My tide of Trust shall tender waves
Upon whose crests my Love will ride —
To wash upon those pagan shores,
And on to shield you at your side!

Dear son of mine, torn from my heart,
Your walls will yield as you await;
For God can walk through
Wall or Gate —
And bend the Will
of
Time and Fate!

THE SHIP THAT NEVER RETURNED

This speedy stallion, known as Chollima, gallops down through North Korean legend. He is, in fact, the dramatic propaganda symbol of this tiny half-country, representing the virtue of self-reliance ("juche"). "Advance at Chollima speed, be a Chollima rider, etc.," urge her country's leaders. A statue of the steed stands in the center of downtown Pyongyang, capital of North Korea.

The Ship that Never Returned
by Eleanor Van Buskirk Harris
Eleanor V.B. Harris 1974

PRINTED IN
THE UNITED STATES OF AMERICA

To Mary Ann (Mae) McClintock — as well as to all mothers, fathers, wives, sweethearts, sisters and brothers of our POW's and MIA's — this book is lovingly and sympathetically dedicated.

Fellow Vigilers: Mae (left) and Eleanor

NOTATIONS WORTH NOTING

Names of certain United States Navy personnel and school pupils have been changed to avoid possible embarrassment, and some situations slightly altered for the same reason. The overall narrative, however, with the exception of occasional flashbacks, remains virtually as it unfolded.

Some of the longer letters, copies of which I saw no immediate reason to retain, as well as conversations, have been recalled to the best of my ability. I am indebted to my fellow-vigiler, Mae Mc-Clintock, for much of the conversation content; for, fortunately for both of us, she possesses a prodigious memory.

I took the liberty of moving nephew Bob's military service back a year or two in order to write him into the story, my justifiable pride proving no deterrent to the normal (?) flow of events.

All persons playing prominent rôles in this sea-swept odyssey of mine have been given the opportunity to read and approve the script. I can only hope they did their homework. Late one evening I gave myself the pleasure of going downtown to our local Chinese restaurant where, over cups of fragrant tea, I read aloud the Christmas chapter to the delighted Tai family. Their son, Peter, was the hero of the piece.

The only performer I failed to locate for a "reading" was one of my Navy advisors who has since retired and gone and lost himself amid the flora and fauna of Florida. With a rigorous New England winter hard upon us now, I can think of nothing more heartwarming than flying down there to flush him out.

This sun-drenched dream will have to remain the impossible one, unfortunately, for I just finished the final pages of my manuscript, my acknowledgements, lying propped and pillowed within the confines of the Melrose-Wakefield Hospital, in obeissance to a thrice-fractured leg.

Possibly because of a medicated memory—they had to keep me "hopped up" after a steel-pin operation due to my "bad trip" on the front porch steps—I neglected to acknowledge the hard-working sisters of my Melrose sorority: *Phi Theta Xi* (incidentally, my most be-spirited book-boosters). Forgive me, girls!

Yes, happily enough, on the local level, enthusiasm bubbled at an all-time high concerning the imminent birth of this first literary love-child of mine. As to that Other World way Out There—well, I trust it, too, will look with charitable eyes upon its innocent face'n form—long after the christening.

The Author

PREFACE

Once upon an autumn, I received a phone call from my dear friend, Mae McClintock, of Milton, Massachusetts.

"Have ye started the book yet?"

"Mae, how can I possibly write a book! You know my schedule, over seven hundred junior high pupils, as well as—"

"Ye'll *do* it! 'If ye want to get a thing done, ask the busiest person ye know'—and I'm asking ye to write that book!"

"But Mae, I have piano classes all day Saturdays and—"

"Ye have a way with words, too, ye do! Now that Steve's and the Captain's and all the other books are out, it's high time ye told ye're *own* story. It's a good one, if I do say it."

"*Our* story, Mae—but few people would believe it even if I could scrape up the time to write it down. Oh yes, then there are my sixteen private piano pupils after school. Just when am I—"

"That's just the reason ye should tell it—all those unusual things that happened—almost as if it had all been planned."

"Have you forgotten my soloist job on Sundays, and Thursday night rehearsals—"

"Ye've already got that notebook ye keep under ye're pillow—and all those letters from the Senators and—"

"Mae, I work *seven*—hear me?—*seven* long days a week—"

"And I'm callin' ye *every* week until it's written, I am!"

And thus, somehow commenced—oh yes, sandwiched in between six weeks of summer school teaching and supervision of same, the Lord, love and history-powered odyssey of a mother—let's make it *two* mothers—who, because of an event of world-wide impact, found themselves in a unique position unlike that of most POW mothers, and who discovered during their vigil that much of their old way of life, and attitudes, had sailed off with *The Ship That Never Returned*, leaving them two changed persons.

This story concerns that change and the extraordinary events that brought it about.

FOREWORD

Now that the lives and fortunes of our returning prisoners of war will for some time lie uppermost in the nation's sympathies, stories of their Far Eastern incarceration are already flooding the readers' market.

First person accounts running the full gamut of human emotion, particularly that of horror, forever lure readers to the book stalls. Yet, despite a literary lust for mayhem, readers, thank heaven, are "human", too.

Thus, the role of raconteur takes a pitiful turn as our POWs, those long-lost lambs from off the Altars of Multinational Quarreling, limp home to the loving ears which will receive avidly, if fearfully, their heartrending narratives.

And let us, who sat out their imprisonment back here in Peaceville, U.S.A., listen closely to our emaciated warriors—to young men lucky enough to make it home in one piece ('though all too obviously, some pieces had to be left behind).

And at long last, when the beloved voices have grown silent, let us not hasten to seal up within our hearts the memory of their awful disclosures. Instead, let this confrontation with truth, untampered with by the will of a conniving enemy, arouse within us an unswerving resolution: to pray with a more zealous faith that a powerful God acts swiftly to mend these young bodies and minds. And of equal importance: *to mend the ways of their Far Eastern jailors, as well!*

Yes, God bless our young men who gave *so much, so far* from home!

* * * * * *

Let us now turn the humanistic Coin of Circumstance to its reverse side:

Does no one who awaited his incarcerated serviceman's return have a tale worth the telling?—no raconteur back home here in Peaceville, U.S.A. who could (almost) match in intensity the narrative he was listening to—*with one of his own?*

9

As beleaguered captives a warring world away sat staring at hostile prison walls, did their loving "waiters" inherit only a comparable legacy of empty longing? Were *they* likewise wandering the same barren desert of doubt, watered only by the tears of terror and frustration—a desert whose sole oasis, for us home folks at any rate, consisted of that infrequent, unnatural-sounding letter from abroad?

To be sure, "they also serve who only stand and wait," but *did* these anxious ones on the home front only *stand* and *wait?*

As your self-appointed storyteller, may I say this Peaceville Piece of mine is no mere Warbling of Woe and Wishing. While it may turn out to be a bird of flimsier feather than those that flew back from the Far East, its plumage flaunts the full spectrum of human emotion, "horror" included, if it's of any use to you.

* * * * * *

I learned to my delight that Fate does not deposit its victims upon the dry shoals of desperation to leave them comfortless. If one can manage to stop sobbing long enough to seek Direction, he'll discover some Heavenly Waters freshening their shores. True believers will go so far as to jump right in and bathe away their tears.

And 'though you may think I'm sailing off course, I actually "saw" whole flocks of laughing gulls flying aloft in the darkened skies. Oh, it wasn't easy to lift an aching head and focus sleepless eyes on their flight pattern, but I learned, at last, the source of their mirth.

And now you'll think I'm so "far out" I've hit a rock, but I must tell you about the fish:

"By all means," a fellow-sufferer warned me, "don't spurn those prophetic *fish* which, if summoned, swim right up out of the seas beneath your sorrow. They *tell* you things you'd never find out for yourself."

But don't worry, these riddles will resolve themselves into practical use as my saga unfolds.

Now. . .getting back to the *fish,* one in particular—I all but crushed the poor little thing to death with a careless heel—the same prescient fish that was able to swim all the way into a POW's lonely prison cell and "see" what was going on![1]

---

[1] A most remarkable prophetess, an eighty-year-old grandma (now a fan of mine), employing her amazing gift of second sight, was able to convey to me what turned out to be near-accurate information concerning the treatment, health, food, surroundings, etc. of my captured son and his crew. Before I had proof of her powers, I passed her off as a daffy old dodo merely bent on currying my attention.

Lastly, encompassed within the glorious lift, which I gradually recognized as emanating from the Everlasting Arms of the Divine Comforter Himself, was the earthly comfort supplied me by fellow-mourners—those who stumbled along the same rocky shoals as I—yet who stooped down where stones were sharpest to wipe the blood from off my feet; and who loved me enough to remind me to stop and pray along the shoreside. But most rewarding of all—who stood by, their tears mingling with mine, to share in the ecstasy of *prayer answered.*

Oh, we homebodies have some stories to relate, too. And as many of you have reason to know, mine is concerned with the Lord-powered, love-powered strivings of one small widow for the rescue and return of her POW son, a U.S. Naval officer. . .alive!

Eleanor Van Buskirk Harris

CONTENTS

PRELUDE

"October's Bright Blue Weather"
Main Characters in Order of Appearance
Sagas of the Sea
Story of a Ship
Precognition Picture on Autumn's Screen

The clear blue sky of a late October morning lifted high over gray ledges, reflecting its endless azure in two flower-rimmed pools beneath. A pair of sparrow hawks played tag over the edge of the cliffs, shooting up and down, in and out of sight as if half crazy with joy at the sudden burst of beauty after the long rain, their silhouettes playing peek-a-boo with these natural mirrors of the garden.

The dishes could wait on a morning such as this, I decided.

Standing on its cliffs two hundred feet above a sea sparkling three miles to the east, this "eagle's nest" I lived in was a perfect vantage point from which to view the world during this bright autumn season —or during any season for that matter—except perhaps on a blustery January night when its upstairs windows were blasted and blurred to oblivion, blotting out even the welcome lights of a dozen or more towns and cities twinkling merrily below.

The young couple seated opposite me, enjoying a late breakfast in the bow window, seemed suffused in a glow of their own, as warm as the one outside, if the mutual exchange in their eyes was any indication.

The Washington wedding had been a lovely one, but all too soon now my happy doves would fly away—a long, long way away. Their detailed planning for a home in Japan had overridden all other topics of conversation, and little time remained of this precious Navy leave for other discussion. I would have to speed up my inquiries if I were to detain these two longer, for I sensed they were eager to finish their coffee and join the sparrow hawks outside.

I crunched down the last morsel of crisp bacon lying on my plate, then pushed it aside to get an unobstructed view of the 12" x 15" glossy news photo my son had handed me this morning along with a copy of a Colorado newspaper.

15

"Stevo," I began, "about this 'new' ship of yours—I was wondering—I can't seem to discover any armament aboard her. What I mean is, where are your guns? Shouldn't she carry some guns, or something?" I studied the glossy closely, then picked up the paper.

"Or something what?" he grinned, not taking his eyes off his bride. "We're not a ship of war, Mother," he went on in the same cordial voice that had earned him a radio job in college years—"just a seawater sampler."[1]

"I can read, Old Dear," I replied placidly. I was used to his comfortable humor. "An 'oceanographic and technical research vessel' it says in this paper, but it seems to me, since this is a Navy ship, you ought to be provided with protection of some sort. With Yokosuka your new port-of-call, homeport, or whatever the term is, you're not too awfully far removed from the war zone. You just might stray into unfriendly waters—well, what I'm trying to say is you might be attacked—or something. . . ." My voice trailed off in embarrassment at the expression creeping over his tanned features, through which his naturally high color still managed to assert itself.

"*Attacked,* did you say?" he returned, his dark blue eyes crinkling in amused disbelief. "Just who is going to attack a *research vessel,* I'd like to know? And I might just remind you, Mother," he added, still smiling at his bride as if she were the only one in the room, "that a U. S. Navy ship doesn't 'stray' anywhere."

My new daughter-in-law laughed softly but not unsympathetically.

"Vuokko, does he badger you like that?" I asked lightly, searching for support. Everyone else called her Esther, her middle name being Esteri; however, "Vuokko" signifies Windflower, a fair blossom of Finland's fields, and I thought the name suited her perfectly— even if I couldn't pronounce it with the delicate nuances she managed so easily.

My "flower" had raised her chic frosted head and was regarding me with soft blue-green eyes the color of a tropic sea. They held a warm understanding which probably stemmed from asking similar questions and receiving equally innocuous replies.

I looked down again at the newspaper with its full-page spread of newsphotos commemorating the commissioning of my son's latest ship. It had been a joint commissioning including the *U.S.S. Palm Beach,* to which the public had been invited. However, the paper had chosen to devote its pictorial page exclusively to the ship Steve

---

[1] An *Auxiliary General Environmental Research Vessel (AGER)* for testing temperature and salinity of water, important factors for sonar findings.

"The Washington wedding was a lovely one... ."

had recently been assigned to and which had been christened for one of its cities.

Although my teaching job had kept me from attending the ceremony which had taken place on the opposite side of the country, I still had the invitation Steve had sent me safely ensconced in the secret drawer of the antique secretary here in the family room. His great, great Grandfather Harris had retained a cabinet-maker to hand-fashion it for such treasures back in 1780.

My late husband had familiarized me with the exploits of many of Steve's oceangoing ancestors, most of whom had stored their hand-written ship's papers in the well-hidden drawer, listing chests of tea, barrels of treacle and salt pork, bolts of calico and muslin, rolls of scenic Chinese wallpaper and other primitive cargo.

Willed through the years to the eldest son, this desk had probably pushed its polished patinas and handcast brass fittings into more briny deeps than these two young lovers would ever see.[2] It was once destined to fall into the keeping of great, great Grandad Harris's first namesake, had the young man not been "written off" in Harris Annals of the Deep as its most mischievous sailor!

Steve had once sent a letter home following a raging storm in the North Atlantic. In sheer disregard of the terror it must have generated for all hands aboard, his description of it was, as usual, hilarious. I was reminded of that other "mischievous sailor."

"Stevo," I asked, "back when the big old *Grand Canyon*[3] was sloshing about 'like a butter chip in a washing machine' in that hurricane sea, and those 'Mt. Washington waves' were 'sudsing up' your decks, didn't you give little old George Harris a sort of mental nod?"

"No, I did *not* give little old George Harris a sort of mental nod," he replied emphatically, then laughed as if in retrospect. "I had more interesting things to occupy my mind!"

(I could see little old George must "go below." After all, *he'd* already left his mark on history.)

Nevertheless, my new daughter-in-law insisted upon an introduction:

The story goes that great, great Uncle George, aboard a sailing vessel in an equally unpredictable ocean,[4] emerged somewhat less successful than his great, great-to-be nephew. (Frankly speaking, Uncle George failed to emerge at all!)

---

[2]According to Steve's great Aunt, this desk had been a voyager to many foreign ports as the treasured possession of Captain George Brae.

[3]A destroyer tender, a huge floating machine shop for ships.

[4]The North Pacific, if memory serves me correctly.

It seems that one summer, back in the early 1800's, great, great Uncle George, at the wise old age of twelve, wheedled and cajoled his parents into allowing him to ship out as cabin boy "for just this one voyage" aboard his own uncle's four-masted schooner plying merchant seas in the tea and spice trade. After all, there would be eight or nine other offspring left behind to do the chores and enliven the hearthside, so why should he be so sorely missed?

Obviously he must have succeeded, for we next find aggressive George aboard the *William D. Roche*[5] out of Newburyport, Massachusetts. Not only do we find him aboard, but busily disobeying orders, i.e., climbing the masts (in lieu of the lovely maples of old Newburyport?). At any rate, during one of those cyclones-of-the-sea, our wayward boy—yes, you guessed it—was torn from the rigging and cast bodily down into "pitching mountains of boiling brine." A seaman, clinging to the stays for his life, saw him go shrieking down, shreds of his white shirt still flapping aloft on the mainmast. Rescue, even by an uncle at the helm, was impossible. Exit to Davy Jones' Locker: one great, great uncle.

Vuokko thanked me, then she and Steve slipped out to the kitchen to make a fresh pot of coffee while I continued to peruse the Colorado paper.

As I heard Vuokko's voice softly replying to her new husband, I was reminded of another (ancestral) sailor's bride, tiny Abigail Brae, who alone saved her husband's vessel from disaster. I must tell my new daughter-in-law this one, for it defied a great sea tradition. (Women's Lib would love l'il Abby!)

Far happier was the outcome of this second stirring episode on an early sailing vessel, but the truth of the matter is, our hero on this precarious voyage "stirred" not at all!

Yes, contrary to the rules of the rolling road, another Uncle George, of more charismatic character, great, great Grandpa Harris's nephew, dashing, brown-eyed Captain George Brae, insisted upon listing as cargo on all his voyages, in addition to his uncle's desk, *one adorable little blue-eyed wife*, plus one dainty maple rocking chair. He simply refused to lift anchor out of any port without them. (What a guy! I fell in love with his daguerreotype!)

Well, during Captain Brae's first bad blow with his dear Abby aboard, an age-old malady with fatal consequences threatened the newlyweds, as well as their craft. Following a long cruise to the Orient, they were turning back with full cargo for the port of Salem, Massachusetts, when only a few miles out of Hong Kong Harbor, in a

---

[5]Here again, I hope Memory has put George aboard the proper vessel.

sudden storm-ridden sea, our devoted Captain was stricken with a high fever and carried insensible to his quarters. (But, take heart, this was not the fatal malady to which I refer.)

In spite of Captain Brae's popularity and reputation for fairness to his crews, his Chinese deck hands lost no time in taking advantage of the situation, and plotted mutiny! (Old salts would insist this was because there was a woman aboard!)

Luckily for the few American sailors present—the only good guys among the crew—there was one potent factor the heartless ship-swiping wretches were too ignorant or hasty to take into account, i.e., *love power!* (It's the best!)

Tiny Abigail, as doughty as she was pretty, and daughter of a sea captain herself, was quick to appraise the situation and forthwith abandoned her tender ministrations and silent vigil in the little maple rocker beside her sick husband's berth.

Unlocking the big sea chest secured to the cabin floor, she seized several pistols and secreted them in her knitting bag.

Realizing that the melee was taking place chiefly in the hold of the ship, our little Bride of the Brine sped out onto the stormlashed deck, locked the cabin door, picked up the lethal knitting bag, and managed to slip undetected to the ship's wheel. Bolstered by a handful of American seamen holding her pistols, on a heaving deck with blinding torrents of rainwater and spume cascading down over her neatly burnished curls and tiny waist, blue-eyed Abby put her small hands to the helm, brought the big schooner about and steered it back to the nearest Chinese port.

Incidentally, the good Captain regained his health, and after a lifetime spent in the trough of the tradewinds, the couple lived to a good-looking old age. Whether clad in the wedding finery of their youth, or basking in the bliss of retirement in the hammock on their porch in old Newburyport, Captain Brae and his winsome Abigail make the handsomest twosome of all those gracing the pages of the Harris family albums.

"So what?" Steve teased after Vuokko graciously thanked me for my storytelling. I must hunt up the old albums as she begged me to.

Yes—so what lay ahead for our latest scion of the sea? Hopefully, nothing of the sort here recounted. Other than an occasional blow on the blue, what high adventure could possibly lie in the innocent trough (or was it before the innocent bow?), of a mere 179-foot oceanographic research vessel,—unless, of course, it "researched" onto the fabulous Sea Serpent—or was swallowed whole by it!

Oh, no, God willing, Steve would serve many more than his intended twenty years in the Navy, for ocean breezes were his breath-of-life; and in due time, doubtless, retire without incident, a weather-beaten old salt with a kneeful of grandchildren spoiling to listen to the tangy tales of his trade, hopefully the worst of them dredged from the depths of his own imagination.

Steve had returned to the kitchen for another helping of scrambled eggs. My thoughts zoomed back to the present:

"What a dry-land name for a ship!" I called out to him rather patronizingly. "Why not *Seafarer* or *Sea Lion* or something more sea*worthy?* Why name it for an *inland* city?"

"Your newly-acquired mother-in-law is woefully uninformed, Dear," I apologized to the vision seated opposite me. "'Admiral Applecheeks' out there in the galley never tells me anything. In fact, I haven't the foggiest idea what a lieutenant's duties are aboard a Navy ship. Is he the guy I've seen padding about the deck with a telescope under his wing?"

She laughed again and placed her soft, perfectly groomed hand over mine. I looked down at the misty shell pink nails. Steve's bride was a couturier's confection from head to toe. It was all I could do to keep from spreading her on my toast.

Whenever I was a guest aboard one of Steve's ships when it berthed in Boston, I always noticed one officer standing with a long-glass under his arm. I knew perfectly well he was called "Officer of the Deck," a traditional figure of Navy lore.

About Steve's new assignment, I knew very little. At least the commissioning booklet he had sent me gave me a capsule rundown on his present craft, originally a cargo carrier, built in South Korea.

Grown weary after ten years of lugging supplies to the South Pacific, this poor old Seagoin' Sal retired—or tried to—back in 1954. Years later, along came a Navy man who "revived" her, dressing her aging form in the most sophisticated equipage money—my money—could buy. Thus emerged a career girl in oceanographic and electromagnetic research, who Dieseled forth as dauntlessly as her years would allow.

It took 22,547 man-days to groom and re-do this Maid of the Rolling Main. They even threw in a face-lift and body-massage. To tell the truth, though I wouldn't have dared mention it to this prideful Navy son across from me quietly adding to his two hundred well-distributed pounds, the idea did occur to me that it might have been wiser for refurbishers to have jettisoned this dated doll and created a new model from scratch. But who was I to dictate fashion trends for the U. S. Navy? (Only a wondering taxpayer, is all.)

Right now I was wondering about safety. Hadn't Steve intimated the ship had had a great deal of steering trouble?

"Stevo, I've been studying the photo of this little ship of yours. Despite what I've read in the booklet, it still looks rather old to me—well, what I mean is—I hope it makes it O.K. *all the way* to Japan!"

"You and me both," archly declared the well-filled lieutenant.

"Well—not a bad morning, girls," he commented as if happy to dismiss the subject. He rose and stretched all six feet into a contented yawn.

Our eyes followed his as he looked down into the valley lying beneath the bow window. Here autumn had emptied her paintbox, spilling colors in every direction—eastward to the strip of blue sea sparkling along a rift in the rosy hills,—westward to the wooded slopes of a state reservation known as *The Middlesex Fells*—and straight south to myriads of rooftops huddled together in city-patches taking the morning sun,—finally dribbling lavender mists in wavy horizontal ribbons across the Blue Hills of Milton, lying beyond Boston.

"Beautiful, Steve!" I sighed, wishing the two could remain weeks longer to enjoy the autumn panorama.

Vuokko's only reply was to move closer to the tall, dark-haired officer beside her who had already put out his arm to receive her. . . .

I hurriedly refilled the empty cups from the fresh pot, hoping to detain them longer. At any moment he'd be lifting his precious burden and swooshing her out the rear door that opened onto the ledges. Right now, this lifting bit seemed to comprise his main source of exercise; in fact, I'd scarcely seen my new daughter's feet touch the floor since she arrived. He carried her over the stairs in somewhat less-than-romantic postures, usually dangling her under one arm, or using "fireman's carry," always with the nonchalance accorded old suitcases. That he was a happy bridegroom I would be the last to deny, even if Vuokko carried bruises to prove it.

"Such amiable-looking people, Stevo. They appear to be the kind you could both work and socialize with comfortably," I used as a retainer, glancing again at the *Journal* photos showing guests at the commissioning exercises.

"I like Commander Bucher's, (how do you pronounce that? Oh, Boo -ker, thanks.), well, anyway, I like his clean white smile. He looks like a 'fun' captain to me, too."

"You're so right, Mother. He's a great guy for a skipper!" Steve bounded back, then smiled slowly as if recalling some amusing incident or anecdote he didn't intend to share.

"His wife looks so attractive standing there on the bridge be-

side him. Vuokko, just look at that adorable outfit she's wearing—
I've always favored wide-brimmed hats!"

Vuokko nodded. "She's a remarkably pretty woman, Mother—
and that's Carol and Ed Murphy standing next to her," she continued shyly in the loveliest voice I've ever heard. "Ed's the 'Exec',
as Steve has probably told you."

She dimpled up at him.

"What's the matter with the guy in the white gloves and sword?"
Steve roared good-naturedly, indicating his own picture over my
shoulder.

"An old smoothie, that's what he is. Who is *he?*" I drawled
nonchalantly.

"But to get back to what's eating you, Mother," he taunted me
prophetically, "maybe we could requisition a couple of Mafia rejects
and put 'em aboard. I wouldn't want you worrying about me while
I'm gone." He grinned down at Vuokko, then his eyes began court-
ing the sunny exit.

"Mafia rejects! You must mean machine guns," I snorted. "Did
you hear that, Vuokko? *A couple of machine guns!*" And I hastily
envisioned two lone Navy gunners, each kneeling at opposite ends
of the vessel, a long empty deck between, fending off, à la TV, two
monstrous warships whose cannon-like guns were blazing and pounding the tiny vessel from bow to stern.

"Oh stop teasing for once! Honestly, Stevo, please be serious.
What'll you do if you're *actually attacked?* I mean it! What'll you
do?"

"Lessee now—uh—oh, I dunno—use *slingshots* I guess."

*Little did I realize the silly phrase would return and repeat itself
a hundred times during the ensuing winter to torture my mind,
since it seemed so aptly indicative of his ship's protective "artillery"
—her potential fire-power.*

"Slingshots" indeed! Even little Abigail Brae's sick husband had
had sense enough to put aboard a chestful of pistols, and his wasn't
a "ship of war" either!

"Get up, Wife!" Steve proudly commanded the blue peignoir who
had sat down to glance at the newsphotos again.

"Wait—why weren't you in these photos, Vuokko?" I demanded.
"Those photographers couldn't have known their business!" In spite
of her shyness, her honey-colored beauty always drew attention.
"A beautiful butternut blonde" papers described her later.

"She hid 'under the bridge'," Steve laughed, swinging her lightly
off the floor and heading for the sun.

"Here we go again!" sighed the willing rag doll, "and thank you,

Mother, for a delicious breakfast," the pretty voice called back out of the blue cloud in her husband's arms.

She'd thanked me at the close of every meal since she arrived. She even had Steve doing it.

The empty cups should have warned me my time had run out. I felt suddenly lonely, sensing the sweet contentedness of the two as I stood at the rear door to the ledges, watching them peer down into the autumn-splashed valley, the morning sun forming dual haloes over their freshly-showered heads.

Oh, for a paintbrush and the power to immortalize such a golden canvas! . . . but the portrait was coming to life—

"Don't break your necks, you crazy kooks," I laughed after them, for they had suddenly turned, and were racing hand in hand toward the open end of the cliffs leading to a grassy shelf below.

I hoped there'd be some wild flowers still dotting the green there. I knew the spot well. Another couple had once shared their dreams looking down over these same ledges. What a pity the beloved dreamer who had left Stephen and me eight years before could not enter into the joys of this sun-drenched morning!

"Oh, the uncluttered lives of youth," I thought wistfully, glancing first at the spot where my dear ones had disappeared down over the cliffs, then up into the ocean of sky, sending into its endless blue the wish that throughout the centuries all parents of newlyweds had wished for their children:—*If only they could always remain as happy as they were at this moment!*

If only it were in my province to reveal to them some magic formula for avoiding, or at least disentangling, the complexities of modern living, somehow forestall the vicissitudes that would all too soon start gnawing away at the vibrancy of young wings.

How delightfully unaware were my two human sparrow hawks out there flitting about in the morning sun that they would soon be flying from simplicity into multiplicity, toward ever-narrowing horizons of pressure and demand, wings inexorably weighted down by the costly encumbrances of our materialistic culture.

In the painful interim that followed Bob's death, I had stumbled upon one beneficent truth: that whatever dreams I still cherished must become interwoven with those of others if I were to rise above self-pity.

Well, I must clear the table quickly to save precious time, as my thoughtful daughter-in-law always insisted upon helping—and Steve, too—although this show of domestic enthusiasm on his part seemed to have eluded me before his marriage.

I emptied the last of the warm coffee onto the plants in the little floor garden on the west wall, then "potted" its queen on her turban:

"Take good care of those two out there, Kuan Yin," I implored the Oriental statue of the Goddess of Mercy standing in the center of its greenery. The dark onyx eyes of the cement deity, however, only continued to glitter back at me coldly from under their swollen lids.

Although the family room still appeared dim to my sun-filled eyes, I decided to take one last searching look at the glossy photo of Steve's vessel, but it appeared blurred. Slowly, as my eyes grew accustomed to the change of light, the little ship came back into focus. No, it did even more than that—at least the sea around it!

Seated alone in the quiet room so strangely devoid of sound and life, I was caught up in the wonder of it. *Could I believe what I was seeing?*

The colorless leaden sea in the photograph I was holding had begun to undulate slowly, and now to my staring eyes—yes, I'd put my hand up to them and they were open—I saw a small ship enter the picture and move toward the larger vessel, circling it twice, then coming alongside, its tiny guns silhouetted against the sky.[6]

Now four others joined it, their guns also plainly visible.[7] They were converging on Steve's small craft! His vessel started to move away, but two of the smaller ships began criss-crossing the waters before its bow while another sped to its stern.[8] Now the guns of the first ship seemed to be. . . .

I put my hand to my heart to see if it was still beating, for consciousness seemed momentarily suspended. I was positive aircraft was about to join the battle.[9] At that very moment, for some reason, I shut my eyes,—but in so doing I lost my strange little vision, seeing once more only a lonely ship lying motionless upon a photographic sea.

Young laughter drifting up over the ledges told me my sparrow hawks were returning to the nest.

I started for the kitchen. . . .

I'd better not tell them about seeing the strange little sea battle. I could already hear Steve's teasing: "Mother dear, you're losing your marbles."

---

[6] A Soviet SO-1, flying the North Korean naval ensign, to be exact, its sailors manning 57-millimeter cannon, sub machine guns, and carbines.

[7] Russian-built P-4 torpedo boats, they turned out to be.

[8] A P-4 with uncovered torpedo tubes, ready for business.

[9] And it did! MIG jets with salvos of rockets!

It had happened so quickly, it was almost as if it hadn't happened at all.   Had my concern over armament prompted it, or had I only imagined this minute-movie?

I knew I had not!

"AVALANCHE!"

January Jinx vs. Funloving Fate
Case of the Crooning Crickets
Element-al Embraces
"Mother's Mausoleum"
Phone Call "Heard 'Round the World"

October's New England paintbrush had long since bequeathed its radiant portraiture to the ground, and Ole January, arch enemy of years past, had now howled its way into a brand new year.

I hoped Steve's ship was safely berthed in its new Japanese port, and that he'd write me again before leaving on the cruise which would not bring him back until spring. He said he'd try to put in a long distance call before the main tour if he could "manage to drop anchor beside a telephone booth."

How I longed to pick up my phone and hear a cordial "Happy New Year, Mother!"—only he'd put it in some crazy way. Knowing I would gasp with joy at the sound of his voice across vast distances, he always keyed it as casually as if he were down at the corner grocery calling back to inquire whether it was dark or light bread I wanted.

After unavoidable delays, my daughter-in-law was at last planning to make the move from the Washington, D.C. apartment to Yokosuka, though, unfortunately, not to arrive before Steve's departure.

(Had he ever gotten those "Mafia rejects" put aboard his research vessel, his non ship-of-war?)[1]

Well, only a week more to go now and Ole January would become a malaise of the past.

Ole January was a month I could do without.

As far back as I could remember, the direst disturbances ever to sour a sweet—and spoiled—little life had occurred in the dead of it.

Take this very newest of Januaries for example:

If, through the eyes of one bogged down in the mires of supersti-

---

[1] Yes, two 50-calibre machine guns, hardly an adequate arsenal!

tion, I were to review the Presagers of Doom just since New Year's Day that had stolen by or up into this pinnacle I slept upon, I would have to blink at their frequency if not at their ominous potential.

Worse yet, even to a confirmed Omen-Scoffer such as I, it became increasingly evident as the wily month wore on, that each foretoken of disaster that had reared its ugly head was perfectly capable of living up to its reputation.

In recent years, in lieu of New Year's resolutions which I used to make with easy abandon—only to abandon with still easier abandon— I chose instead to project but one sterling plea to Old Father Time. This year's directive was as simple as it was succinct: "Stow the usual humdrum, hackaway Hannah routine, Popsie, and for once *put something BIG on the AGENDA!*" (But, naturally, I hardly expected the venerable gentleman to take me so seriously!)

No sooner had I beamed my dream to the ancient Keeper of the Clock, it seemed, than a Funflinging Fate appeared, pushed the feeble old Reaper from off his dais and grabbed his scythe for herself. Moreover, when she rolled up her sleeves for the garnering, I must have been standing directly in her path!

First thing she did was to "scythe" me out of my warm nest on New Year's morn straight down onto my only pair of reading glasses, mincing them beyond utility. Loss no. 1.

Only the night before I had scarcely finished the first chapter of Anne Morrow Lindbergh's *Gift from the Sea* when Funnygirl forthwith scythed me out with the tide and over the bay into the dreamy arms of Morpheus, slipping my glasses between its pages, of course, before she whisked the little volume onto the floor.

Putting out my second eyes failed to provide sufficient amusement, apparently, for when I bombed out of bed, she had me sailing across the glossy surface of *"the Sea"* with such a list that my left elbow struck my night table with force enough to send an exquisite china bedside lamp out to the trash barrel, and at the same time etch a branchlike crack across the mirrored face of my night table as her official signature. Loss no. 2 and 3.

"A fine *Gift from the Sea! I hope it never brings me another!*" I thought darkly (and I might add, *prematurely!*)

This breakage bit proved the puniest of her pranks.

Precisely at midnight I'd first heard the whisper of her scythe. I recognized the witching hour, for I was awakened by roaring crowds in Times Square via brother Gilbert's TV in his downstairs bedroom.

This gal Fate wasn't fooling around. Knowing full well my music-oriented eardrums would never be able to bear up under such piercing and repetitious repertoire (acoustically cellars are flawless), she had engaged the services of a chorus of raucous-voiced crickets to carry on her charade in the vicinity of the furnace. The songsters were undoubtedly refugees from our little family room floor garden who had inadvertently been dumped to their subterranean theatre via the laundry chute.

I had for some time labored under the illusion that crickets cricked only in balmier months, but perhaps because I turned up the cellar heater sky high to ward off a terrible chill,—keeping me home from two New Year's parties—, they mistook it for Queen of the May, as my overheated brother who lived with me suggested.

At any rate, half frozen after attending the drafty concert in "evening dress," I crawled back up into my warm bedroom, hoping to fall again swiftly into the soft embraces of the God of Dreams. Recurring recollections of an old movie, *Teahouse of the August Moon,* unfortunately, blocked my path to Slumberland, for I kept mulling over the scene where almond-eyed natives hold up cages of these same *good fortune* harbingers to actor Glenn Ford.

Since killing a cricket in the Orient equates killing a mockingbird in Feathersville, Florida,—or so I've been told—I prayed such Oriental influences would remain glued to their own side of the globe. If not, then under the circumstances I had better say it while I was able— "Sayonara"—for I had just bounced a whole bucketful of *good fortune* out into Ole January's snow! Had I put an Oriental "hex" on the household? We didn't really need one.

Perhaps I forgot to add that I had to *walk under* good brother's wallpatching *ladder* to get to my cricketeers, as well as act as referee to *two* shaggy *black cats* who fairly knocked me down ("crossed my path"?) next morning when I went out onto the porch to feed my woodland denizens the breakfast my sore throat refused.

Staunch Unbelievers such as I, naturally, would characterize such precarious phenomena as pure nonsense—that all this had "nothing to do with the case,"— (i.e., a case of influenza, to be exact.) Yet, let's face it, a few hours later I was back on my downy couch and into "*the Sea*" again, this time with a magnifying glass, trusting it's brine would cool a fevered brow; for my head was pounding in painful rhythm to the accompaniment of whining snowplows on the steep hills below—or, did I neglect to mention the fact that the opening blizzard of the New Year was presently in progress?

Freewheeling Fate was loaning her steel to Miss N.E. Winter now, for by midnight our lonely crag was locked in the death grip of the sky battle, the beruffled bier I slept upon shaking as if a giant hand were gentling an oversize baby in her bassinette. The embroidered blossoms on the canopy over my head began mixing their colors in pretty confusion, while just beyond my louvered doors I could hear the glass prisms of the candelabra on the music room mantelpiece playing a tinkling concerto to a trembling chimney well.

Temperatures had slammed down to a 20° below zero, and to the accompaniment of shattering ice pebbles the size of marbles in a fourth grade pocket in springtime, I heard Miss New England Winter outside my bedroom window shrieking and clawing at clapboard and shutter, her insane orgy but a prelude to the next movement.

With earsplitting regularity, the baseboard pipes in the lovely music room began bursting. Above the sound of shuddering beams, twenty eight sonic booms rent what was left of the inner stillness, sending gallons of water rolling over the hems of satin overdrapes and across the pale blue faces of Oriental carpets.

Because of the flooding, electrical fixtures down on the lower floor burgeoned into busy waterfalls, inundating everything beneath them.

Although my own situation brought me no side-splitting chuckles, this whole bit reminded me of a movie I once saw of some expert plumbing "executed" through the combined genius of that incomparable duo, Laurel and Hardy-ha-ha.

As expected, the two fumblers enter a splendid mansion and proceed belligerently and untidily to get their wires crossed. When all is restored to order and the bosomy estate owner is ushered in to appraise their accomplishments, Mr. Hardy proudly turns a gold faucet, only to burn his plumpish hands under the flames which belch forth. Naturally, the climax comes when friend Laurel flicks the electric wall switch for a huge chandelier, which retaliates by flinging fountains of water into astounded faces. There seemed to be a slight corollary here somewhere. I headed for drier ground.

Gilbert bounded upstairs bucket in hand, meeting my fiery form (temperature 103°), flying to the safety of Steve's empty bedroom below. I crawled between the cool sheets, burning, yet trembling with cold anxiety—Steve's vessel was on its way to Japan now. How was *he* faring in this savage northeaster? Had its frigid fingers reached out far enough to fasten themselves onto his little ship at sea?[2]

Yes, January was a month I could do without.

If Funstinging Fate hadn't tricked me into earning my own keep— for keeps—I'm positive I'd have surveyed[3] Ole January straight out

---

[2]They had! This "maiden" voyage from Bremerton, Washington to Yokosuka, Japan had churned up a nautical nightmare for all hands aboard, their frail little barque pitching and rolling at 44-47 degrees in an angry sea. Barely missing skerries and shoals, the battered ship had to take shelter in the lee of a nearby island off the west coast of Kyushu.

[3]Navy term for dispensing of no longer useful encumbrances (heaving something over the side?).

of my psyche, climbed down from my cloud, and gone off a-baskin'
with Bill Shakespeare "in a somer seson whan soft was the sonne"
—or if he didn't compose the luring line, with whichever other ancient bard didn't know how to spell—

As an additional "snow job" on my dreams of baskin' away Ole
January, Fate had also handed me a passel of Fourth Graders, for
once straying out of her true character to bestow such a heartwarming prize on my loneliness.

I couldn't very well bask off and leave behind my greatest little
band of cheerleaders, now could I? (Well,— yes, there *were* days
when I thought I could!)

Then, too, in this educational era of divisive designs upon the integrity of the Happy Classroom Family, it would pain me—even for
one month—to will to some strange individual the "individualizing"
of twenty-eight such adoring individuals. Such alienation of affection
via "breakage of sequential curriculum" seasoned with "pre and post
testing," all packaged under the appetizing label "Contract Strategy,"
might end in divorce!

You could say, if you were the egocentric I am, that I'm a member
of that paucity of educators who, while they may not "love their
work" (with apologies to Horace Mann and his ilk), *do* love their
workers!—and that goes for any Ole month.

On this red letter Tuesday afternoon—we had early school dis-
missal in snowy months—I coaxed my flu-weakened limbs over to the
old apothecary chest in the downstairs family room, upon which
rested a pair of binoculars Steve had brought me after a cruise to the
Middle East. I trained them on the skies outside the east window.
Holding them steady was not easy following a tenacious high temperature.

Well now, in addition to the deluge-dealing blizzard that fell out
of her January Joke Box, what other goodies did Miss New England
Winter have hiding for me in the folds of her maxi-cape? The skies
looked surly.

I'd hoped she'd keep those Wild Wind Boys of hers on leash a
while longer; yet I could see the lady had already put them to work
orphaning a huge family of purplish clouds which rolled about in
motherless confusion as if mulling over her nasty temper. Were these
weather-workers joining forces for another Tonight Show—a second
debacle driving its icy javelins in from the deep? If so, would Steve's
little ship be out in it somewhere? If only I could hear his voice—
would he really phone me from Japan?—or had he already sailed?

It was easy for my tired arms to drop the lenses to the valley lying 150 feet below my roost. How desolate it looked! The broad white fields of Pine Banks Park were empty now. There were no happy screams in January—no shouts of recognition when I walked out onto the circular sundeck to clear away the ice and snow. A stray dog, a snowmobile, or a child being drawn on a sled were the park's only visitors in winter.

Yes, during these first four despicable weeks of this very newest of years my "January nerves" were grateful that my home-away-from-home, the Decius Beebe Elementary School, was welded solidly to a valley of the city. Living out the remainder of the day and night tiptop this unprotected promontory known to Melrose citizens as *Boston Rock,* a wind-mopped mountain of stone whose ledge-laden brows rise up only to stare down at a dark, woodsy beard—was quite another dish of tea.

So close to the sky dwelt I, in fact, that with a soul-shrivelling crack, the contours of my center chimney threatened to disintegrate as punishment for getting too clubby with certain electrified clouds. Poking the black nostril of its snowy flue up into the private alter-cations of the elements, until I armed it with lightning rods, brought naught for its pains but a barrage of ammunition in the form of lethal bricks.

Just how lethal would be the "bricks" about to fall upon me now, as a result of the world-startling lightning streaking toward my household? Would they knock me clear through the Gate of Heaven —or just far enough for me to open it a crack and get a good peep at its propensities?

Of course, if you stood down there on Main Street near Sylvan and bent your neck back, you might decide I was halfway to heaven as it was. My high east bank lay open to a deep valley that led to the sea, the same sea that stole away a son, and sent its salty squalls to sandpaper the paint from off my windowsills—a sea that loosed whole squadrons of garrulous gulls to autograph my upstairs picture windows when gale winds put curves in their flight patterns.

I replaced the binoculars and turned my thoughts back for the dozenth time to the most baffling morning of all Januaries to date, *this* morning! What a debilitating day—what a *scary* day it had been from about eleven o'clock on! What did this once-in-a-lifetime exper-ience signify? Was I so weakened by my recent illness that a copped-out brain conjured up this hallucinatory situation? A situation *that brought a spirit emissary* or whatever the non-physical Weirdo What-sis was, *strolling unseen into a fourth grade classroom?*

Even now I could feel the presence of "The Presence" right here in the room with me—seated over there in that gold chair opposite mine in the big bow window, to be exact! How trying at this impasse to remember that I was an Omen-Scoffer! This spook was for real!

With stormtime approaching, I tried to dispense with my "ghosting" for more comforting indulgences. I had already decided the stairway to my bedroom was insurmountable, regardless of the fact there remained several hours in which to recuperate before attempting to prepare supper for Gilbert.

No, crawling back into bed only to start wondering about Steve— or, worse still, to listen vainly for the call that might not come, or to count for the hundredth time the blooms growing in the canopy garden over my head—a sort of compelling preoccupation for idle minds—appealed to me no longer. I must "think away" my visitor!

Perhaps peering into the nostalgic mirrors of the past would prove a placating diversion. Yes, escaping into Memory's corridors just might serve to "erase" the unseen emissary, entity, spirit or whatever The Thing was, still sitting so patiently over there in the bow window!

* * * * * *

Twelve years earlier, following the heart attack that caused the untimely death of a devoted husband, I marshalled the fragments of my courage and put them to work planning this home as a memorial to him. Its location had a sentimental significance.

An undertaking as ambitious as this, I reasoned, i.e., becoming mother-architect to a cliff-dwelling, should serve to uproot me, temporarily at least, from heartbreaking reminders of a glorious but all-too-brief togetherness, as well as bedding me down within unfamiliar walls—walls without memories. Learning to live without Bob's all-encompassing love was not easy.

I prayed that as a result of a prolonged, challenging enterprise, a better You-Know-Who would evolve out of it; and that this newly-acquired tendency to self-pity might fade in its intensity; though sadly enough, I realized it would take more than Bob's tragic death to bring about the complete demise of a frightfully spoiled, egotistic, over-ambitious, latent tomboy spirit that had dominated my exuberant existence since only heaven knew when!

Hopefully, if this new venture endured as long as I estimated, even if I were unable to heave a Funpoking Fate from off its signpost, perhaps she'd weaken for once and assist me in placing my self-centered limbs along the Road to Recovery, or at least "scythe" me part way up the path to becoming the "terrific little doll" my husband blindly believed me to be.

Just one thing worried me: Was I, in this thrust for self-improvement, about to join ranks with those wonderful people I knew whose lives appeared to have been kindled to beauty solely via the onslaught of severe and multiple trials?

Must my life require not only challenging endeavors to lift me out of myself, but added tragedy to extinguish the last embers of a fiery pride? (Oh,—heaven forbid!!)

Arming myself with pencils, an outsize pad of art paper, multiple erasers and an elbowful of favorite Architect Royal Barry Wills' volumes on New England Homes—Mr. Wills used to live in Melrose—I went into the Wyoming Hill attic and ferreted out my old drawing board. (Wyoming Hill was my childhood home.) Closing the door to sympathizers, I went to work.

Weeks later, after shelving whole sheaves of personally rejected plans, with my heart crying for the companionship of my late husband, I watched the white body of my artchild lay itself gracefully down—all one hundred feet of it—across the granite forehead of our favorite lookout and picnic spot.

On clear days, from the rim of this historic ridge, one could peer past wooded mounds and swatches of toy suburbia into the very heart of downtown Boston, seven miles to the south. The bronze *Reference Station* marker that the *United States Coast and Geodetic Survey* had cemented to the ledges beneath the columns of the rear portico, lifted me to 211 feet above sea level, which is lofty enough when you consider that if you just turned and looked down to your left, you could watch the sea itself sparkling a little over three miles to the east, i.e., three miles as the seagull flies.

Like son Steve, my brothers and I could never live happily-ever-after in a house from which we could not catch a glimpse of the ocean, for we hailed from a family of sea-lovers, probably due to some horn-headed Viking or other who sailed into our ancestry, or at least to Scandinavian forebears. The bulk of our progenitors were English, undoubtedly seadogs (pirates?), as well.

Not realizing the full extent of my briny background when we were first married, the slow discovery of it was a source of delight to my husband, and on many a storm-tossed night we donned our oilskins, jumped into the car and sped to the wildest waterfront we could think of. Standing at what we considered a safe distance from some sea wall, fascinated by the jousting peaks of foam rearing and smashing themselves into a soapy frenzy for our enjoyment, our faces would be streaming with rainwater, augmented by swampings of seawater, our stolen kisses laced with the tang of the surf.

Even saltier than my own was my husband's genealogy, for sea captains had sailed out of nearly every generation of his. That he

My late husband, Robert Somerby Harris (Steve's dad).
"Ledgewinds" was built as a memorial to him.

chose to become an instructor in law, government and history was a far cry from that of the seagull; nevertheless, his heritage did not go unheeded, for he became a lecturing member of the Boston Power Squadron, taught sailing during his summer vacation months, and even pulled back the canvas on our small boat "anchored" in off seasons in the side yard of our first little house on Mt. Hood.[4]

On many a mild winter evening I looked out to see Bob in his heavy jacket under the rays of the post lantern, sitting in the stern of the *Sea Comber* (combing nothing but the snow on the lawn), puffing away on his pipe with that summer-sea look in his eyes.

Directly after his death, with my heart still under the canvas, I sold the boat even before I sold the house, for I couldn't bear the empty sight of it.

In considering the United States Navy as a career, our son must have felt these ancestral tides on both sides of him sweeping him along to his decision.

Life was a whole new ballgame now, and like my buddies in the park below, I must try to play it cheerfully and abide by the rules.

Visitors to "Ledgewinds"—the name we put under the post lantern—who shifted gears or cursed silently scudding over winter ice in ascending the steep hills to get to it, or who climbed or biked its hills in the heat of summer, as dozens of my former junior high and elementary pupils did, upon reaching the summit, unanimously pronounced it worth the effort. ("Ooooooh, Man!")

There were U. S. Navy visitors, as well—

Like the legendary Lorelei lying in wait for unwary sailors on a rock along the Rhine, my Siren of the Sky,—or *Mother's Mausoleum on the Mountain,*" as Steve dubbed it,—had likewise lured her quota of seafarers, though hardly for the sport of wrecking their vessels in order to dine upon their succulent young bodies. Oh—quite the contrary! The Naval Shipyard in Charlestown was a mere seven miles from Mother's Mausoleum's well-stocked larder, and I must say the house hardly sounded like a repository for the dead when Steve filled it with fellow officers whenever his ship came into port.

Historical accounts associated with my new location became more meaningful now. During King Philip's War, Boston Rock was a signalling station for the Wampanoag tribes, as Gilbert and I discovered when we unearthed arrow and spearheads while shoveling out soil from the rear ledges for natural garden pools. Here, also, once dwelt a heartbroken hermit who fairly cried himself to death. His do-

---

[4]One of the many wooded promontories on the rim of the city.

Views from "Mother's Mausoleum on the Mountain"

Music Room Views: Collage of First and Third Picture Windows — Pine Banks Park Below (left)

mestic plantings still flourish alongside wild rock flora. Most hair-standing of all, is the mystery of a reappearing apparition which rises right out of the sea and roams the rocks after a rousing nor'easter! (You'll meet this Phantom of the Foam later on in my story.)

While I steered as much "busyness" as I could manage into the "aching void" after Bob's death, I found I leaned upon Steve's judgment as never before.

Indeed, my greatest solace, and at the same time the most poignant reminder of my loss, was the growing awareness that Steve, while not the Adonis his father was,[5] was very much like him, endowed with the same loyalties,—"square" ones like respect for God, home, country, job, fellow man, etc., reflecting his dad's cheerfulness and love of life, all modestly ruled over by a logical mind which hid its propensities behind a mask of comfortable humor.

Yes, the affable disposition beneath the ruddy boyish complexion ruffled no one, and while he was a nice guy to have around for his "spiritual" aura, he evidently hid a more practical one, for when he shouldered his Navy bag for ports unknown, all household appliances were found to be repaired or improved. "Mr. Fixit," his dad and I used to call him,—a real wizard with wires.

Even the more reserved manner we all noticed following the death of his most beloved companion (his dad, who died during Steve's junior year at college), did not prevent him from carrying the joy and love of the household right out with him whenever he went to sea.

There was little solace to be gained from the skyrocketing tax rate once my brainwave bounced off the drawing board, however, an enigma which nudged me into remaining longer than anticipated on my job as a career teacher. Despite Steve's protracted pilgrimages, between Gilbert's dry humor and my fourth grade funsters, I achieved a noteworthy triumph over loneliness. I was deliriously fond of youngsters, anyway, and found that by returning to elementary teaching from Junior High (General Music), I was entering a welcome change of enrollment (a splashdown of 710 to 28 pupils, to be exact). Not only that, my vocal cords were salvaged between Sundays.[6]

This package of nine-year-old pixies I was teaching now furnished

---

[5]My husband, in his off hours, modeled for clothing and general magazine advertisements, if coaxed hard enough. A neighbor, a professional photographer, talked him into it.

[6]In four years of teaching General Music in junior high, my songsters in Coolidge School mushroomed from 650 to 710, and the countdown to a mere 28 elementary pupils represented (besides marking 710 report cards) a valid reduction in responsibility and tension. A soloist job on Sundays kept me in tune, to prevent my becoming crazy enough some year to go back "Up the Down Staircase" to Melrose Junior High—(which, incidentally, I did!).

me with all the maternal bliss of a busy mother hen. This year there seemed to be more than just those few lucky prizes hiding in the annual carton of cherubs. Along with their occasional blurbs of sheer wisdom, they loosed bright shafts of hilarity into each day of the fast-moving schedule. At times my mopsters carried their mirth clear into my dreams, for on many an ice-capped evening my big canopy bed seemed warmer and less empty when I lay there reviewing the more pithy of their home anecdotes or classroom quips, sententiously smiling myself into oblivion. ("Why sure, Kathy, you know what a *Chihuahua* is—it's one a' them l'il Mexican jumping beans!")

Second only to my affection for its youth, was my starry-eyed fixation for my native city, homesite of four generations of my family. Once called *The Bedroom of Boston,* later *The Spotless Town* (little crime, no Sunday movies, no sale of liquor, debt free), today it is known as *Hockey Town, U.S.A.,* a well-deserved label, for Melrose has sent to Dartmouth College alone (in Hanover, New Hampshire) at least *ten* of its varsity team hockey captains.

A musical city, Melrose owned one of the three greatest pipe organs in the country at one time, and gave lungroom to several grand opera stars,[7] and house room to Phineas Upham, to whom most historians credit the salute to the flag. We had a Navy King, too.[8] Yes, Melrose is a fair city of rocks and rills, woods and templed hills—and my heart with rapture thrills to live in it—(until my taxes come due!).

Fondly I viewed its remains (it looked pretty dead in January) each morning from my bedroom windows upstairs at the front of the house. Even now at 3:33 p.m. it appeared more pristine than it probably was, napping down there under its blanket of snow.

I forfeited the red chair for the emerald velvet cushion in the bow window in order to watch the 3:35 threading itself between rows of red brick, white-columned apartments lining the hollow. In a couple of hours, more frequent commuter trains would begin disgorging our Boston toilers into these fairer and sweeter-smelling environs in which to slumber. Gilbert, the bachelor brother who lived with me, would be among them.

As I walked past the gold chair, I could feel the "eyes" of my invisible imposter upon me!

---

[7]Geraldine Farrar, Elena Kirmes, Marion Selee, Louise Bernhardt, Dorothy Schultes—(and almost me!).

[8]Steve was proud to serve aboard the destroyer *Forrest Sherman,* named for a Melrose man, Admiral Forrest P. Sherman, a U.S. Chief of Naval Operations, and the youngest Naval officer ever to hold this high post. His brother, Paul, a Brigadier General, was in my Melrose High School class.

Yes, despite its tuneful advent, Ole January, as always, had not proved "cricket" at all.

Nevertheless, this morning had started out as the first commendable exception, occasioned by Mother Hen's triumphal return to the Beebe Elementary Nest at 8:15 a.m.

My three week's absence from Coop 4 apparently had endeared me to my chicks the more—and vice-versa—if the chirping, jumping and clinging were a reliable barometer. The "barn," at any rate, was flooded with sunshine despite leaden skies without, and the children whizzed to work as if Santa Claus had come to town.

Oddly enough, shortly before noon, a feeling of impending disaster swamped my thinking and clouded out the "sun"; while at the same time Grade Four's room temperature—or should I say "climate"?—dropped to a chilling level. It was at this juncture our nebulous "visitor" drifted into our midst and decided to remain—really quite unlike any caller I had entertained in my many years of teaching!

My frostbitten nerves signalled that something,—but some "Thing" had surely strayed in fresh from the Psychogenic Sphere of Seers and Spirits,—or wherever such Air-Walkers hail from!

Male or female and entirely unseen, Mr. Psychic Vicissitude or Miss Prophetic Paranormalcy, or some such entity bearing another metaphysical pseudonym (that augured evil?) was truly in our company.

What in Heaven's (Hades'?) name *was it trying to tell me?* Well, shades of Edgar Cayce, whatever it was, was giving me a sick headache!

Round-eyed attention under the Reading Tree gave way to intermittent sorties to my side. Had my little ones sensed the ominous advent as well? They seemed unduly affectionate.

As the morning waned, moreover, Mother Hen herself seemed to be approaching the brink of a sort of mental precipice across which she had to lean in order to reach her babies, a precipice over which she had no desire to peer.

Oh brother! Wait 'til the Teachers' Room crowd heard this one! They'd think the flu-bug had bitten away my brain. Should I tell 'em "It" had followed me home, too? (No, they'd be sure to rate me Fresh Fodder for the Funny Farm on that one!) . . . .

My eyes fell on the lovely star-shaped lantern Steve had brought from India. Suspended above the floor garden window, the pretty treasure was trembling on its long bronze chain as if recoiling from insults being hurled against the storm sash by wanton tongues without.

"Keep the lamp burning, Mother!" my voyager always sang out when he left me.

Was he serious? His subtle teasing defied certainty—but I'd keep the lovely thing lighted, anyway, this mariner's beacon, day and night. I'd shopped the Boston stores until I uncovered a powerful ruby-red bulb which I'd put down inside it, wondering if its roseate beams could possibly extend their radiance clear out to Lynn Harbor!

Even my thoughts proved tiring on this mysterious day of days, and out the big window that crowned the cliffs I could see the Purple Cloud Family turning sullen, their swollen faces glowering down on darkening ledges, whose ice-covered peaks charged upward as if to pierce their frowns with lances of polished ebony.

Dusk was marching early.

Miss N. E. W.'s Wind-Boys were now spitting bits of razor-sharp ice into the pretty face of the garden window. Ole January had never seemed nastier.

Oh, dear Heaven, *where was Steve and his lonely little craft on this frigid January night, anyway?*

As if in answer to my silent query, the phone beside me jangled into my reverie. The pain in my head sharpened, yet my hand trembled in anticipation as I reached for it. (Twenty-three days seemed an interminable time to wait for a call when you'd counted every hour of it!)

"Stevo!" I all but cried aloud. . . .He must have returned to the Japanese port for some reason. I knew this call was important to me. It must have been important to my "house guest" as well, for I was aware it had vacated the gold chair and was *standing right beside me!*

"Mrs. Harris?" a cautious male voice began. (How different from Steve's cordial greeting!)

"Yes, this is Mrs. Harris." (I hoped my disappointment was not too apparent.)

"Is this Mrs. Robert Harris, mother of Lieutenant Stephen Robert Harris, Research Operations Officer aboard the U.S.S. Pueblo?"

(Research Operations Officer? So that's what his title was! Other than oceanographic, what sort of "operations" was Steve researching, I wondered? Could it be he was in some area of Naval Intelligence? They couldn't have made a better choice—)

"Mrs. Harris?"

"Yes, yes! I am the mother of Lieutenant Harris. Please continue."

Despite its cool courtesy, the voice sent a sickening surge welling up in my throat, and, to my horror, I found myself listing over the very edge of that—

"This is the First Naval District of Boston, Commander Lowrey here. We've been trying to reach you. We have received an important message concerning your son."

The precipice! Was I about to be shown what had been lying at the bottom of it since noon? This man's voice sounded too impersonal. It had a studied steadiness, as if trained to convey heartbreaking messages with no trace of emotion—

"We have received the following telegram from Naval Headquarters in Washington—Please listen carefully—"

(Dear God! What would his next words be? My head was bursting now—I could scarcely hold the receiver—)

"The U.S.S. Pueblo to which your son is assigned has been boarded by the North Korean Military while the ship was operating in international waters in the Sea of Japan, and has been towed into Wonsan Harbor.

"The Department of Defense has announced that the Pueblo is a Navy Intelligence Collection Auxiliary Ship.

"We will notify you when we have further information on the incident. Do not leave your telephone."

"—Navy Intelligence Ship?—boarded by the North Korean *Military?*—towed into?—"

I begged the Commander to repeat the message, then, in rapid succession, asked all the questions other Pueblo parents and wives must have asked.

At last I was starkly alone. *The Presence* had left the room,—simply evaporated, as if its earthly mission had at this precise moment been fulfilled—

What in the world had Steve been doing off the shores of Communist North Korea?—to be boarded by the *Military?*—then towed into Wonsan!—Wonsan?—Where was Wonsan? My eyes jumped to the big Atlas over on great, great Uncle George Brae's seagoing desk.

If they were *towed,* they were *captured!*

Dear God! Had my only child, this pleasant-hearted, open-faced, self-effacing yet ever-so-promising and dearly beloved son of mine been dragged into limbo—into that cruellest, most callous of all living deaths—become a PRISONER OF WAR?

The floor began to swim slightly.

Did anyone ever faint sitting down?

Act II

ENTER THE VILLAINS

Backdrop
  "Mercy" in a-Basement
    Mother Hen Returns to Nest IV
      "Spirit"-ed Caller to Classroom and Castle
        Questions Without Answers
          Hot Line to Heaven

Due to enfeebling events prior to the epic pronouncement, I most certainly was not in the best of health to receive it.

It was not until Sunday, January 21st, rounding out a three-week battle with influenza, that I descended to the family room fireside for the first time, weaker, if not any wiser for the ordeal.

"After this latest parade of calamities, there's one consolation I can offer you, Good Brother," I greeted my taciturn attendant in a fever-gutted falsetto.

"We've run the gauntlet of disaster. There's absolutely nothing left of a cataclysmic nature that could possibly strike this household now, except the bomb!"

Over the chicken broth he was heating in the kitchen on the other side of the carriage wheel planter, my listener maintained a stoic silence, his customary response when rating my remarks incorrect, superfluous, zany, or all three. This dearth of retaliation on his part today left me a little uneasy. Was it because he was too busy tallying previous devastations to our "new" dwelling?

While not as extensive as that wrought by this latest newsmaker, storm damage suffered before gave local hardware stores a windfall in purchases: pounds of longer nails and screws, rolls of weather stripping, plus pumping, painting, bolting and anchoring devices.

Even the oil truck proved an unfriendly monster, no respecter of amateur landscaping surely, for it chawed and flattened whole clutches of evergreens hidden under windrifts of snow lining the steep driveway.

Spring, summer and fall proved to be no less tempestuous seasons than that ruled over by Miss New England Winter. The hot tongues of autumn woods fires, fanned by dry winds until they licked the edges of our summit, had been kept at bay until reached by city firefighters only by the speedy use of our garden hoses.

Not only had summer thunder showers spanked our inquisitive chimney, there was always that Spring and Summer Sprinting Bee to retrieve our garden umbrellas, a race we invariably lost. Loosening our stoutest bonds to bend to the will of the winds, the billowing beauties first turned themselves inside out, then bounced down over the cliffs into mangled masses of colored rags and steel wire, only to become impaled like broken kites upon the treetops below.

Most dismaying of all was the work of super-muscled vandals, who converted metal garden furniture into a morass of matchsticks when they jammed it into the rock-bottomed pools out back.

Gilbert's chicken broth was approaching me now, and topped off with hot buttered toast smothered in Doris's spiced apple conserve, it helped to inspire pleasanter recollections. Dear Doris and brother Robert in Vermont!

How Steve longed to join us when we drove up there each autumn for our annual apple-picking feast, wandering the grassy lanes of mountain orchards,—leafy green branches all but breaking under the weight of their red-purple or topaz gems. And on down clear to the shores of Lake Champlain, and to Fort Ticonderoga, where our great (can't recall how many greats) grandmother was gently but hastily carried into the safety of its fieldstone walls to give birth to a son. Cannon booming on the ramparts outside told her the Indians were attacking Vergennes again. Years later, an Indian arrow sank deep into her back, killing her as she worked in her little kitchen garden.

Yes, while Steve envied us these apple-chomping, cider-sampling junkets, we envied his being at sea, salt water to our forebears— as well as to us afterbears—being preferable to apple juice.

Donning my new reading glasses, I leaned back in the red easy chair to enjoy a three-week's harvest of get-well cards and messages. Aside from Gilbert's brusque but efficient nursing, nothing promised to speed my recuperation like the packet of letters from my Beebe School banditti I was holding in my hand. These belletristic pearls, replete with poetry and bold-crayoned illustrations of teacher languidly lying abed while they toiled on unabated, were the crowning coup de coude to recovery.[1]

---

[1]One Lord Byron wrote (with reconsiderations):

> Mrs. Harris looks embarrass
> As she lays upon her bed
> We all miss her and will kiss her
> ~~If she isn't dead~~
> When she mends her head.

The Young Men in Her Youth

Robert

Gordon

Alden

Gilbert (Bert)

Willard (Bill)

Author at age three
"I must be a throwback to my Grandmother Van
who served tea at precisely four o'clock
each afternoon."

Gilbert was presently clearing a path for the oilman, for several inches of white flakes had already sifted down.

Where was Steve's little ship on the high seas now? It had left the port of Sasebo on January fifth, rounding the southern tip of Kyushu to the Naval Base at Yokosuka, arriving on the eleventh, Vuokko had written. How long before his ship would leave for the Tsushima Strait and on out into the vast Sea of Japan? Would the crew then head north into severe cold?

With Gilbert outside, here was my opportunity to perform a small rite that brought instant cheer whenever I envisioned it from my sickbed.

Following my husband's death, my five brothers lost no time in spoiling their only little sister, having been rather good at it in the first place. I was now removing the filmy pink cloud-with-lace Robert and Doris had sent me from Vermont.

Rolling up the full sleeves on its matching nightdress, I noticed my act, as always, being caught by a pair of black onyx eyes. Truly, it would appear my little Oriental Goddess of Mercy standing in the floor garden was in league with a Funfooling Fate, and if so, a vixen mala fide she had become. (Of course, only superstitious sillies would believe such supernatural talents seeped out of a chunk of cement!)—(Had those freeze-dried crickets been in cahoots, too?)

Everyone took it for granted the statue had been bought at some Oriental bazaar and carried over the blue by Steve, when, as a matter of fact, I myself had discovered her in, of all places, an antique barn in Maine, lying under a pile of fringed shawls and ancient damask, still fragrant with sandlewood and some other indefinable incense.

"Stonebrains, Baby," I silently saluted her, "you are about to go bye-bye. My Christmas poinsettias will provide a more pleasing sight than those ominous orbs of yours! Your cricket consorts await you."

Summoning more stubbornness than sinew, I placed my arms around the cold, solid neck, yanked her out of her verdant domain, and inch by inch, puff by puff, bopped the 4½ feet of malevolence down over the cellar stairs. If there were any more hexing to be done, let it be to the furnace!

* * * * * *

The following morning, Monday, January 22nd, found me not one iota more robust than Sunday morning, January 21st; but on Tuesday, the 23rd, I decided to make the best of it and return to school, even rising before the sound of Gilbert's shower.

Two hours later, my soda-straw limbs lifted me up long enough to greet the twenty-eight youngsters awaiting my re-entry to scenes of cerebration in Room 12.

With the enthusiasm accorded the first astronauts, they welcomed me back to "earth," the more agile girls leaping up, since I wasn't much taller than they, to plant a kiss on the nearest cheek, the smaller ones leaning hard (a little too hard) against me, grabbing onto anything, even the pleats of my salmon silk suit Alden sent from Saigon.

However punitive, these were the sweetest moments to be alive— if only half-alive. Since Bob's passing, Room 12 had become my little heaven on earth. While not inhabited exclusively by angels, our schoolroom floated on a cloud of mutual admiration. There was no loneliness here, and I could afford to be a strict disciplinarian with no loss of face, for the Voice of Authority flowed from a friendly heart.

With my arms around as many as I could encompass, I managed to sort out and give replies to the guileless questions rushing up at me from the crushing circle, most of them demanding a more detailed accounting for my prolonged absence.

My turn to listen, at last, to their newshoard, the ham in me assumed the rapt expression and bulging eyes required to designate complete enthrallment.

As with all news nowadays, most of it was bad:

Two Classmates down with mumps—"both sides."

One brother soon to be off to Vietnam.

One father home from Vietnam!

One housecat "creamed" by a passing truck (that word again)! Plan Book note: Needed: Lesson in "proper verbs."

One new baby sister, as yet unnamed. (Many on-the-spot suggestions.)

Two dead hamsters—cause of death undetermined, although a younger brother stands accused of substituting lux flakes for dry oatmeal. ("Good clean way to die", one voice commented.)

One runaway brown rabbit—address still unknown.

One miscarriage. (Events leading to "Aunt Mary's" loss given in detail until switched to another channel.)

Complaints that not only the substitute, but the substitute-for-the-substitute were both "chicken" and wouldn't let them go over to the playground on cold days; and not only that, couldn't sing for sour apples—"the way *you* can"—weren't as pretty, etc. (Lesson for today: *Want to be considered pretty? Smile at a young child.*)

One freckled enthusiast hastened to inform me that his arithmetic grades had improved considerably since my absence—did I get his letter?

Eventually Grade Four sat down in earnest to the day's lessons. I, too, sat down with my Group Captains for consultation under the snow-sparkling limbs of our classroom *Reading Tree*.[2] The morning moved slowly, but the noon bell sounded at last, sending one youngster zooming out of his seat to my coat closet. (Teachers were required to accompany students as far as the sidewalk.)

"Thank you, Tim," I said to the agile legs leaping up to get the heavy raccoon coat over my shoulders. "I noticed you held this pet of mine nice and high to keep his paws off the floor." (He was holding it upside down.)

Getting teacher's coat and helping her into it seemed to be the prize assignment of the day. And how its dimunitive worshippers cottoned to this ancient relic of college days,—pulled from its moth crystals whenever raccoon was "in" again—and whose striped-tail pocket rims remained miraculously resilient after years of pupil-pawing and patting. Personally, I've never heard a raccoon bark, but I used to when they "stroked" me at recess.

Recess was a time anyone could be a little silly. Even clucking like a mother hen kept my charges together as no words ever could crossing a convergence of busy streets to get to the playground area, a sort of Dr. Doolittle in reverse.

And now it was lunchtime—but I wanted no lunch. I threw the heavy coat over my arm and panted into the teachers' room as soon as I'd finished my shepherding.

"Girls, something 'wicked bad' is happening somewhere! I must have ESP or Psycho-Sensitivity or you-name-it," I greeted the noon-tide munchers. (I noticed the TV wasn't turned on.)

"Honestly, I feel as if I were teetering on the edge of a precipice, trying not to slip to the bottom of it." I sank into the only unoccupied chair. Not one of our all-female faculty stopped chewing, neither the meaty sandwich-eaters nor the dieting salad-sippers, for noon hours have a way of slipping past "on little cat feet." There was

---

[2]Reading or other study groups actually did sit down to work under a bonafide tree cut from the woods below my cliffs and painted white. During the spring season, it blossomed with multi-pastel crepe paper flowers, their green leaves in two shades "growing" amongst them. Commencing with brilliant hand-cut leaves in the fall, we changed to silver-glitter-snow in winter.

Although a good-sized specimen, we set it on the reading table and let its branches spread out high over our heads. It had an enchanting effect, especially on visitors. It made its greatest hit during the spring season when we filled its branches with hand-painted cardboard birds and hid a bird-song recording under the table with its "green lawn" tablecloth. The effect was truly realistic, not to mention delightful.

always that batch of math papers to correct and marks to record before the bell rang.

"You poor thing, you may have returned too soon after your illness," observed one teacher, going over to the hot plate for coffee.

"Too soon was not soon enough, Gracie. I've been bedded down for three solid weeks!"

"And to be so sick during that blizzard, Eleanor, must have been doubly upsetting," Ruthie Hoyt sympathized.

"I'm glad you could get prompt service after that awful flooding when your pipes burst," Ruthie Odegard added. "Our mutual plumber told me about the damage you suffered."

"We were thinking of sending a St. Bernard up that mountain of yours with a bottle of wine—or is it gin they actually carry?—if you hadn't returned soon," another muncher added. All mumbled in amused agreement.

"Yeah, thanks a bunch. But seriously, girls, I'm worried. I keep thinking of my brothers, Bill and Gordon, way down there in Maine. Maybe they've gone out in deep snow, got separated and are lying hurt and helpless, lost in the frozen woods, or maybe—"

They seemed to find this comical. I suppose I did sound melodramatic to healthy people with hearty appetites. I could eat nothing myself, although intermittently offered tasty snacks on approval. I usually drove home during lunch hour, since I lived reasonably close, to pick up my mail, and get something hot into the empty void besides coffee. But seeing the icy road shimmering like a pale blue ribbon between white drifts, when I accompanied the children out to the sidewalk, suggested nothing of the sort. Yet why the compelling urge to *get on home?*

"Look, dear," the first grade teacher suggested, "if you've got to worry, why not worry about that handsome hunk of brother in Saigon—the Airforce Colonel, the one who had that pizazz suit made for you—is that Robert or Gordon? They're all so good looking."

"It's *Alden*, Ruthie," I replied, smiling ruefully. "He's with AID[3] at the American Embassy. These days, embassies are prime targets. No, I'm positive it isn't he, but don't ask me why.[4] His own son is in Vietnam now, too, a Green Beret Captain.[5] Those blasted rockets

---

[3] Aid to International Development.

[4] Alden was Commanding Officer of the 1946th AACS Squadron at Tempelhof Air Base which operated the Berlin Airlift.

[5] Alden's son was eventually to receive the silver star (among other decorations) awarded at his Fort Belvoir Virginia Hospital bedside by his father.

being fired into Saigon worry me continually—but honestly, some awful thing is—"

"Where is your *son* now, Eleanor?" an older colleague broke in cautiously, a little too cautiously, I thought.

"Steve? Oh, he's off on sea duty again, possibly in the Sea of Japan." (It loomed large and lonely on the Atlas in Room 12.)

"He's aboard an oceanographic research vessel. They're carrying scientists along with the crew to do salt water sampling for some Navy project or other. I miss him terribly—Vuokko, too—since he left the country—such a wonderful guy!"

"He certainly is," returned my friend, Ruthie Odegard, who knew him best. She started to say something else, but decided against it. She seemed to be studying my face, then looked over at Doris.

"Why not have some of our coffee to get you through the afternoon?" the second grade teacher suggested.

I managed a polite refusal to Doris, my mind again immersed in troubled introspection:

"After all," I was thinking, "whoever heard of a United States Naval vessel being lost at sea,—in a *storm*, that is?" I certainly had not! Yet, if that temperamental steering gear had "freaked out" during a bad blow, and because of it the men had drifted helplessly into some alien port, would "slingshots," in effect, represent their only power of resistance to attack?

* * * * * *

And now the "Naval storm" *had* broken (into print all over the Free World) and a ship *was* "lost" in it,—and most terrifying of all, her crewmen, as well!

As I sat stunned in the red easy chair beside the telephone trying to remain conscious, the guarded tones of my official Navy announcer echoed through my thoughts. And even after the message had been repeated, and the voice at the other end of the line grew warmer, few of my many ensuing questions could be answered.

I was shivering uncontrollably and pulled the faithful old raccoon coat, still lying in this chair where I had dropped it, back over my shoulders.

—"Commander Lowrey here"—

"Mrs. Harris? Mrs. Robert S. Harris, mother of—Research Operations Officer—important message concerning your son—Navy Intelligence—ship boarded by the Military—towed into Wonsan"—!!

Yes, this was the message that would rock the world, that would send me hurtling down a precipice for certain. But that which I would encounter in descending to its fullest depths, might prove quite a different story from that which the world about me would normally expect.

"The rest is history" as the saying goes, but in the case of the *U.S.S. Pueblo,* an unprecedented history of shock, insult, dismay, and affrontery that would stun not only the world's "greatest nation" but the entire Free World as well,—this act of ruthlessness unknown in the history of modern sea warfare, this brazen kidnapping of eighty-three U. S. Navymen by a fourth-rate Mini-power which called itself *The Democratic People's Republic of Korea!*

A sovereign United States vessel flying its country's colors, pirated neatly off the Sea of Japan entirely without benefit of military aid, and quickly closeted in the silence of an alien fortress, was something historians would have a field day writing about! (*Would its victims live to tell their version?*)

My aching brain clunked on:

In any dangerous crisis hadn't I read somewhere that there is an instantaneous communications system of some kind between our far-flung U. S. military units and the War Room of the Pentagon? What had happened to it? Had SOS messages concerning the *Pueblo's* plight not been able to pass through all the indeterminate stations in the military chain of command?

(*Yes, Pueblo's cries for help had been stymied en route, just as the warning by North Koreans concerning the harsh treatment to be accorded "the next U. S. ship to 'spy' off their shores" had been stymied, never reaching responsible ears!*)

Why were the men captured at all? We were not at war with North Korea!

Did "intelligence collection" ship really mean *spy* ship, and if so would the men aboard her be considered *spies*—and be *shot*?

To what degree had human frailty affected *Pueblo's* capture? Who was accountable for it? How many were accountable?

But that all could wait—

Where were our lost sons now? What was happening to them? Were their strafed bodies lying mortally wounded on *Pueblo's* decks? There must have been some sort of confrontation with the North Koreans. Who was hurt? How badly? When would we know?

Another question struck me now: Had Vuokko received word of Steve's capture? Or was she already on her way to Japan?

I phoned her in Washington immediately, praying I could muster strength enough to complete the call. She answered at once.

"Yes, Mother," the broken little voice replied in tones so soft I could scarcely hear them. "I knew before they called me that something was happening to Steve. You see, I had—well, it was really a vision. I awoke to see Steve standing before me, in uniform, with a deeply troubled look on his face. Just as I called his name, the vision faded. When official word came a short time ago, I knew then what it was he had been trying so desperately to tell me!" She paused as if fighting for control. (So she had received a forewarning, also! Someday I would tell her about mine—seeing the little gunboats surround the ship!)

"I was just about to call you, Mother," the sorrowful voice in the distance went on. "My Navy advisor agrees that it may be best if I avoid reporters entirely. I don't want to say anything that will jeopardize Steve or his crew. (As if she could!) I have an idea his work on that ship was very important. That's why I'm planning to 'get lost', as my advisor puts it."

"I am also sorry to have to tell you, Mother, that Aiti (Eye-èe-tee—Finnish for "Mother") has now suffered a relapse. I must go to her at once in Montreal. I'll send you a card with the address. They'll (reporters) never find me there, and just as soon as she is better, if there is no change in the news, I plan to take an apartment on the West Coast in order to be near Steve when he returns."

(Neither of us wanted to think "*if* he returns".)

How many other fringe victims would *Pueblo's* capture claim? Had it precipitated Aiti's stroke? Both Vuokko's parents seemed exceedingly fond of their new son-in-law.

"And remember, Mother, God is with Steve wherever he is—You will both be in my prayers—"

Spoken like a dutiful minister's daughter I was thinking, yet I had never been prouder of Steve's bride than I was at this moment. In spite of her compounded tragedies, she would include me in her prayers! Well, this dear child was already sweetening mine. The pretty voice, so tinged with grief, lingered with me like a haunting fragrance. No wonder Steve loved her so deeply. I loved her, too. How keenly the young people must be suffering!

I managed with trembling hands to place long distance calls to Robert in Vermont, Gordon and Bill in Maine, to my husband's sister, Elizabeth, here in Massachusetts, and to other close relatives. I even considered calling Alden at the Embassy in Saigon. I'd simply have to stop worrying about him and those rockets now! Then I realized the news had probably reached him before it got to us, and it would be like him to respond by sending a tape full of excellent advice. He had his very fingertips on the war there and should be able to explain this hostile move.

In the days that followed the newsblast, it seemed as if all other Americans had received the same disrupting phone call I had, so vocal was their anger against the tiny aggressor nation, so vehement their disgust, amazement, their clamor for the immediate release of the defenseless crewmen.

Yes, people everywhere, via mass media, reacted to the vicious act as if their own flesh and blood, their very own sons, were in the clutches of these soulless pirates whose regard for human life was known to be about as tender as a chess player's for his pawn. More than likely, this crime of shiplifting would set the stage for an International Chess Tournament at that!

What merciless yellow hands would clutch the living bodies of our beloved sons and move them about at will?—And when they had served some ugly end, toss them off the chess board to die?

Still sitting in the red easy chair by the telephone, I dropped my head like a rag doll down over my knees to allay the faintness, endeavoring in my frail condition to absorb the stark reality of this newest Ole January nightmare.

Was I, though a rank amateur, being slowly pushed into the company of those "wonderful people" I knew who had undergone fearful trials, presumably to mold them into nobility?—If so, then to Hades with becoming a "wonderful person" via the refinements of torture! —the important thing in this instance was not simply to bear it "nobly," but to *act* in the main victim's behalf!

The blood flowing back into my brain told me Fate was winnowing out another detour in my joyful journey through life. Daily existence, once again, would cease to be that sunflecked sea into which I plunged each morning, breasting its mental challenges, drifting along its currents of artistic and musical adventure, while from its shores, well-wishing friends and relatives tossed fragrant little bouquets of encouragement upon its waters.

My widowhood brought the usual marginal benefits: People were a little kinder, particularly the professional surfers who rode those energy-depleting crests of creativity with me daily. Teachers, who together over a period of years, have charted and channelled the forensic and frenetic forays of youth, enjoy a rapport that is unique, I believe—that I might label "enviable" among people in other professions.

—But now the waters of my singing sea were troubled, the only face rising above its darkening swells being that of my lost sailor. (82 other young heads were also bobbing about in the background of this restless turbulence.) Had I the strength to swim out to my dear one as he clung half-alive—if alive at all—to some pagan reef?

Could I summon the courage, the stamina, the faith, the brain power and vision needed to reach him at Destination Unknown? For who knew where the crewmen had been taken for imprisonment—or execution? I'd lost faith in my country's rescue-power.

In the few tragic moments my life had known, my initial move had been in the direction of God. Why, in these latter years, had I waited only for sorrow to send me to Him? Whatever had become of that transcendent Oneness I used to know, when in some church choir I sang my way to the very Gates of Heaven?—or thought I did!

Oh, to recapture that celestial rapport I'd so carelessly mislaid along the Paths of Time!

I felt certain that if Steve had had to abandon ship, he'd have managed to seize his Bible and secrete it somewhere on his person.

(This turned out to be true, although he was forced to surrender it when a submachine gun pointed to the bulge in his Navy jacket and a vicious hand reached in and tore it from him.)[6]

Somehow I could not bring myself to turn on the TV in Gilbert's bedroom on the first floor. I had managed to catch him at his bank, relaying the news and asking him not to remain in town for dinner as originally planned, but to hurry home as soon as possible.

A terrible weakness came over me—a familiar loneliness—

"Prayer is the means by which God's power is released into human life" were the words which came to me.

Was the Great Comforter already speaking to me down through the bleakness of the January night?

I slid to my knees beside the easy chair, turned, and cradled my aching forehead in the cups of my palms, resting them heavily against the wide seat for support. A feeling of emptiness, of frail humility and utter dependence suffused my whole being:

Had the loving life of this only son of mine merely been loaned to me by heaven—for a little while? Must I return the Golden Gift to his Creator now? No! No! I must "reach" both Heaven—and beyond a prison wall—"According to your faith be it unto you—"

---

[6]Probably believing it to be a code book. Even the crudely fashioned cross of a devout sailor was kicked about his room by a North Korean "Room Daddy" as if it embodied some supernatural power. Who knows?—perhaps by this time a few N.K.'s with the necessary education have read Steve's Bible and "seen the light!"

"Dear Father in Heaven," I pleaded, "send me the strength to bear this burden as I know you are sending Steve the strength to bear his—wherever he may be—

Restore my health, Dear God, that I may serve him effectively, through Thee.

Place Thine everlasting arms, I beseech Thee, beneath him and his crew, supporting their young bodies, and preserving their minds, throughout the pressures of whatever ordeals lie before them.

Remain with them! Watch over them! Embue them with Thine immeasurable affection—and spare them for those who love them so dearly!

This I ask in the name of Thine own dear Son, Jesus Christ.

Amen."

* * * * * *

During a sleepless night, I "wrote" to Steve:

Journey in Faith

Dear son of mine, torn from my heart,
　　Behind unyielding walls you wait—
Walls that promise no escape
　　Without the Will of Time and Fate.

But I shall find your prison walls;
　　My compass rose God's Hand does bear;
I'll smash each lock, and burst each bond
　　By Force of Faith—and Pow'r of Prayer!

My Tide of Trust shall tender waves
　　Upon whose crests my Love will ride—
To wash upon those pagan shores,
　　And on to shield you at your side.

Dear son of mine, torn from my heart,
　　Your walls *will* yield as you await—
For *God* can walk through Wall or Gate,
　　And bend the Will of Time and Fate!

Act III

"HELL WEEK" AT HOME[1]

Music of the Press—Opening Chant by Off-Key Trio
  "Illuminated" Lessons in Grade Four
    Pain by E.S.P.
      Housebreak—Heartbreak—Newsbreak
        Communists in Cliffsville?

The same Tuesday evening of the ship's capture the phone was abnormally quiet; however, it was ringing lustily when I left for school
Wednesday morning. Assuming newshounds had already caught the
scent of a Bostonian aboard the ill-fated *Pueblo*, I chose to bypass it.
Moreover, since "not leaving my phone" had earned me no further
news from headquarters, I phoned them, requesting the First Naval
District people to refer all calls to Beebe School during teaching
hours.

My good principal stood ready to do battle for me after learning
Steve was among *Pueblo's* captives, knowing there would be an onslaught of newsmen once he was identified and they learned his
mother's whereabouts. I told her if they persisted in seeing me to
give them my home phone number "for use after five." I had no
intention of looking up and seeing them "sitting under my Reading
Tree" as Gilbert had forewarned, nor playing games with me at
recess, either. I had my suffering all cut out for the day, thank you!

As I drove my little car down the snowy hills to work, my brain
was throbbing with questions:

Were there other Massachusetts men aboard the stricken vessel? If
so, had their mothers slept as fitfully as I? Were their scanty dreams
charged with the faces of their captured sons and remembered bits
of their last conversations together? (*"Seriously now, Steve, what
would you do if you were actually attacked?*—attacked?—attacked?")
His carefree answer as he caught up his beloved in his arms persisted
in playing a tattoo on my mind the whole night through. ("Huh?—
oh, I dunno—use *slingshots,* I guess—use slingshots—slingshots—slingshots, I guess—")

---

[1]As opposed to "Hell Week" in North Korea. (Final week of torture.)

Had Steve ever succeeded in getting those "Mafia rejects" put aboard?   And if so, why hadn't they been used against *seagoing* gangsters?

> (The two 50-calibre machine guns, *U.S.S. Pueblo's* only "heavy" weapons, were snugged down solid under frozen tarpaulins.   Rear Admiral Frank Johnson had even suggested to the ship's captain, "Pete" Bucher, that he keep them hidden below decks!   "You're not out there to start a war," warned he.)

Did other *Pueblo* relatives feel as stunned, helpless, and sick-at-heart as I this first morning after the shipnapping?—sick that our giant of a country had so stupidly declared itself vulnerable to a midget of a half-nation?   Was it a case of the elephant and the mouse, or our sea watchers not getting this tiny *Pueblo* twig in their sights because of the forest?

Like Gilbert and me, had wives and parents, young brothers and sisters huddled together glued in anxiety to their TV's and radios as long as news was carried into the night, straining to hear the word "*Pueblo*" or "crewmen?"   If so, they'd not been disappointed, for the brazen act of piracy on the high seas was on the lips of every newscaster.   Both they and the terra firma sea strategists were having a ball.

For the loved ones keeping the night-long watch, however, it was no ball—yet there was always a flickering hope that some intercepting bulletin would mercifully end the shattering pain by announcing that the whole bit had been a gigantic hoax of the North Koreans, just a freedom-of-the-seas "Imperialist"-defying gag, a bit of briny derring-do for propaganda-mongering.

If, after demonstrating to a wide-eyed world that our sovereignty of the seas was pure saga, would the pranksters then return our men to us?   All, that is, except those who got in the way of their toy pistols?

Regrettably this was not the intention of the North Koreans.   In fact, there was no information whatsoever issuing from abroad concerning the whereabouts or fate of the Navymen.

> (At gunpoint they were herded together and forced to squat on the fantail and forecastle of their vessel, some lightly clad, in below-freezing temperatures.   Sheets were ripped from bunks and made into blindfolds, and many a mouth, head, or stomach felt the maiming thrust of a rifle butt.   Eventually the men were driven like blind cattle off the ship and put on buses.

"Capture Class" No. 1.

"Capture Class" No. 2.

Later, arriving in strange territory, they heard and felt, but could not see, a spitting populace who jeered at the parade, armed with clubs they were restrained from using. One guard,—Steve thought it must be a guard because of his brute strength,—stepped forward and smashed him full in the mouth. Not only was he unable to see his adversary, but because his hands were tied, the warm blood flowed unchecked down onto his neck and chest, and froze into a solid mass.

That was just for openers. Upon arrival at their first destination, husky North Korean soldiers lined up on each side of their 82 blindfolded captives and lunged at them from both sides as the half-frozen men walked the gamut of shock and pain to "the Barn," their first bleak prison.)

Solons at the Capital, for all their frothing at the mouth, were equally devoid of news if not of noise; for politicians of varying stature feverishly emptied all manner of hypothetical notions into defenseless mikes, with absolutely nothing of substance to report.

Certain Senators "Know-All," and fellow armchair sages from the states of "Should've" (particular favorites of *Pueblo* sailors) fairly wagged their wattles off for televiewers: "They should've scuttled the ship, they should've opened fire, they should've made a run for it," should've, should've, should've. (All of which Gargantuan Guessers, as Brother Gilbert pointed out, *"should've" shut up!)*

(Information based on the testimony of Gene H. Lacy, *Pueblo's* Warrant Officer at the Naval Court of Inquiry revealed that her crewmen could *not* have scuttled the ship within any reasonable space of time, for her pipes (she had no seacocks) were well nigh inaccessible, and the procedure would have taken at least two and a half hours. The ship, moreover, was standing in only 30 fathoms!

During these "heroic" hours, would crewmen simply have shifted from one foot to the other waiting to die? or like movie versions of "great tradition," stood stiffly at attention until the frigid waters gurgled over them?

If they had done so, they would have "heroically" given the North Koreans 82 well-trained young American lives in addition to their ancient ship, all two-and-one-half million dollars-worth of its highly sophisticated electronic equipment, and every secret paper intact.[2]

---

[2]Newspapers placed its value at one hundred million. Its actual value of two-and-one-half million, however, is nothing to sneeze at when you think about it. H'm? Divers could have recovered the papers easily from only 30 fathoms (180 feet) of water.

Oh, by all that's Navy, "Don't give up the ship!" No, give up 82 healthy young men instead, and all their secrets with them!

Commander Bucher did exactly the right thing in this mother's estimation. He fought for *time* and *life,* keeping the armed aggressors baffled, while his men and Steve's broke their backs to destroy everything their meagre devices for destruction allowed.

"I saw no reason to send men needlessly to their deaths. It was a slaughter out there." (Ship's Captain)

"There wasn't a man among us who wouldn't have given his life for his country if it had done any good. Scuttling the ship and going down with her would have been easy compared to what we had to go through!" (*Pueblo's* Crewmen)

Brooding over the lost captives brought me a realization of how tragically their counterparts were reflected in the ancient classic which, when I read it to them, always brought big, sad eyes to fourth-graders. For as with the Pied Piper of Hamelin, the mountain had yawned open, swallowed our children, and left us standing dazed and lonely in the deathlike silence.

With a mind torn by anxiety, I waded into the day's lessons. My pupils, along with students the country over, were abuzz over this high-seas hijacking of a U.S. Naval vessel flying its country's flag.

An excited class welcomed "Newstime" as never before. In their textbooks and on display maps and globes, chubby fingers pressed down on the Sea of Japan and North Korea. Several found them quickly after seeing maps in the morning papers. Wonsan Harbor did not show clearly on our big wall atlas. Were the men still there, or had they been spirited inland to some unpronounceable hamlet— and become lost to the world?[3]

I thought it prudent to withhold my secret a while longer. Knowing teacher had had a son aboard the famous vessel would bring chaos to an already high-keyed classroom, as well as vocal explosions that in my sleepless state would not be particularly therapeutic.

With deadpan expression, I drew my chair into the slower-moving group in Social Studies, a logical subject on this eventful morning. The remainder of the class pushed their desks together, forming self-propelled cliques, depending little, if any, upon my remote control (unless argument proved more abrasive than reason). Group cap-

---

[3]Lost to the world—and to the World of Washington, as well!

tains and secretaries had been coached previously for leadership.

"The country of Guatemala," a childish voice in my small circle started reciting—

(Guatemala? No, Dear, *North Korea!* Let's learn more about the people of *North Korea,* their history, their ideology, their characteristics. Characteristics? My wandering thoughts remembered a certain young flier, a prisoner during the North Korean Conflict,— brilliant, charming, the son of a friend of mine, just a human vegetable now. They'd pulled the wire too tight, too long, around his forehead when they tortured him.)

"My paper is about climate," another little voice, a bit unsteady began.

"The climate of El Salvador is—" (freezing, freezing, the men are freezing, wounded, dying in the cold,—sick, starving, bleeding, but where? Oh, not in nice warm El Salvador, my pretty one!)

> (One *Pueblo* crewman was horribly wounded in the lower abdomen, with no hospitalization for days. He bled profusely and his roommates kept him alive with whatever they could find to stanch the flow. Eventually the stench from his festering wound became so overpowering, his "nurses" opened the door to his cell and vomited into the corridor, inadvertently forcing the guards to do something about it. Removed, at last, on a blood-soaked stretcher, he was operated on *sans anesthesia.* Worse yet, soon after being returned from the hospital to rejoin his roommates, still weak and half sick, he was dragged out and beaten as severely as the others.)[4]

I must force my meandering mind to adhere to the lesson. These little moppets sitting around me studying my face so intently must not be deprived of love because of my own deprivation. I must give them the whole loaf, as always—

"Now, Cindy, think carefully. Was climate the real reason for your choice of country? Have you done enough background reading on Central America to make a fair selection?"

The blue eyes rolled up to mine gratefully. "N—no, not really, Mrs. Harris," and dimples slowly sugared the little face.

"Know somethin', Mrs. Harris?" squeaked a tiny lad in the group, as if Cindy's dimples had reminded him of it, "you f'got to smile at us this morning."

(Had my tenseness reached them, despite the close guarding of my secret?)

---

[4]Fireman Steven E. Woelk.

"You don't say, Teddy! How's this?" and I did a Bugs Bunny with eyes a-poppin', my new reading glasses teetering on the tip of my nose.

The class cackled in noisy appreciation. Teacher was really a rocket!

Lesson for today: *A bit of ham now and then is highly recommended for "scholarly" refreshment.*

The morning moved slowly—would eleven o'clock ever arrive? (Radio newstime)

"Six times four is twenty-four," two lively opponents were chanting in the Magic Clock Math contest. "Zero times four is"— (Zero! Zero in and help those Navy men! Why didn't you zero in, you fliers!??)

"One times four is four." (Only four bowls of rice for eighty-two men? Zero bowls? How many days does it take to starve? How many men were wounded? Three times one or three times twenty-one? How many men were dead? One times eighty-three? Was Steve still alive? Oh, when would I know?)

The ten o'clock bell was ringing. Milk Time! I snapped out of the doldrums and called cheerily, "Attention, Milk and Cookie Captains, kindly remember to wash your hands thoroughly before attending to duties."

(Wash! Could a solid-thinking, knowledgeable twenty-nine-year-old be brainwashed? I simply couldn't imagine a person with Steve's broad understanding of human nature and sense of humor being brainwashed. Or would North Koreans play more lethal games with their electronically-educated victims?)

> More cruel, for certain. ("You could hear men screaming twenty-four hours a day. They had a way of torturing you that left no marks. They were experts at it, trained in Moscow.")

"Wash your hands." Had crewmens' hands been tied tightly for long hours in the sub-zero weather, cutting off circulation?

> (Steve's wrists were bound so tightly across his chest that both hands swelled to the size of small footballs and turned black. He could feel nothing in them for days and thought he would lose them after a surly guard had grudgingly cut the cords.)

The pre-recess fable having reached its happy and moralistic ending, I smiled my thanks to the little owl-eyed librarian wearing glasses, who was not only returning *Aesop* to the Browsing Bookworm's Book Bank but straightening all the other volumes there as well. Fourth graders had not yet graduated to the "do-as-little-as-possible-and-get-as-much-as-possible-for-doing-as-little-as-possible" school of thinking. This age-level still clung to the tenets that labor is laudable, school is not a drag, and that people like you better if you're polite.

"The milk is nice an' cold today," whispered Frankie hoarsely to a friend across the aisle, punctuating the observation with satisfying slurping sounds. I didn't correct the curly-mopped culprit, for the little girl's glasses had alerted me to another terrifying possibility:

Steve's eyes! Had Oriental fists smashed at them, jamming his contact lenses deep into them? (Not quite)

> ("If he wasn't satisfied with the 'sincerity' of my replies,
> the guard snapped his fingernails into my eyes. The pain
> was sharp. I saw lightning every time.")

The chocolate cookies going the rounds of the class melted horribly into mutilated black pupils filling an entire eye socket!

> (Steve's contact lenses steamed off with the purloined
> prize in his shirt pocket, along with 500 pounds of prime
> beef steaks, the latter loss being more keenly felt than that
> of the lenses,—really not surprising when subsisting on a
> sparse daily ration of warm drinking water, rancid turnip
> soup, reeking fish, and cold, glue-ish rice. Artfully, Steve
> used his loss of lenses as an excuse for not being able to
> read the propaganda literature thrust upon him, which ruse
> came to a swift demise when a guard gifted him with a
> pair of crudely fashioned spectacles.)

I must try to anchor my thoughts to this side of the world:

"Thank you, 'Captain'!" I said to the youngster holding out a carton of cold milk in pudgy grip. I worried it down, but declined the cookies.

"Don'tcha like these kind, Mrs. Harris?" asked a solicitous Cookie Captain. "If ya don't, there's a few left with raisins in 'em at the bottom of the tin up back."

(*This* kind, Kevin—and no raisins today, dear boy; they'd probably be black and dry anyway, like say—*dead crickets!*)

"Thank you, Kevin, but I'm afraid I left my appetite at home today. You've been very thoughtful, however, so you may have my cookie."

The intercom buzzed. It was my principal, and her voice had its usual pleasant timbre, suggesting no reporters had invaded the front office—yet!

"Just wanted to know if you're all right? . . .Good, then why not have a student teacher take the children over to recess, and come down to the teachers' room and turn on the TV. Then tonight, go home early. Remember, just go with the children."

How kind she was! I was reminded of the dark days following Bob's death. The voice was continuing—

"Eleanor, dear, *really now,* how is everything going so far?" ("So far"? Yes, *so far—North Korea was so far, far away!* Would these "lost" sailors ever find their way home? Would the 82 be abandoned after years of imprisonment only to drift off one by one into strange terrain to starve and die? Or eventually be shipped to parts unknown to slave out their days in some labor camp? Long-lost American prisoners of war reportedly had been seen working in the mines of Siberia!)

Through my mind flashed the true account of a World War II father, a widower whose only child was reported missing in action. Refusing to believe his beloved son was dead, the grief-stricken parent spent the remainder of his active life wandering from country to country, hospital to hospital, prison to prison, and finally grave to grave, eventually drowning in his own Sea of Agony—for he died in a hospital for the insane.

"Uh—oh, I'm sorry. Yes, the children have been wonderful, really, Irma! Thank you for your thoughtfulness. Now that trouble has come my way once more, may I say again I am ever so grateful to be teaching at Beebe!"

* * * * * *

U. S. S. PUEBLO SEIZED IN INTERNATIONAL WATERS
KOREAN REDS SEIZE U. S. SHIP
CAPITOL IN TURMOIL ON PIRACY
SHIP WAS U. S. *EYES AND EARS*

Was Steve the officer in charge of both "Eyes and Ears?"

Why hadn't the U. S. Navy used fishing trawlers for monitoring unfriendly shores just as the Russians did? When a Soviet trawler went ashore off West Africa, as soon as the tide went down, her long bottom was seen to be bristling with sonar devices for listening to underwater movements!

As my little car ascended the steep hills to home port, I used my free hand to find each new headline in the papers lying on the seat beside me:

CARRIER ENTERPRISE UNDER WAY
(You're too late with that lassoo, Enterprise!)
REDS REFUSE TO RETURN PUEBLO
DOES INCIDENT MEAN NEW WAR?
(The Prize Poser)

Yes,—Would our country forsake its 82 Navymen rather than risk launching World War III?

Within seconds after I hung up Ole Raccoon, the telephone was ringing—but so was the doorbell. Had newsmen followed the car? Although clearly seen from any vantage point in the city, Ledgewinds was not easily located.

"It's probably Phyllis," I decided. She knew about the *Pueblo,* and it would be like her to come bearing consolation in the form of something delectable from her spotless kitchen next door. But, no, she used a familiar knock, or called out to me.

I dropped my aching head against the back of the chair and let everything ring away.

Oh, for a drink of cold water! I could feel my temperature trending upward again. My auditory nerves, nevertheless, proved more sensitive than my thirst. I started for the door—

("Just cackle like a worried mother hen." More likely a very dumb chick! Brother Gilbert had advised me thus in dealing with reporters.)

Why should the life of a fine person I loved be laid bare to mollify some scribbler?   Or worse yet, the information end up being used as a fulcrum to aid the harsh inquisitors of North Korea?

I opened the door to find a trio, one with the inevitable camera, peering through the picture window on the front porch, whose identical twin at the opposite end of the dining room wing framed Boston seven miles beyond. Ascending the steps on a clear night, one came face to face with a panorama of scintillating beauty. The three men were enjoying its daytime appeal.

"I'm sure you gentlemen realize my delicate position as the mother of an officer held by a hostile nation," I demurred in response to their questions. "Undoubtedly the North Koreans maintain a clipping service in this country, and I don't intend to supply information that will feed it. The less they learn about my son and his crew the better, and I'm positive he would want it that way."

I tried to sound stoic above my parched throat and willowy legs, not to mention my *Pueblo* headache, a star boarder since the fateful telephone call. (Aspirin or any of its rival medications only nauseates me.) "I'm sure you men can appreciate both situations."

If my three interrogators did appreciate either one, they had a strange way of showing it, for the questions purred on, taking devious avenues of approach to coax out replies. I could scarcely "draw their attention to the view out back then shut the door," for they had already seen it from the front, were securely inside, and obviously had no intention of early departure. I sank again into the easy chair, my flu-weakened knees pure H_2O. I'd give the soft-violin approach a whirl:

"I realize you gentlemen have to earn a living from whatever news sources you can uncover on your daily assignments. I have to earn my living as well. However, I must protect the interests—the life of my son—since the situation he is now in must be extremely dangerous—I might say 'explosive'. Whatever you write could provide grist for the North Korean propaganda mills and be used against the crew. For all I know, at this very moment they may be torturing Steve for facts about his background. I'm sure you understand, gentlemen," I concluded.

They nodded sympathetically, then went right on pressing—sotto voce. And while one was vocalizing, the others glanced about the house, wandering unobtrusively from kitchen to family room, peering out the bow window at distant vistas and murmuring complimentary remarks, during which exploration I thought I caught the sound of a distant click or two. Were they taking pictures of pictures?

I was relieved that the stairway to the second floor was out of sight. There were three gorgeous wedding photos of Vuokko on the piano up there, and I had no intention of letting them know Steve was married.

Oh, to have a naval advisor as my daughter-in-law had! This being a "secondary" relative had its drawbacks!

Eventually I dredged up a knockout punch. This should really ring down the curtain!

"Gentlemen, may I remind you that as yet we *Pueblo* relatives have received no directive from the Navy Department concerning our rôle regarding news coverage," (my thirst was killing me), "another reason I'm being conservative, and that is all I have to—"

Instead of ringing down the curtain, my "knockout punch" rang it up on Act II, for one man zoomed to the phone and started dialing while another explained with some exhilaration that their paper had access to just the source I sought and would even pay for the call; and although our mutual "vibrations" had not meshed from the start, I took the phone in hand, trusting this was the shortest route to getting rid of them (as well as getting a drink of water!) and conversed with what did turn out to be an official source.

My Navy "contact" in D. C. seemed not surprised to hear from me and even approved my stance, although sermonizing at the outset that we had a "free press" in our country (altogether too "free," sometimes turning a nauseating pink in reporting military happenings, I was to learn).

My telephone advisor went on to inform me that Pueblo relatives would not be "muzzled" as people were in Communist nations; that in my case, however, now that I must be aware of Steve's duties aboard ship, it would be wise to act with perspicacity. I could both aid the North Korean propaganda machine and do my overseas prisoner a disservice by revealing unnecessary facts. (Our "vibrations" meshed perfectly here!)

Yes, my advisor sounded as if Steve really had been in charge of the ship's priceless surveillance instruments!

I reported the Navy man's suggestions to the trio hovering so cozily, although undoubtedly they had overheard all of it.

For some reason during their visit, my inquisitors kept referring to Steve as *Executive Officer,* and I did not correct them, for I was not absolutely certain what his duties or rank entailed, myself. Then, too, a devilish impulse to toss a few grains of sand into the gears of the North Korean propaganda machine smothered my initial desire to alter their impression.

> (A regrettable omission on my part; for naming Steve Executive Officer (instead of Ed Murphy, the real exec.), may have set in motion the vicious lie that this affable son of mine and Commander Bucher were not on friendly terms. They have *always* been on friendly terms, regardless of the division of command (a ship within a ship) with Steve in sole charge of its thirty technicians.
>
> Commander Bucher and the real executive officer, it turned out, did not enjoy good rapport.)

Feeling like a withered balloon after the trio left, I commenced my unsteady journey for the carafe of ice water in the pretty aqua refrigerator that matched the walls and floor of the open kitchen. I had progressed as far as the room divider, the planter with the vine-covered carriage wheel, when I had to throw out both hands and clutch the spokes of it to keep from falling!

From out of nowhere a stabbing pain sliced down, tearing into my vitals as if someone had pushed a knife through them, while at the same moment a dreadful truth clicked into my consciousness. I crouched down in agony, one hand still clinging to the wheel. "*Steve*

—*Oh Steve!"* the mother in me moaned, "What are they doing to you? *What are they doing to you?"*

The searing pain, a hundred times more powerful than my *Pueblo* headache, crawled up through my body and brain. I shuddered uncontrollably, digging my nails into the hard wood of the polished wheel, my palms crushing the cool leaves of the philodendron to a limp wetness.

The pain then receded slowly, its only after-effect being a strange foreboding. (of death?)

As I drew myself back up to a standing position, I knew for a fact that the source of the awesome hurt lay thousands of miles away in a Far Eastern prison, "sent" by some force beyond man's computation, perhaps generated by a deep human need, as if the very soul of this offspring of mine were straining across miles of sand and sea to tell me something. Tell me *what? Did I really want to know?* Could I *bear* to know? *What did this skirmish with psychodynamics infer?*

> (At this precise hour Steve was summoned before a stone-faced general and "court" of the North Korean People's Army and told he *would be shot to death at sundown,* along with the thirty men who served under his command! Commander Bucher was informed that he would be required to stand by and watch the execution of each of the 82 survivors, one by one, commencing with the youngest and then be shot himself!)

Toward the end of the week we learned that during the one-sided sea battle, four men had been wounded and one killed. "Was it my son, my husband?" each relative would ask, for no names were revealed. (North Korea's psychology of delay and frustration to force capitulation of some kind?) How well they knew we Americans are impatient people!

I was positive the young Navy man who was dead was killed while destroying classified material, possibly blown up by one of those modern push-button mechanisms news media promised us would be aboard the ship. Had "Mr. Fixit," with one thought in mind, rushed to his "wires" and given his life to them?

> (In desperation Steve's men, while he himself was "pounding to powder" sensitive, costly coding devices in his own quarters, began feverishly piling up materials for a huge bonfire which they hoped would destroy all materials in one holocaust—until he reminded them that the vessel's fuel tanks lay immediately below. There was not

enough ventilation for effective burning, anyway, as it turned out, and the one slow-moving paper-shredder kept blowing fuses. (Reams of documents went out portholes.)

As for Duane Hodges, ship's fireman and much-loved musician, hurrying to burn sacks of secret documents, he was hit by a North Korean shell which tore his abdomen so badly, he was left with one leg hanging. A crew corpsman, Herman Baldridge, managed to locate morphine to ease the dying youngster's pain—but the body had fallen in the narrow passageway leading from the Special Detachment Spaces to the main deck. As the battle raged above him, the fatally wounded sailor lay in a welter of his own flesh and blood, walls and floor running with it—while his open wound, in spite of attention, continued pumping blood over the deck, making it difficult for sympathetic but frantic crewmen, slipping and sliding through it, to get to the sea and jettison their top-drawer cargo. The youngster was tenderly removed, but stone-faced North Koreans, pistols levelled, pushed aside his attendants!

Young Duane had sung a final salute to his Maker the very night before he gave his bright young life to Him: Accompanying himself on his guitar, his voice lifted in praise, his last words being "How Great Thou Art!")

* * * * * *

The full story of Steve's life appeared in the newspapers that same evening, possibly much of it lifted from his college yearbook, augmented by other personal records the newsmen had evidently gained access to. The picture they used was his graduation photo I had displayed on the old sea captain's desk.

My deprivation from sleep made bitterness my new companion.

What, after all was *said* and *done* (and certainly more was being said than done), was the life of a young U. S. Naval officer compared to the Almighty Dollar? "Get the story at any cost" was obviously still paramount.

Didn't newsmen follow any ground rules at all, even their consciences? Couldn't our courts safeguard the sacred rights of its citizens from such pilfering scribblers—and more important, save servicemen from writers whose tenderest heartbeat was the click of a typewriter—and whose capacity for fair play stretched the generous length and breadth of a ballpoint pen?

Teachers, lawyers, doctors and other public servants have to pass critical tests and be licensed. What criteria for dealing at will with human lives did reporters have to meet? What standards for fair judgment, for personal integrity? For intimate exposure?

Yes, just how long were we going to allow this "free press" of ours and all other mass media to "run the country," brand its leaders, color its thinking and literally take things into its own inky or tube-twisting hands? ("Ring in the valiant man and free. . .the larger heart. . .the kindlier hand. . . .")

*   *   *   *   *   *

Piece by piece, however disjointed, the puzzle of the purloined *Pueblo* began dropping into place, and while all the pieces didn't fit perfectly and several were missing (not to take their rightful places until the *Pueblo* crew returned to fit them), the story began to unfold in all its stark realism to a stunned and waiting nation. It produced repercussions that welled into a grand state of international tension, teetering on the brink of a third world war!

Devoid of North Korean fabrications, the simple facts appeared to be that the ill-fated vessel had left Sasebo, Japan, twelve days before its capture. Its exact position off the coast of North Korea was ever a subject of baffling controversy both here and abroad. Even the State Department sounded not absolutely certain the vessel had not drifted "over the line" in the final analysis. Had they or had they not trespassed North Korea's territorial waters as their captors screamingly claimed? This was the largest puzzle piece of all and was never satisfactorily dropped into place for the American public until the *Pueblo's* men returned, dispelling all doubts.

> (The truth of the matter was, the ship, obeying its original orders, *at no time penetrated North Korea's territorial waters,* even though long-suffering, sick, and emaciated crewmen were beaten half to death in order to coerce them into backing up this totally false accusation.)

Via Gilbert's TV, I saw again with disgust the bald, inscrutable expressions on the faces of Russian diplomats at the United Nations Security Council Meeting who backed this same black lie in the very face of U.N. Secretary Arthur Goldberg's brilliant presentation of the facts, i.e., proof via navigational charts of *Pueblo's* position in international waters, based upon intercepted radio messages emanating from enemy ships themselves. The Russians first stamped his presentation "professorial," but their endless haranguing branded him a liar!

Yes, the very first pieces of the puzzle showed a Soviet-built patrol boat (SO-1) approaching the lonely ship around 10:00 p.m. on Tuesday (Boston time), and signalling, "Heave to or I'll open fire."

With flags, *Pueblo* crewmen signalled back, "I am in international waters."

Four more patrol boats hurried toward the defenseless vessel,—*just as I saw them in my minute-movie,*—their men at general quarters manning the guns, one North Korean captain ordering Commander Bucher to follow in his wake.

Shells were now flying across *Pueblo's* deck, destroying part of the flying bridge and life boat, Bucher and several of his men wounded. Yes, for the record, *Pueblo's* men were hopelessly outgunned and outmaneuvered. Her radio operator had been desperately calling for help. That rescue planes would soon be winging their way to the stricken craft was only a bright promise.

Five North Korean armed vessels, guns bristling, torpedo tubes open for business, surrounded the helpless *Pueblo* while Russian-built jets roared in overhead, sending salvos of rockets into the sea. There were also fifty more MIGS standing on strip alert on Wonsan's shore. One patrol boat, with armed boarding party, backed toward the vessel. "Have been requested to follow into Wonsan" the Captain had radioed. "Have three wounded and one man with leg blown off. How about some help? These guys mean business."

At 12:32 a.m. (Washington time) at the "All stop, we're going off the air,"—the last message anyone ever heard coming from the doomed U. S. vessel,—apprehension reached a new high at the Pentagon. Walt Rostow, Johnson's security affairs advisor, appeared at the White House. Dean Rusk, Secretary of State, and William Bundy, Secretary for East Asian and Pacific Affairs were also notified.

Regardless of the impressive roster of names "called to the colors" in Washington, why was there such a sluggish response to the alert? Why the long delay before waking the President to inform him of the ship's capture? Did this delay allow the bantam bandits the time they needed to snag their prize and get it safely into port before any of our airmen could make the scene?

> (Isn't it possible this crucial hour of waiting might have changed history had it been used properly?—saved unspeakable agony for eighty-two young Americans—not to mention the destruction of secret devices, costing millions?
>
> Such sophisticated paraphernalia was meaningless to North Koreans. "They asked all the wrong questions.")

Had Russia conspired with North Korea and certain U. S. traitors to grab this unarmed goldmine?

Did Russian agents make up the *Pueblo's* subsequent "crew," or did Red Chinese agents walk her decks after the Americans were removed?

Wasn't it South Korea's turn to come to the aid of her allies?

Why did the *Enterprise* arrive so late? Why were orders reversed?

To top it all off, why didn't *Pueblo's* men ever "get the message," the warning sent to Washington by North Korea *that the next U. S. ship to spy off their shores would be "blown out of its waters?" Yes, why?—why?—why?*

Via mass media, North Koreans next mouthed the myth that the *Pueblo* had "fired first" (with what, "slingshots"?), had given "arrogant resistance," that "several were killed" in so doing, and "many wounded." Thankfully, in a short period of time our State Department straightened out their statistics on this one, thereby giving me a half-night's rest, the other half keeping me awake wondering just which *"one"* really *was* killed.

Pueblo relatives agreed wholeheartedly with Secretary of State Dean Rusk and other Navy authorities that the incident was a "matter of utmost gravity" and an "act of war." But, like me, were they praying that our nation wouldn't gird its loins until our P.O.W.'s were removed from the front line of the battle zone?

President Johnson eventually made the ball field and called up 14,487 Air Force and Navy reservists to duty, while Coach Rusk in the same breath cautioned the opposing team to "cool it." At any rate, to one small mother, this show of force posed a certain heartening possibility: It might convince the kidnappers they'd best mail back our men!

I had to admire our Secretary of State's forthright manner in dealing with the situation. The problem was being taken from justifiably angry Naval heads and placed in the hands of State Department solvers, and, while I found the changeover disheartening, Mr. Rusk seemed equal to the task.

"I'm going to see that guy if Steve doesn't return within a reasonable time," I promised my brother as we continued to watch Washington reactions via TV.

"He's canny," I went on. "I've noticed our Secretary of State is careful not to make these TV command performances give-away programs for hostile listeners. I hope those senators *allow* Mr. Rusk the privilege of playing it 'cool!'"

(Even now, after seventy years, historians still scratch their skulls and wonder if we didn't botch badly by sending a battle wagon into Havana Harbor when the diplomatic situation was so "hot." *("Remember the Maine"?)*

A few years ago, when driving home to Melrose after singing in a Concord church each Sunday, I had to pass through Woburn Square. Being a sea-lover, I never failed to look over at the big glass case standing on a pedestal in a grassy triangle which housed one of the *Battleship Maine's* crumpled funnels salvaged from the Havana Harbor explosion. That any seagoing tragedy would ever mar my little landlocked life in Snug Harbor never occurred to me!

I was encouraged now to learn that a public negotiating session had been held at Panmunjom, but unfortunately this opening gesture fizzled out on a pie-slinging B-movie note.

It seems that while Rear Admiral John V. Smith, Senior Member of the U.N. Armistice Commission (with whom I struck up a cordial correspondence later), was a deft debater at the conference table, his invective lacked the Oriental charisma. No, our side of the debating team at Panmunjom would never win blue ribbons at these name-calling contests, and that's all the North Koreans intended them to be, i.e., a bid for propaganda time. Indeed the N.K. vocabulary, at sewer level, definitely had the edge on ours. So strongly did it reek, in fact, it rolled down the curtain.[5]

Yes, Washington decided the public had been sufficiently entertained by these off-color N.K. comedians. Conferences would be private from here on in. So *private* they became, unfortunately, we didn't hear a peep out of either adversary!

Wednesday evening also launched me into a non-stop telethon—on the receiving end, that is. Now that my tenderless trio had sung their opening chorus to the world: *"All About Steve,"* local and national papers were composing additional stanzas, his mother's aid being continuously solicited. I tried keeping the receiver off its cradle, but the ensuing howl was as nerve-fraying as the ringing. I would have had the telephones disconnected, or begged the operator's assistance if it hadn't been for the fact that Hope springs eternal, even if it had to spring all the way from North Korea! I knew Steve would call Vuokko and me, if possible, even if the act were only a facet of some propaganda scheme.

All I wanted to do at the moment was to close swollen eyelids for a couple of hours, if only to open them on a new day of agony.

Truly, in what seemed a matter of minutes, Thursday of this his-

---

5"Your mouth smells of rotten mutton." (N.K. appraisal of a U. S. negotiator.)

toric "Hell Week" (Gilbert's label) dawned, and found me still employing brother Robert's recommendation that I allow reporters "just enough of nothing to get them off my back." Brother Gordon's advice was simply that I should advise all reporters and phoners to descend en masse to a balmier region, in the same breath suggesting a "warmer" way I might negotiate personally with "iron-willed, peerless-patriot, omnipotent-ruler, genius-commander" Kim Il Sung. ("My funny uncle," Steve used to call Gordie.)

As I stood now at the corner stove this Thursday morning preparing Gilbert's hot cereal, snatches of the night's cacophonic conversations bubbled up at me from the cream of rice kettle. (Rice! Did Steve like rice? I couldn't really remember, but was he getting enough of rice—of anything?[6])

A hopeful idea flashed briefly: Could it be that Steve and his men were captives aboard their own ship, eating their own food stored in the hold, sleeping under their own warm blankets? Second thoughts told me this was probably not the case.

> ("We counted the dogs that ran by our window every morning. If one was missing, we wouldn't touch the stew that day; it was foul-smelling anyway, and we often found animal teeth, eyeballs and hair bunches in it. Some of us became so ill with dysentery we missed the "bombsight" (hole in the floor of common room for toilet)—for which, sick as we were, we were beaten unmercifully.")

Yes, my ears still echoed to the stacatto voices of my night callers.

"This is the *Boston Globe* calling—This is the *Boston Traveler.* Is this Mrs. Harris, mother of—*Record American—Associated Press— United Press International* (they must have worked fast!)—Is your son, the Lieutenant Stephen Robert Harris, Intelligence Commander aboard the—Was your son the officer responsible for—etc., etc., etc. Sorry to wake you at this hour—As his mother, do you think your son's ship should have had—"

"I'm sorry, but I'm hardly in a position to judge what sort of protection my son's ship should have had." (I simply did not wish to be quoted, although I harbored some good practical ideas on what sort of protection I thought his poor little ship *should* have had!

"Mrs. Harris, can you tell us a bit about your son's—and do you think the Navy—"

---

[6]"If you couldn't chew it, (it was a solid mass, sometimes), it came in handy for gluing 'House Rules' notices to the walls of our cells. The bread, what there was of it, was like statified cinder block. I longed for cheeseburgers and strawberry milkshakes continually!"

"No, I feel I would be doing my son a disservice to discuss his past. I'm sorry, you must realize I'm not a military strategist, only an 'anxious mother.'"

Once, close to 5:00 a.m. to some overseas publisher, I remember mumbling "only an anxious *mother hen!*", which slip of the tongue struck me as so hilarious I clunked down the receiver and laughed until I felt sick to my stomach. Oh, I really "freaked out." I couldn't wait to tell Gilbert his "anxious mother hen" might have laid an egg of international proportions.

Little lesson for tonight: A sense of humor insures survival,—if you're not too weak to laugh.

The following morning the phones commenced anew.

"Why do they persist in posing all these military conundrums? Ye cats! Just because Steve is a naval officer, do they think his mother is an authority on marine warfare? Steve, as you know, is not the chatty type."

"They just want a dumb mommie's views for laughs," my breakfast buddy philosophized. "Let the thing ring and eat your breakfast. You're beginning to look your age."

"Thanks, but I certainly hope this powerful Navy of ours is going to sail up and drop an advisor on my doorstep one of these days. I'm running out of ideas, along with red corpuscles!"

After school, I found newsmen had already scaled "Mrs. Harris's Mountain." The telephone idea had evidently gone astray, and while Irma Pendleton, my good principal, had dusted them out of the school office with the dexterity of a seasoned diplomat, they had evidently mobilized for a second sortie. I gave them virtually the same answers my night callers received—innocuous information.

With the approach of the dinner hour, I left both phones going full blast in order to make my nightly roll down to Wyoming Station to pick up Brother G. The night was cold and clear, and as I stepped out of the house and peeped back through the dining room picture window, the lights of Boston leapt up to dazzle me.

Yes, "the night had a thousand eyes," much brighter than these two "burnt-holes-in-a-blanket" I was wearing. But thanks be, *no telephones!* How peaceful it seemed as I rolled down into the night,—ever so peaceful, until a car approached from the left on the steep incline. It was filled with what I could have sworn were *five Korean men!* They were grimacing and pointing up the hill, but took little notice of my Volkswagen since a larger car was ahead of me, blocking their view.

The scene was so demoralizing, I felt I was meeting Steve's captors face to face!   And it was only by a quick turn of the wheel that I missed dismembering a beady-eyed cat (or was it Kuan Yin?) crossing the road!

"Every Oriental will appear to be a North Korean about now," my chattering teeth tried to tell myself.

The car's occupants could have been Japanese, Chinese, Hawaiian or even Russian-Oriental types.   Yet my intuition told me they were Koreans—*North Koreans,* by Harry!

I was still trembling when I reported to Gilbert on the confrontation.

"They're just a bunch of foreign students in a car pool, Jitterbug," he chided me in that offhand way of his. "The woods is full of 'em, and so is Harvard."

"Well, if the woods is full of them," I retorted, angry at being laughed at, "they must have been hiding behind the trees, for I've never seen them before. Besides, they were too old to be students."

I drove around the brow of the hill several times, always finding it deserted.

What would their next move be?

That evening Gilbert muffled the bell on my night table phone. "This phonecall business may bug your ears, but it's only the opening scene. TV will be putting you on for laughs next."

"I can assure you it's no laughing matter!" I replied hotly, not even thanking him for fixing my phone, "so cool it!"

Now why couldn't my genes and chromosomes have more closely resembled those of my departed mother? Why did the tomboy in me have to rise so crassly to my defense?   Oh, to be the "wonderful person" she was!

Yes, how would my angel mother have reacted to this dilemma? *She* didn't have to knock herself out to act like a lady; she *was* one, Canadian born, an honor graduate of McGill University with a scholarship to its School of Medicine.   Unlike her bubbly tomboy daughter, nurtured in self-defense on such fare as bag-punching, ice hockey, track and a smidgeon of wrestling, she had a quiet dignity and personal beauty her six offspring secretly admired, never tiring of watching her as we sat around the dinner table. Men running for office sought her signature on their nomination papers. Even today when I go shopping, tradespeople tell me how much they miss her.

Oh, to be as restrained, yet as gracious as she was—But it was a sure bet I couldn't look as pretty while *being* it!

Second lesson for tonight: *The better you look, the better they listen!* (If it weren't for my notoriety these days, Grade IV wouldn't be doing much listening.)

I read somewhere that one must hold a clear mental picture of what he wanted most in life in order to achieve it. This made good sense to me and I struggled to keep a mental picture of Steve and his men *returning* in the forefront of my thoughts. I'd envision a healthy, if not heavy body, a rational, if not happy mind, and a spirit constantly lifting its cup to heaven to be filled. Could such positive thinking help Steve?

* * * * * *

If I had expected to find my cherubic host at Beebe School sympathetic toward my involvement in the *Pueblo* crisis, I was mistaken. They were ecstatic! In their eyes, I was no anxious mother, but a famous one, one they could brag about to their friends and relatives. They exploited my questionable status further by seeing to it that I turned on the news promptly at eleven o'clock on the radio Beverly Stewart (who taught in the next room) had thoughtfully carried to school for me.

On this Friday morning, for special help in modern math, a group of pupils was seated with me under the Reading Tree, its cotton and glitter-adorned branches (i.e., "snow") sparkling bravely in the pale rays of a winter sun. It was almost time for the noon bell when a knock sounded smartly on the open classroom door.

With reluctance I rose to greet a toothless first grader who, when she spotted me, skipped in blithely, bearing a directive from the front office which she slapped with aplomb on my desk. The class adored these interruptions by "the tiny people" and although pretending not to notice, were secretly hoping for some humorous *faux pas*.

Standing on tiptoe and spreading ten fat fingers like pink starfish against my desk for support, my miniature messenger lifted a little moon-shaped face that looked quizzically into mine and asked: "Uh—aren't you the lady that had a son on the U.S.S. (her "S's" were jet-propelled and a youngster sitting close by wiped his cheeks absently)—uh, the U.S.S.—(her parents must have helped her read the letters from the newspaper) uh, wait a minute now—Oh, yeah, I think I remember now—the U.S.S. PABLUM?" (I had a feeling Irma had already been asked the question and had sent Little Bo-Peep upstairs to give me a lift.)

By afternoon the weather had turned so warm and foggy, I found it treacherous even walking the children across the busy intersection for games on the Old Gooch School playground.[7]

_____

[7]The old school building has been torn down, but the open area is still used as a playground and park. The great corner elm marked the meeting place for Melrose's Minute Men.

The news had turned murky, too. North Korea, still heady over the world-shaking success of its ship-stealing coup, declared itself "fully combat ready" to deal an "exterminatory blow" to the United States (failing to mention whether Muscovian or Chinese nuclear warheads would be employed for the purpose).

All was not bird nest soup and saki, however, for N.K.'s national blood pressure zoomed to the boiling point at the idea of our carrying their slick trick to the attention of the United Nations Security Council. Their broadcasts warmed up as well, as they declared the United States had "no right to discuss the seizure" and that we were raising a "frantic war clamor" by bringing the matter before this august body. Were they now realizing their brashness had gone beyond international acceptance—that "faces" along their half-peninsula would be "lost" if scrutinized closely by an articulate world organization?

In order to draw attention away from this unpalatable prospect, they made the eyebrow-lifting pronouncement to their vast new audience that while the eighty-two surviving crewmen were "in good health at present" they would be *"tried"* and *"punished by law"*— which everyone knew would mean only trumped-up charges in a mock trial, ending in *execution by a firing squad!*

What a chilling new threat to carry home! At closing time, Irma insisted I leave at once, and dazedly I backed into my faithful raccoon being proffered by the butler-of-the-day.

Execution! My *Pueblo* headache soared to a new ceiling of pain.

Well, that meant, at least, that the men were still alive—but for how long? "God, grant Washington the wisdom to reach them before—!

"Now, don't you worry, Mrs. Harris," came the small voice of my coat-holder directly behind me, as if he had peeped into my mind and wanted to give comfort; "we're gonna be awful good while your son's in jail over there in North Korea, because—know something?" (No, I don't know anything anymore, Herbie). "We're making a scrapbook for you and your son and—"

Several children protested vigorously as if my valet had given away a super secret, but allowed him to continue. "Yeah, we've collected a wicked lot of newspaper clippings already. We call us the *U.S.S. Pueblo News and Scrapbook Committee.* I'm gonna be Captain and Joyce is Secretary."

"We're all gonna be secretaries, Herbie, you said so!" came the spontaneous complaint from all classmates. I was too numb to go about quashing the argument, but not too numb to see into their hearts. The "gonnas" and squabbling could go unchallenged today, for "the hearts of children hold what the world cannot."

"Know something?" I returned as they croaked with glee at my use of the verboten phrase, "I think *you* are all *'something'*, you, Captain, and your staff of twenty-seven secretaries here—something very special, and very dear to me!" (And their beaming silence and glowing eyes told me I wasn't "freaking out" this time!)

Lesson for a dark day: *Turn a bright face to the world. Some of the light rays may refract to the point of returning the glow.*

* * * * * *

Although faculty friends had held no open discussion on the subject, glances I sometimes intercepted clearly signalled, "Our Eleanor looks awful, doesn't she?"

Their concern was openly expressed, however, when upon arrival each morning I found shades up, lights on, the room aired and a small bouquet (in January, yet) or homemade treat lying on my desk. Had I been as thoughtful of these salt-of-the-earth confederates during their own personal trials?

This very afternoon, standing alone in the downstairs corridor after recess, staring back at the dismal world outside while my bundled brigade bounced upstairs, I was startled to hear the voice of my ever-stunningly-attired principal beside me:

"Eleanor," she began, studying my half-moon gold earrings with the little pink stars the children admired, "do you remember my telling you I have a friend in the jewelry business in the Little Building? I've been trying to remember ever since Christmas vacation to bring you a necklace that matches those earrings exactly. Each link contains a pink star and ends in a rose sunburst on gold filigree; you'll love it!—and I want you to have it. I'll bring it tomorrow," and she turned back to the office to answer the phone.

I wouldn't tell my generous boss such things meant nothing to me now!

As I ascended to my eyrie after the trying day, the fog was the fabled consistency of pea soup, and only the snowy blobs of evergreens lining each side of it charted my course along the steep driveway. I moved up cautiously, thinking how appropriate the setting was for this horror movie I was playing in.

As far as I could make out the place was deserted. Nary a reporter roamed the reefs, yet I found the stillness forbidding. Ragged ledges loomed like gray ghosts guarding their smoky ravine, singing winds having abandoned them to the silence of sifting mists. Yes, for once it did have the atmosphere of a mausoleum!

A grating noise quite in keeping with a haunted house accompanied the turning of my key in the porch door lock, and I couldn't quite stem the feeling of apprehension that welled up in my throat as I stepped inside. But I stepped no farther—for as clammy air from somewhere bathed my face, I saw the rear door to the cliffs closing slowly, ever so slowly on its metal bar! The sight was terrifying, yet there was an ineffable sadness about it—almost as if the spirits of my two newlyweds had just drifted out onto the ledges for the last time. . .I began to feel sick—

Abruptly the true significance of what I had just seen turned my blood to stone, and my feet congealed to the carpet. Had real flesh and blood intruders just gone out or just come in?

I listened as if my life depended upon it, as well it might have; but all I could hear was my own heart drumming its alarm to a rather hollow stomach.

My answer lay on the floor around me as I beheld heaps of familiar objects scattered the length and breadth of my vision! Kitchen cabinets yawned open to reveal disarranged, half-emptied shelves. Beneath them, clutches of broken dishes made shabby islands on the sea-blue linoleum, with rivers of sugar and coffee grounds winding among them, open cannisters lolling in the mess at crazy angles.

In the family room, papers and notebooks from the old sea captain's desk lay scattered like windswept leaves over the prayer rug before it.

Hearing nothing, I felt my emotions sliding downhill from anger to dismay. There is something deeply disturbing about the ravaging of one's home, the pushing about or destruction of its intimate appointments by the iniquitous fingers of strangers—yes, almost as disturbing as having one's beloved only child plucked off the seas by them!

I slid out of my boots and padded about in my stocking feet, the fact it was familiar territory giving me false courage. Noiselessly I stepped over family room papers, only to discover Gilbert's floor and bed were similarly littered, empty containers and the contents of his highboy drawers strewn in wild abandon. Here, also, showered over the room like supersize snowflakes, was a more formidable blizzard of white envelopes and papers.

The same enraged bravado carried me silently up over the winding staircase to the second floor, where I felt a resurgence of dismay at the vast job of un-housekeeping the burglars had accomplished in my own quarters.

The white louvered doors to my closet lay open to a mauled interior, shoes and hat boxes flung helter-skelter over hanger tops and floor; while over on the newly-starched lace of my delicate bedspread, summer and winter pocketbooks sprawled open or stood on end, the fleecy white rugs below them heaped with the dumpings of dressing table drawers.

Lingerie, scarves, and my New Year's gift of nylons from Gilbert spilled from the half-open drawers of my dresser. In another corner, I noticed my pink cut-crystal container, from which I filled my purse flacon weekly with "flowery perfume, the expensive kind" lying on its side on the vanity. The last few drops of it were rolling across its mirrored face to cascade down into a dark circle on the rug.

My alarm peaked a second time, as while reaching for my bedside phone to call police, I spotted flung in a corner my string of Christmas pearls from Alden.

Sinister thoughts erupted. Were the thieves not after valuables at all but something pertinent to Steve? My mind snapped to attention. The tape recorder! Alden's tapes from Saigon!—The tape I was preparing to cheer dear Vuokko—what had I said? What had Alden said? Did they all contain information the "robbers" wanted? I saw again five grinning Oriental faces in a car, pointing toward the house.

I dropped the phone and slid in cold panic down to Steve's room on the first floor. Yes, it too had been ransacked—but the tapes and recorder on his desk appeared to be untouched. Would the intruders, therefore, return to finish the job, including *me*, if they knew I was alone?

With fingers of foam rubber I fumbled to lock every entrance to the house, yet continued to feel dank air flowing in from somewhere, but where? And then I saw it,—a great ugly gash in the dining room window fronting the ledges, twin to the one on the porch. On the floor beneath it lay the heavy copper crown of the sundial Gordon and Martha had given me for a housewarming present, its handcast arrow severed and lying a few inches away.

The room began to shimmer and darken. How much could a gal take anyway? Since my knees seemed unwilling to support me further, I let myself down slowly to the floor.

As if the broken picture window were not supplying sufficient oxygen for the occasion, I slid along on one hip to the yawning aperture and thrust my head through, too dazed to care very much whether my jugular vein dropped down to become impaled upon the razor-sharp prongs of plate glass jutting up from below!

The phone interrupted my deep breathing exercises with its usual tenacity. Blast those reporters! I wanted to call the police! Yet something urged me to answer it.

I started to take one last deep pull of the foggy air, but it ended in a gasp, for I beheld a *dark shadow moving furtively across the ledges!* I could only hope this was but the result of one of Miss N. E.W.'s gentler Windboys reaching up to tease the branches of my lone sentinel, the one tree at the rear which I'd been able to rescue from bulldozers when the house was being built.

I dragged my partially revived torso over to the phone and fell into the easy chair. Pushing up the sweat-congealed curls from off my brow, I tried to find my vocal cords:

"Hello?"

"Mrs. Harris? Oh, Mrs. Harris!" a gentle but excited voice cried into my ear, "I suppose everyone has been calling you. This is Mrs. Wilson, your former neighbor on Wyoming Hill. Listen, my dear, your Stephen is alive! I just heard his voice on the radio—he's making some sort of confession."

"Alive! My darling's alive! (Dear God, I do thank Thee!) What station did you say, Mrs. Wilson? . . .But a *confession?*—What on earth is he confessing to?"

I remembered reports of the captain having "confessed" (to a lot of rot). What would Steve be forced to say? My teeth were chattering so I could barely thank this good woman, for I could swear the shadow outside had moved closer. *Steve, alive!*

"Oh not now, whoever you are! Don't shoot me now." I silently begged my shadowy assailant. "It wouldn't be fair; I must hear Steve's voice first. I must know he is really alive!"

Oh, why hadn't I retained presence of mind enough to ask Mrs. Wilson to call the police!

Hardly daring to remove my eyes from the window long enough to dial the radio station, I felt questions nudging through my terror: How long since the recording was made? Was it really Steve who made it? Was he alive even now? Had the N.K. fiends half-murdered him to coerce him into making his so-called "confession," then done away with him? Perhaps *Pueblo's* crewmen were actually dead and only actors taking their places to delude us into thinking our dear ones were still alive! My mind felt as sick as my body—

No! I must force back the right "picture" to mind, Steve and his men *returning.*

It seemed almost comical at this impasse that I had locked doors so feverishly when at any moment a man (or Shaggy Red Bear) could step right through that gaping—

A pleasant male voice broke into my reverie to inform me that it would be quite impossible to obtain the tape as it had been filed away.   And, because the announcer was in the midst of his news program, the area couldn't be entered.

I must hear Steve's voice!   Desperation dictated I inform this radio station man who I was, even if it meant answering a barrage of questions in repayment.

"I simply must hear my son's voice," I pleaded in conclusion. "This is the first inkling I've had that he's alive!"

"Hold on, Mrs. Harris, you just hold on," a voice with new interest boomed back.   "I'll get that tape for you somehow." (Of course, he'd want me to hold on; he'd have more news to broadcast now. I just prayed I wouldn't have a bullet in my brain by the time he returned!)

As I waited, I felt a cool breeze from the broken window freshening my burning cheeks, and noticed with indescribable relief that the fog was lifting in long slanting ribbons from off the cliffs, as if being summoned aloft by the brightening heavens. Shadows were darting like happy apparitions everywhere now, my faithful little tree the cause of them. Mrs. Omen-Scoffer did an about-face.

Might it be HOPE dancing out there, and not DEATH, after all?

Act IV

A PUEBLO FRIEND IS BORN

"Hell Week" Sizzles On
  Phone Call That "Saved" Two Lives
    Men!—Newsmen, TV Men, Cameramen, Clergymen, Navymen
      The Big Black Limousine
        Sunday Punch
          Rerun
            Saga of Saigon

"Two more days to go," Gilbert remarked philosophically when I had pacified newsphoners and returned to a plate of cold food, which I hadn't wanted anyway. Obviously he was referring to the finale of this nightmarish week. Phones rang again. There'd be no sleeping tonight. Steve's N.K. "confession" was tops on the hit parade.

National magazines had by this time joined my tormentors, and papers as far away as London had acquired my phone number.

Between calls, Gilbert and I commenced tallying our burglary losses. Truly, Steve was the only "loss" we were much interested in retrieving. As to material possessions, it takes weeks to recall everything you had in the first place, as anyone who has had a housebreak can tell you.

I had a few keepsakes of my mother's, the theft of which hurt most of all. It was days later, when I remembered to search the secret drawer in Grandpa Harris's ancient desk for the purple velvet case containing my own Grandfather Westman's Queen Victoria medal and my mother's diamond engagement ring, that I decided the robbers had best never meet me face to face!

Police inspectors had passed rather lightly over my five-Koreans-in-a-car observation, since I hadn't taken down their license number anyway.

My supper companion, who had lost over two hundred dollars stashed away for spring house projects, was in no better mood than I. "You would have to open your teeth and tell those guys (inspec-

85

tors) that 'in view of your greater loss, this robbery disturbed you very little.' You'll have to have an alarm system installed now. That'll disturb you very plenty."

His eyes wandered to the floor garden. A mischievous gleam came into them.

"I hoped they'd stolen that stupid statue of yours. What's she doing down cellar behind the furnace, anyway?"

("Plenty, brother, oh plenty!" Mrs. Omen-Scoffer was tempted to report.) Instead I retorted:

"Oh—to heck with everything in this blasted house! ('You're pretty vain about that house of yours, Mother') The only thing I really care about in this whole cruel, cockeyed world is seeing Steve safely home again!" (Was the spoiled darling pushing out of her candy cocoon?)

"You'd better shift; you're stripping your gears," Steve's uncle warned quietly but not unsympathetically. "There's a long pull ahead—they're not finished with those guys yet."

"You mean?"—Thinking back on the tape of Steve's "confession," the labored sighs punctuating the stilted phrases, the toneless timbre of his normally vibrant voice, I couldn't bring myself to say "through torturing them to death?"

"I mean they'll squeeze them for all they're worth propaganda-wise," he explained quickly.

—And then?—"God, spare them for those who love them so dearly," I prayed silently.

Shaking with fatigue, I put everything I thought thieving hands had touched down the laundry chute or into the dishwasher. Why did those heartless reporters have to tell the underworld—or was it five North Korean spies—that I was a school teacher, thus revealing that I'd be away from the house during the day?

Somehow I'd found time to dash into the Red Cross Building down on Ell Pond and get the staff busy tearing a vent in the North Korean curtain.

"I can just see American agents peeping from behind every bush outside Steve's prison compound!" Elizabeth Hersey of our Melrose Red Cross staff comforted me. "Eleanor, I have a friend in Geneva connected with the International Red Cross there, and I'll have him try to reach the men. I'll report to you later."

When I phoned Griffith Couser, Steve's ex-Naval-officer Department Head at high school, he responded with both good counsel and a list of influential people to contact. East Asian authority Professor Edwin Reischauer of Steve's Alma Mater cautioned me I should expect to wait "at least a year" before seeing Steve again. Naturally the learned professor could promise nothing definite. Who could, in dealing with Communists? ("The words of their mouth are smoother than butter, but war is in their hearts; their words are softer than oil, yet are they drawn swords." Psalm 55:21) I, for one, am no Communist Sympathizer! Their underlying goal is to rule the world, a fact which we in our One World idealism, are prone to forget. I remembered Alden's fight to feed the city cut off by them!

Between calls, I'd gotten off letters to Dean Rusk and Arthur Goldberg commending them for their efforts on behalf of *Pueblo* captives, both letters executed in my most painstaking cursive script. (One summer, elected by fellow teachers, I had handwritten dozens of sample lessons for the Melrose Elementary Schools' Manual of Handwriting.)

My ego-idea brought results. Each of the celebrated statesmen dictated a personal reply to me via his secretary, for the official seals on the letterheads were embossed by hand.[1]

As I anticipated, each man promised relentless efforts toward the rescue of *Pueblo's* sailors, each, moreover, paying me the compliment of passing my handwritten letter around his office to colleagues working on the case. Did such promises mean effective action?

Saturday morning I shook confectioners' sugar over the plump strawberries left from last night's dinner, combining them with fresh pineapple Gilbert had carried to the train from Boston's Fanueil Hall Market, while the golden orbs of fresh eggs slowly glazed over in the little steamer he had bought me at a local church fair. With crisp Canadian bacon and some of sister Elizabeth Harris's cranberry and tangelo crush spread on hot buttered toast, I intended to see that brother, at least, regained some of his lost vitamins. We had a dual contest going: Who could appeal to whose appetite most? He bought to lure mine, and I cooked to lure his. Thus far, neither side seemed to be winning.

Papers had grown silent on L'Affaire Pueblo, a state more ominous than headlines; "Confessions" had been wrung out of each of the *Pueblo's* six officers. But now that N.K. propaganda mills had been replenished, would the hapless victims be allowed to live?

"Ouch!" I must try to keep my fingers from trembling in getting the sizzling bacon onto its brown paper to drain.

I found myself listening again to Steve's T.V. confession, voice

---

[1]My Navy advisors explained this mark of authenticity when they came to the house and studied the replies.

strained and toneless—timbre and message quite unlike anything I had ever heard issuing from his lips. It disclosed only too clearly that he had been, and still was, suffering!

I thought back on what Gilbert had told me about "obtaining" such P. O. W. confessions:

> ("They keep their victim awake for nights on end, never allow him to drift off for a minute—keep slapping him awake—torturing—pressing for what they want—and finally, when the guy doesn't really know what he's doing anymore, he—")

As the sound of Gilbert's shower poured into my ears, so did the much-publicized phrases of the trumped-up message. It was the sad labor behind Steve's words, however, that lay heaviest on my heart. I learned later that the prospect of seeing his thirty technicians shot, one by one, if he didn't mouth the following "confession," forced him to the decision to read the phony document for taping: "I admit the crime committed by the armed espionage

> ship *Pueblo* and myself in conducting intelligence activities after having entered deep into the coastal waters of the Democratic People's Republic of Korea—" (Quite a status tag they'd pinned on their half-country!)

> "I apologize for our crime. We openly committed hostile acts against the Democratic People's Republic of Korea that are entirely unjustified."

(Unjustified—or essential to our survival? Monitoring vessels of key nations are busy listening on unfriendly shores the world over.) *"And it was a very dirty game."*

(Did I detect "a touch of Steve" in this last phrase? At a "news conference" carried via TV later on from North Korea, he talked with a straight face about snaring information for his "goodies bag." Were these expressions obliquely inserted by the captives to alert the home folks to the fact that this entire "news" and "confession" parade was a farce? One man apologized for his "naughty crimes.")

> "The Johnson Administration and my Commanders forced me to commit such a crime and I hate them,"

the dull voice dragged on. (Steve must have known many of those sleepless nights to sound this infantile! Or was this last phrase spoon-fed to him?)

> "I deeply regret and sincerely apologize to the Democratic People's Republic of Korea and beg you to forgive me my crime."

("It is our opinion that internal evidence in the text of
the statement [confession] clearly points to a fabrication."
—State Department appraisal)

Brothers Robert and Willard (Bill) both telephoned long distance
to apprise me of the ingenious ways tapes could be erased and
spliced, that actors were sometimes employed as imitators, or
that the natural timbre of the victim's voice could be retained while
inserting within it the insidious message so cleverly "even his own
mother" wouldn't know the difference (only his own mother did
in Steve's case!)

("I hope you didn't swallow any of that garbage, Mother!")

No, I didn't "swallow" it and trust no listening or reading American did, although Steve's airforce cousins Russell and Rob, as well
as many strangers telephoned frantically to tell me "not to believe
a word of it!" Bless 'em!

I did "gag" on it, however; for if considered "criminals" instead
of prisoners of war, what exactly did the term bode for the hapless
Navymen?—the hangman's noose or a bullet in the heart?

Accounts of the treatment of U.S. airmen imprisoned during World
War II came burning through my brain:

Fliers were stripped naked in sub-zero weather, chained to a pole
in some public square and left to struggle until they exhausted
themselves and fell into the frozen sleep of death.

In a warmer theatre of war, prisoners were hung by their feet from
tropical ceilings, and when they could pull up their weary heads no
longer, hung downward, slowly drowning in their own hot blood.

* * * * * *

REDS SAY HARRIS ASKS FORGIVENESS
(Rubbish!)

MELROSE OFFICER ADMITS WAR CRIMES REDS SAY
(More rubbish!)

U. S. NAVY BUILDUP IN SOUTH KOREA
(Our answer to the Pueblo seizure?)

Well, at least the papers were Pueblo-izing again, even if most of
the "quotations" were, as one Navy friend poetically described
them: "Sweet Swill from the Swinetroughs of North Korea's Propaganda Farms."

I placed the morning editions beside Gilbert's plate as he issued
blond and shiny from his shower clad in his Saturday garb. I ladled

the cold diced fruit into a glass compote and poured the sweet juice over it.

"For Pete's sake, call up this poor woman!" my breakfast buddy suddenly demanded, tearing a long article from an inside page of one newspaper. I scanned it quickly—

Another mother with a son on the *Pueblo*!

"I can't eat, I can't sleep since poor Ralph was captured! I just go through the house crying," the distraught mother, Mrs. Ralph McClintock of Milton, Massachusetts, was quoted as saying. "Where is my poor boy? What have they done with him? What will happen to him—?"

       ("Well, why shouldn't I look like this? For weeks I was
    fed from a bucket in a dark room—")

I left my plate untouched and hurried to the doughbox table to get out the telephone book. "Dear God, I thank Thee for Thy countless gifts of love, for this solace to my grieving heart," *for only a mother can measure a mother's anguish.* Yes, here it was, "Mc-Clintock, Ralph—"

"Hello, Mrs. McClintock?" I began. A high-pitched, worried voice answered.

"Mrs. McClintock, this is Mrs. Robert Harris of Melrose," I continued pleasantly. "I've been reading about you in the morning paper, and thought it might be of some comfort to you to know that you are not alone in this crisis. I, too, had a son aboard the *Pueblo,* Lieutenant Stephen Harris, Research Operations Officer."

"Oh my! Oh my dear—is it Mrs. Harris?—and ye say ye had a son on the *Pueblo,* too? Oh my dear! Oh, I'm so glad you called me!" The relief in the voice was good to hear.

"Oh, our poor boys! Isn't this awful! What'll they do to them do ye suppose? Our country doesn't even know where they are! Did ye know that, Mrs. Harris? They may all have been shot!" and she broke down sobbing. "I haven't slept a wink since my poor Ralph was taken off that ship! Are they all dead, do ye think, Mrs. Harris?"

My heart went out to this warm-hearted stranger with the pretty brogue. I knew only too well the frustration she was experiencing, the helpless groping for answers that never came, the hungry hope that our dear ones could be found and rescued alive, and some assurance that our government was doing something about it.

"Listen, my dear Mrs. McClintock, I know just how you feel, and if I didn't have to go out and teach school every morning, I might be crying the hours away myself. (This was no time to tell her I adhered to a No Tears policy.) Listen carefully now, I may have a few comforting thoughts to leave with you."

"Yes? Yes?" The dear soul seemed utterly dependent upon me, and I intended to give her everything within my power to lift her spirits.

"Mrs. McClintock, our sons cannot be dead! They're too valuable to the North Koreans alive! As you've probably read, South Korea has been going ahead of North Korea industrially by leaps and bounds, and they're (North Koreans) angry and jealous about that. Of course, I've never once believed that little ship ever sailed over into enemy waters! Never!"

"Oh—well—who knows about the ship? Mrs. Harris, do ye mean they'll just use our boys, then let them go,—maybe?" The plaintive tone wrung my heart.

"That's exactly what I mean!" I was merely parroting what Dr. Adrian, my dentist, Bill Cooper, a Melrose High teacher, both ex-Naval officers, and other Navy friends had told me.

"Can we do anything for our boys, do ye suppose?...if ever we can find them!" Her voice was on the verge of tears again—

"There's plenty we can do for them, plenty!" And I mentioned my letters to Arthur Goldberg and Dean Rusk, listing others I intended to write.

"I never waste a second, Mrs. McClintock; I even make notes while I'm watching my pupils at recess. Listen, my dear, we must contact every person in a position to help us—locally and nationally. I use the latest *World Almanac* for addresses of key personnel in the Navy and State Departments. You can get a copy at your stationery store. Let's keep pressing for an address from the State Department, also, so we can write to Ralph and Stephen"; —and I told her how my local Red Cross chapter was endeavoring through Geneva to reach the men.

"Oh, Mrs. Harris, ye've given me hope, ye have! That's wonderful, your doing all that. I'll start writing today, I will! Oh, how can I ever thank ye enough? Ye don't know what your calling me has meant to me! I hope ye'll call me again," she concluded wistfully.

"We'll keep in touch, you can count on it. *I need you as much as you need me, Mrs. McClintock! Don't forget that!* Get out your pen now, and put away that handkerchief!"

Returning home from grocery shopping on the same Saturday morning, another new experience awaited me. I wasn't able to get my little car up my own driveway!

"Hello—do you know where I can find Mrs. Harris?" a young man's voice called from a parked sportscar.

Judging by the number of vehicles—cars, small trucks, and huge
TV sound trucks parked in the driveway, Gilbert must be hosting a
houseful of callers already. I was under the impression the speaker
had already found me missing and believed I was a neighbor bearing
a basket of goodies to the stricken household.

"Present, unfortunately," I smiled, stopping for breath and loosening Ole Raccoon's ample collar.

"Oh!" he said, jumping out and grinning down at me in guarded
surprise. "You'll pardon me, Mrs. Harris, but I expected—"

"I know, 'Silver Threads Among the Gold' with a weeping widow
underneath."

It was apparent he found me "youthful" as people usually do,
rigors of capture notwithstanding. He seemed in no hurry to join
the inner conclave and kept me answering questions out on the driveway until, despite fur boots, I was forced to tell him that Miss New
England's frigid fingers were getting a toehold. He laughed apologet-
ically, and keeping his eyes on me, swung my pretty embroidered
market basket over his arm, thereby giving himself a gallant excuse
to follow me into the house (where he promptly resumed his eye-
to-eye questioning!)

Once over the threshold, however, he all but lost his chivalry (plus
the groceries) lunging through to the kitchen table.

Lights, cameras, wires, busy men, and purposeful activity were
everywhere! Horror Haven was jumping out of its doldrums. The
arrival of the prima donna was scarcely noticed in the bustle of stage
preparations.

My dim view of newsmongerers was due for a pleasant reversal, for
I found Ken Wayne, Andy MacMillan, Dick Pansullo and the other
TV announcers I was destined to meet, charming and considerate
people, who, while they asked searching questions, endeavored to
keep them to the pattern of security I requested. Newsmen, it turned
out, were not all scoundrels. Nevertheless, I kept reminding myself
of Gilbert's sage advice: "Keep to the anxious mother hen theme—
sob a little; it'll give you time to think." I'd adhere to the first half,
anyway, no trouble at all.

The "team" decided to use the music room for its word games.
"Right over here by the fireplace, Mrs. Harris—got your light meter,
Harry?" I hoped the *Pueblo* Case was receiving as much attention
in Washington as I was from these TV technicians!

(If only my little TV fiasco could help the cause!)

"May I just run a comb through my hair? I've been so ill —"

"Certainly, Mrs. Harris, we've a few more things to adjust here
anyway."

I drew together the four louvered doors of my bedroom that formed a wall between me and the music room, flipped my flowered blue jersey from its hanger, pinned on the silky golden crown of hair and added some pale rose lipstick. Butterfly was not quite dead.

"Not too much light, please," the ham in me suggested to "Harry." During my light opera days I always had to use a darker-than-natural makeup since my coloring is extremely fair. (Someday I'd write the thrilling story of that "other career" and the subsequent loss of a Superb Songstress to the World of Music Theatre. But right now—)

"When and where did you first hear of the seizure of the Pueblo?" *"What can you tell us of your son's background?"* For security reasons, the second question drew a polite evasion.

"Does your son expect to make the U.S. Navy his career?" (An unequivocal *"yes"* here—if he lived to make it. How could I get it across to televiewers that the U.S. Navy was Steve's very life?) Well —too late. The next question was coming at me from Ken Wayne's microphone:

"What would you say has sustained you most during this ordeal, Mrs. Harris?"

"My greatest sustaining force during this ordeal stems from the solace of *prayer,* (If Ken only knew it, I was praying every minute he was interviewing me!) the knowledge that God will come to my aid, especially if I solicit His love earnestly and untiringly." (Turning to Him "as a little child," I was really thinking, "praying unceasingly" as the Apostle Paul directed.)

A good friend put the next idea onto my lips:

"I like to think that the countless prayers being offered by concerned people in all parts of our nation and the Free World-at-large are forming a sort of protective shield over our sons in North Korea."

Yes, this very morning when I was downtown filling my pretty Puerto Rican basket, I ran into Ruthie Hoyt who stopped to paint this gratifying picture for me. Was she recalling to mind the words of Psalms 3 and 5?

> "Thou, O Lord art a shield for me; my glory and the lifter up of mine head. For thou, Lord, wilt bless the righteous; with favour wilt thou compass him as with a shield."
>
> (Our Navy sons' own prayers were already yielding up concrete results: "Praying didn't stop the torture, but *it helped us forget how bad the pain was* between torture sessions. God erased the awful memory—")

* * * * * *

I served hot coffee "between the halves" to TV personnel and all News Party crashers, opening my big box of doughnuts still warm from *Sugar and Spice* ovens. Anyone braving the heights of Ledgewinds in winter—even newsmen—deserved nourishment. My former Junior High pupils walked miles in the snow to sing with the organ upstairs or to dangle their sizzling feet in the cool garden pools in summer—and I invariably fed them all.

"That's what keeps them climbing, Noodlehead," Gilbert scolded. But he would have missed them almost as much as I, had they stopped showing up.

I must be a throwback to my paternal grandmother who always served afternoon tea precisely at four, even if I were the only guest present—only Grandmother didn't drive down to the *Sugar and Spice, Wyoming Bakery* or the *Muffin Man* for treats. Her frosted breads, tea cakes and hot buttered rolls were lovingly fashioned by hand, and fruit desserts, served in gold-edged, dainty, deep-cut-glass dishes, were her own luscious jewel-tone preserves.

Well—it was curtain-time for Act II:

"Do you think your son's spy ship should have had protection?" Dick Pansullo asked.[2]   Here again I borrowed an idea, Gilbert's this time: "A show of protection would have been provocative for an 'oceanographic research' vessel." I'd been asked the question a dozen times and hoped my answer would meet with Steve's approval—if he ever got wind of it.

"Do you think our country is doing everything it should be doing to obtain your son's release, Mrs. Harris?" (Another of those oft-repeated inquiries!)

After the last visitor had manfully shaken my right hand to a pulp, and left me with every conceivable good wish for Steve's repatriation, I reviewed this final question as I cleared the coffee cups —with my left hand—from the kitchen table.

Yes, *was* my country doing "everything" it should be doing to free our sons?   Despite personal reservations, I had decided my duty at this closing point was to cheer all *Pueblo* relatives and other mourners who might comprise my TV audience—or better still, to discourage those radical writers who used a pink shade of ink while newscovering our Service Men!

"I have implicit faith in the power of my great nation to resolve

---

[2]The term "spyship" (frequently employed by various news-carriers) is a misnomer, since spying is a covert activity.   Electronic surveillance or intelligence gathering in international waters does not break accepted international law and is an approved military technique conducted under the principle of freedom on the high seas. (From *Bucher, My Story.*)

*this dilemma with honor and dignity—and may I add that I am proud
to live in a country where the life of the individual is still considered precious!"*   Put that in your honey jar and lick it, Little
Red Writing "Hood"—wherever you are!

"You looked like a defrosted ghost," was Gilbert's appraisal after
the 6:00 p.m. TV newscast. (Harry Light-Meter had ignored my
warning.)

That Brother referred not at all to my mouthwork must be con-
strued as complimentary.

Saturday afternoon following my TV "special," I fell into bed.
Gilbert answered the first phone call. "It's Phyllis," he called upstairs. "She said she promised to call you if there was anything in
the paper about the *Pueblo,* but—"

Grabbing Ole Raccoon en route, I was out the porch door almost
before he could say more—anything, anything but this Washington
silence! I dashed over to Phyllis's back door, which due to precip-
itous ledges, opens into her living room on the second floor.

"Lost captives of the U.S.S. Pueblo" I read, "whereabouts still
unknown." My heart sank—one more day to go!

I heard a familiar step on the stairs,—Gilbert's! Phyllis's husband
must have let him in on the lower level—I never saw his face look
waxy before.

"You'd better come back over," he began, not raising his eyes
to mine. "There's a big Navy limousine arriving, and Mr. Radtke just
stepped out of his car at the foot of the driveway."

Reverend Warren Radtke was the new minister at my church
whom I'd never met.

I sensed that Gilbert didn't wish to alarm me further by adding
that the driver of the limousine was a Navy chaplain. My knees
turned to jelly—

"Are you going to tell me what I don't wish to hear," I bluntly
greeted my Episcopal rector at the foot of the driveway,—a pleasant
round-faced man in his thirties,—my tones issuing like hollow echoes
from some faraway cavern.

His friendly countenance took on a puzzled expression:

"Mrs. Harris, I can't 'tell' you anything. I came up to get acquainted. I just heard about your son being on the *Pueblo* and—"

For some strange reason, I found it difficult to believe this—the
stage seemed so perfectly set for tragedy.

Was it because of the big black limousine and the solemn face
beside it looming at the top of the driveway?—Or the Navy overcoat
on the visitor with the *gold crosses* on its shoulder boards?

The florid features of the broad-beamed priest broke into a pleasant smile, reminiscent of a kindly St. Nicholas, when he confronted this small shivering soul, who, after asking the same awful question, fully expected to be skinned alive by the scythe of a Funscreaming Fate.

"Dear Little Lady, I can tell you absolutely nothing. I wish I could. The Navy simply sent me out here to see what I could do for you. I'm Father Mulhill." He extended a big friendly paw to each of us as Reverend Radtke introduced himself. I wanted to give them both a swift sample of my tomboy temperament, but my angel mother flew down and saved her confederates just in the nick of time.

Panting with fatigue and the shock of their simultaneous arrival, as courteously as I could, I thawed the ice from my veins with a rather warm warning:

"Well, thank you for your kind concern, gentlemen, but I certainly hope that no other mother of those unfortunate sailors has to face up to the dual nightmare I've just had to,—for they'll be sure to believe, just as I did, *that their sons are dead!"*

Reverend Radtke put a protective arm about my furry waist and we went into the house.

After the two gentlemen left, I did some thinking. Why hadn't all three of us gone to our knees for *Pueblo's* cause? I wanted so much to "reach" my Heavenly Father! Surely He would have heard the prayer offered by my two clerical "comforters",—His Faithful shepherds!

Cushion for a Worried Worshipper: *Prayer clothed in the language of the Cloth wears better in High Places.*

I phoned Mrs. McClintock that evening, for I was concerned for the welfare of this emotional, tender-hearted mother with the sad music in her voice.

The dear lady sounded overjoyed to hear from me; but when I tried to amuse her by telling her about the simul-sailing of my spiritual navigators onto my Beachhead of Distress, she found it no laughing matter, bless her!

She next reported that, barring incoming telephone calls, she had been writing continuously since our morning conversation, to President Johnson on down to less prestigious plenipotentiaries.

Our conversation led to the *U.S.S. Pueblo's* real mission, to the whole modern field of automated spying. I read my new friend excerpts from newspaper articles on the subject, which I pulled out from my "library" (located under my bed)!

"Before counter-measures can be taken, precise details of an enemy radar must be known—location, frequencies, power, length of radio pulses etc., the job of the elaborate electronic snooping system now operated by major powers."

Mae urged me to continue. The information was vital to us, even if we had a sticky time of it ungluing its technical terms. The last paragraphs told us that—

> "The U. S. Navy, under the National Security Agency maintains three 'ferret' ships of the *Pueblo* type.
>
> "The *U.S.S. Pueblo's* primary task was to listen in on Communist tactical communications, especially those line-of-sight frequencies that cannot be detected beyond the horizon. The dome-shaped objects of her foremast were direction-finders and triangulators for locating the precise positions of North Korean radios. (So that's what those blobs were up on her mast!)
>
> "The antennas mounted amidships were used to pull in radio signals.
>
> "Below decks technicians work in a special detachment unit facetiously dubbed the SOD-HUT by its manufacturers. (Special Operations Detachment), the compartment with radio receivers, flashing computers and clattering teletypes. All *Pueblo's* receivers were connected to banks of tape recorders, and thirty specialists deciphered messages with the help of computers, passing on data to the N.S.A.[3] headquarters in Maryland for highest-level analysis."
>
> "The capture of this floating mint of delicate instruments and highly trained crew was a major coup in the shadowy war of electronic wits!"

"My Stephen's job aboard ship must have been to research these listening operations," I interposed. "He may have had full responsibility for this area of intelligence on this dangerous mission!"

"Oh, I think you're right about that, and ye know, Mrs. Harris, my son Ralph is a technician too, a graduate of Huntington School and Wentworth Institute. He was probably serving under your son!! Wouldn't that be something, now! Oh, I do hope they're all together and not locked up separately in some damp, dark place!"

> (Officers were put in isolation. Eight crewmen were crowded together in each small room, neither one a luxury accommodation!)

---

[3]National Security Agency.

"I certainly hope not, too, my dear—but, who knows, Ralph may be saying to Steve right now, 'Do you suppose your mother in Melrose had gotten in touch with my mother in Milton yet?'"

"Yes, yes! Perhaps he is," she replied, brightening. Then tears muted her pretty voice: "Oh, how I wish we knew where they are! It's terrible! Every night I keep seeing a flag-draped casket, Mrs. Harris! I can't get it out of my mind. Yes, I do—*I see a flag-draped casket being carried off a plane. The plane is big—it has no windows and a big black belly. It slowly opens on its side and sailors walk toward the plane to act as Pall bearers*"—and she started to cry again. "I'm so afraid it's Ralph! I can see it as plain as day!!"

I scolded her gently, saying she was really not being fair to Ralph to keep such a morbid picture in mind. Then I told her of my decision to adhere to a mental "photo" of *Pueblo's* men *returning*.

She agreed to give my idea a whirl.

"Ye know, Mrs. Harris," the same worried tone went on, "I wouldn't be telling ye this, but ye sound like a very sympathetic person. It's about Ralph's tiger cat, 'Sister.' I have two cats, a pure white angora we just call 'Kitty' and her sister, 'Sister.' That tiger, 'Sister,' is as bad as I am since Ralph was captured—hardly touches her food, just keeps jumping on and off Ralph's bed, and then crawls under it. She was never as restless as this when he went to sea before, except when he was cruising very far from home. She looks so thin, I'm beginning to think I'll have to take her to the Vet!"

"Oh, I love animals, Mrs. McClintock! Do take good care of 'Sister!'" (So she'll be alive when—if?—Ralph returns!)

I didn't add to her worries by telling her that while she was worrying over Ralph's pet, I was worrying over my own darling pet, Vuokko! Her letters from Montreal were becoming more brief and polite. I knew she was withholding a landslide of suffering, since she wouldn't confide in either parent for fear of increasing their burden of anxiety, her ailing mother not being expected to live. I must call Vuokko soon!

Wishing to end our long conversation on a lighter note, I put Mae to sleep with some of the poems I'd scribbled in my subpillow notebook, the last one, a crazy jingle I once wrote in school (and got punished for), she loved:

> If you can't stand the pace
> Of the Human Race,
> And are "falling from grace,"
> Fall back on your face,
> (But with "grace")
> —Anyplace!—

As soon as I had replaced the receiver, as expected, the phone rang again. The call I had been anticipating had come at last:

"Mrs. Harris? Commander Ross Winship of the First Naval District of Boston. What are you doing tomorrow evening?" (trying to stay sane!) "May I drop over?"

I liked his brisk cultured voice. "By all means! Do join tomorrow's News-in, Commander. This Grand Central Concourse of mine has been spinning with strangers all day." (My mother would have put it much nicer, sans sarcasm.)

"Yes, I don't doubt it. That's just what I'm coming to see you about. I'm sure you'd welcome some help and advice." (You're so right, Commander, I'd have welcomed some a week ago. Aren't you a trifle late? I mean, the Pen, Press and Picture War is about over, isn't it?)

(My mother's wing brushed my tomboy mouth lightly.)

I politely gave directions for locating Ledgewinds and went to hunt up something for Gilbert's supper.

Brother Bill was right when he wrote me the old saw: "There's the right way, the wrong way, and the Navy way." Nevertheless, I'd always had a "list" toward sea-going males. Even the ocean-mad members of the Boston Power Squadron, to which my husband belonged, possessed a sort of wholesome sincerity not always found in landlovers.

"I find seagoing men delightful. Is it because they are used to viewing horizons more broadly?" I once asked my husband.

"Viewing more broads on the horizon," he laughed.

The tall, rangy officer, in his late forties, with a clipped moustache, rather British in bearing (he'd been stationed in Bermuda for a long tour) and whom I was told to call "Ship," proved as efficient as he was good-looking. He informed me that a Washington paper, a "reliable" one (*The National Observer*) had read the account beneath the headline: PUEBLO MOTHER'S WEEK OF WORRY (it hadn't occurred to me to ask the police to keep our robbery out of the papers), and as a result, was sending a well-established correspondent to my home for an interview. The writer had just seen Rose Bucher, and would probably hunt up Mrs. McClintock, as well. The Navy had okayed it.

"I'll be right here beside you," he promised, smiling down into my eyes. (I'd have jumped into his lap, if he'd asked me to.) But I got the message: Little Mother of Intelligence Officer S.R.H. must not open her little pink mouth too glibly. He needn't have worried; my mental acuity (ego?) rated higher than that indicated by my baby brow.

In a few days, "Ship" was turning me over officially to a Commander Richard Bordeaux of the Naval Reserve Training Station in a city not far from my own. He left me with a gallant salute. The house seemed lonely after he'd gone—just as it used to when Steve left for a long tour of duty.

Mae McClintock was likewise being assigned to an advising officer, a younger man, who'd probably only remind her of "her Ralph." Personally, I hoped Commander Bordeaux would be a wise old sea monster with kelpish hair.

What I hadn't revealed to "Ship" was that I had every intention of inviting Mae McClintock to join me at Ledgewinds for the *Observer* interview. After all, this was my home, and why shoo our writer clear across Boston to Milton? Mae and I were ever so anxious to meet in person, anyway.

By Sunday morning, my *Pueblo* headache had reached the point of nausea. Nevertheless, after swallowing one of Gilbert's prescriptions, (he had intended to study medicine until World War II caught up with him) I revived sufficiently to attend services at Trinity. I must move toward that "closer walk with God" I was seeking. Fortunately, this year I was not soloing elsewhere, so I could attend my own church. Anyway, I owed good Reverend Radtke a return visit.

"You and Mrs. McClintock should get off the phone and open up a *Remember the Pueblo* Headquarters downtown. You know, like *Remember the Alamo!*" Gilbert had suggested at breakfast. (Rose Bucher must have been thinking identical thoughts on the west coast!) Such a thought, however clever, right now seemed overpowering. With school to keep, I had all I could handle. (Teachers were already talking about getting out a Rescue Petition to send to the President, I was happy to tell Gilbert.)

—And now, what on earth would I have for dinner? I should have stopped in on the way home from church at the one store open on Sundays. Yes, maybe Mother was "losing her marbles" after all! How I hated to take Bugsie down the icy hills again; but, wait,—was I seeing things?

As I rubbed the frost from the windowpane, I beheld a small safari of food (?) carriers advancing toward the house with hampers, covered dishes, and even a huge bouquet of golden chrysanthemums!

I ran out coatless to welcome the little army. Hugs and kisses rained down upon my generous friends, Ruth and Arthur Odegard, the Reverend Dr. Lord of the Methodist Church, (where I began my soloing at eighteen years of age) and dear Mr. John Perkins, my first music chairman, now ninety years young! Dr. Lord placed the sunny altar flowers in my arms.

After unloading their cargo on the kitchen counter, my dinner-bearers visited just long enough to admire winter's handiwork from the big windows upstairs, to lament the ravages of the New Year's storm on music room furnishings, and to laud me—over-zealously—for my remarks on television. (My ego, as usual, lapped up these compliments like a kitten over a saucer of cream.[4]) Finally, they wished me a speedy reunion with dear Steve, and all assured me they were praying nightly for his return.

"Prayers' blessings will reach him even if the U. S. Navy cannot," I returned wistfully, again thanking them heartily for their thoughtfulness.

Had I ever thanked my Heavenly Father for providing me with such friends? I knew I had not.

"By the way, Eleanor," Ruth asked as she passed the floor garden on the way to the door, "what's become of that pretty statue you used to have standing here under Steve's lantern, the Oriental one with the slinky eyes that followed you around everywhere? She gave me the creeps!"

Gilbert and I sat down to a sumptuous feast, truly manna from heaven: piping hot lobster newburg—and lots of it—to be spread on toast triangles, still hot and crisp,—a rosy-hued fruit salad full of my favorite bing cherries, topped with Ruth's own creamy pink dressing,—hot homemade raised rolls already buttered, a jug of cold cider —since neither Gilbert nor I drink coffee—and a quart of butter pecan ice cream—not to mention Ruth's sourcream chocolate cake with thick mocha frosting between each layer!

She and Arthur had attended church, Dr. Lord informed me, then hurried home to finish preparing all this, then asked him to join them. Dear Mr. John Perkins's Sunday newspaper contained an article proposing prisoner exchange, but of course I didn't tell him I'd already read it and had grave doubts about its fruition.

To be captured was a disgrace to Far Easterners. So why should they want these "lost faces" of theirs returned? . . .

Abruptly the warmth of the golden chrysanthemums faded. *What had Steve dined on this frigid noonday?*

—Phones were ringing again—

"Mrs. Harris? Commander Richard Bordeaux. I know I'm supposed to call you on Tuesday, but I wonder if I could see you

---

[4]Lesson for an egotist: For an overdose of vanity, swallow a little pride. (My Junior High pupils called these little blurbs of mine *"Harrisisms"*. Two of their favorites were:
(a) *Listen,* and *Learn. Fool*—and *Fail!*
(b) *"Picturing"* the faults of others develops *Double Exposure.)*

tomorrow night instead? Good!" He gave me directions for finding the Naval Reserve Training Station. The voice was businesslike and brusque—not at all like "Ship's",—but I was grateful. I hoped I could stay awake during the interview.

At five o'clock on Monday I was encased in my kicky new aqua wool suit with its fluffy white fur collar, all misted over with Brother Willard's birthday gift of "flowery perfume." An attractive advisee should certainly elicit more "advice" than a drubby one.

* * * * * *

The short, thickset Frenchman, not much younger than I, eyed me shrewdly as he stepped forward to greet Gilbert and me in the Navy Training School office. Was this my "dependable old sea monster with kelpish hair"?

His hair was not in the least like seaweed, but as neat as the rest of him. His round face shone like Bert's more angular one did when he emerged from the shower. Orderlies came and went out of the all-male-appointed pine-panelled office.

It was soon apparent this mature officer wasted no time, yet commanded respect. He appeared to like Gilbert, but I sensed a slight antagonism when it came to me. Maybe he didn't welcome this additional assignment, or was he afraid an emotional female was about to inundate the polished decorum of his all-male setup? He needn't have worried. I was dry as two bones.

My sturdy "advisor" hadn't read nearly as much as I had about the *Pueblo* seizure and I felt it to our mutual benefit to prompt him several times. How in Hades could a man advise you who didn't know as much about the case as you did? He questioned me at length concerning press interviews and I went into full detail. His ideas matched those of "Ship", but like "Ship" his advice was a bit overdue.

"The United States will never apologize—never!" he finalized with proper Navy aplomb. (Wannabet, Commander?) Audibly I replied, "Then our men will die! Do you mean to tell me, Commander Bordeaux, that our nation is going to allow eighty-two innocent young men, who were only doing what their country required of them, to slowly rot to death, go into slave labor, or be executed because we refuse to scribble down a few words?" (I knew my principle was wrong, dead wrong, but I didn't see why a full ship's crew of healthy men, who hadn't done the North Koreans an iota of harm should be sacrificed in cold blood for no good reason! A "senseless waste of life" as their good captain commented later.)

"Of course you feel that way, because you're a mother," he acquiesced, "but our nation will never apologize!" ("Mother" welcomed neither his expertise, nor his vehemence.)

"I'd better impound my reaction to that pronouncement, Commander," I smiled, with the coolness of a snake who'd like awfully to strike. I thought I caught a glint of humor in the seablue eyes.

"By the way, your phone will be tapped," he informed me perfunctorily in parting. "Be sure to call me a week from tomorrow," and his firm hand clasped mine in a Samson-like grip. For a minute, I thought I was going to faint.

Oh, that cocky rooster! I could advise him about a few things. The nerve of his saying our country would never apologize! (Was it sheer worry that was making me so angry?)

"Call him Tuesday?" Phooey!

I threw the lovely blue suit back on its hanger and slid the closet doors together with a bang. My days of glamorizing had just bowed out.

"You're a poor judge of character," Gilbert chided me at dinner. (We were enjoying the last of Ruth and Arthur's hamperload.) "I liked the man, a real man's man. He liked you, too, only you upstaged him. He couldn't possibly read all the *Pueblo* news. He has hundreds of men under his command there. You'd better phone him as he asked you to. He gave you some good advice. There's a lot you don't know about Navy policy and—"

" 'Navy policy,' blah! Some Navy policymaker broke his compass on this cruise! And something tells me if those poor men ever get out of wherever they are alive, they'll be blamed for it—being captured, I mean!" (How right I was!)

—So our phones would be tapped! We must be more careful!

I lettered for each of us, before I went to bed, a Code Card Mae and I could place under our bedside phones, if we found it necessary to discourse on political or military subjects, especially on the ship's seizure or our sons' interests and backgrounds.

* * * * * *

Tuesday turned foggy and warm. Arriving home from school, I chugged up the misty driveway thinking how closely the scene resembled the fateful Friday before. But the big picture window was securely boarded over now with new locks on all outside doors, as well as an order placed for an adequate alarm system.

I stepped inside the porch door, and although everything appeared

OUR TELEPHONE CODE WORDS (Partial List)

Pueblo: The Pill
Crew: Waiters
Sons: Souls
N.K. Prison: Restaurant
U.S.N. Advisor: Doctor
Apology: Apples
Make Apology: Get the apples
    in the bag
Washington: Dullsville
Congress: Rolling Stones
L.B.J.: The Team
Sec. State: The Coach
Sec. Navy: Flipper
Navymen: Sand Fleas
Intelligence: Goalies
State Dept. Attaché: Panda;
    Willie, the Wrist-slapper
Senators: Do-Gooders—(?)
Capitol: The Zoo
Beebe School: The Farm
Milton High: The Plant
Pupils: Chicks
Navy Greeters: Gulls
Money: Sand
Food: Ink

North Korea: Disneyland
Captors: Baboons
Pyongyang: Nankee-Poo
Ransom: Meat
Communists: Grizzlies
"Spies in the U.S.": Cubs
Red Writers: Hoods
Red "Bug" on Phones: Fuzzy-Wuzzy
Sea of Japan: Soup
Russia: Red-y-Maid
China: Dragon-Daddy
Kosygin: Clarabelle
N.K. "Task Force" (U.S.A.):
    Mod Squad
Kim Il Sung: Kimchi, Ole Sun-of-
    a-Nation, Moonface, Sickle-
    Seeker, "Overrated-Over-
    Stated"
Phone: Stove (stove hot=line
    busy)
Bed: Think-Pen
Picture (photo): Insult
Write: Pray
Letter: Candy
Office: Tent

Sample: Dorothy passed my candy around the tent.

Translation: Dean Rusk passed my letter around the office.

to be in order, a chill went up my spine as I heard feet running across the invisible ledges at the rear! Something urged me on to the hallway door leading to the cellar. It was ajar, its smashed lock lying in a pile of wood dust and splinters on the carpet at my feet! Believe you me, I'd waste no time calling the police this trip!

The phone rang. Oh no! Was it going to be a rerun of last week's Horror Movie? A dark figure loomed beyond the glass panels of the porch door, but thieves don't knock. The phone was persistent but so was the dark-suited figure. A young police officer stepped in.

"There's a car parked down on Sylvan Street by the woods under your cliff, Mrs. Harris, and we thought the occupants were headed for your house."

I reported what I had heard and found. The officer started down cellar as I went to the phone.

"Hello," I began impatiently, hoping to rid myself quickly of the untimely caller.

"Hello, Eleanor!" came a faint, cultivated voice I barely recognized as that of Alden's wife in Virginia. The connection was poor. "Have you heard the news?" (Heard the news? After the week I'd been through?)

"Yes, of course, Dear," I replied, vaguely puzzled. "They phoned me from Naval Headquarters in Boston. I've tried to call you and Bab (my husband's sister) several times. Isn't it terrible; I'm so sick I—"

"Naval Headquarters? Why it just happened—it just this minute came over the radio!"

"What just came over the radio, what, my dear?"

"Why, the news about the Vietcong shelling the U. S. Embassy in Saigon! We had to land helicopters on the roof. There was a regular battle and you know Alden, he'd be right in the midst of it!"

Alden! A nagging bubble had burst at last!

The police officer was waiting to tell me something but seemed to sense that the phone call was important. The old weakness came surging back in full force. Could I keep the floor down where it belonged this time?

"Listen, my dear, God help us both. I thought you were referring to Steve! His ship was the *Pueblo!*"

"Eleanor! Oh, no! *Not the Pueblo!*"

* * * * * *

When I phoned Mae that evening, oddly enough, her own situation had worsened:

"Oh, Mrs. Harris! Thank goodness ye called! The doctor has just left. I must be goin' daft or something. Today when I got home from school, guess what happened to me?" (She assisted dieticians in the lunch program at Milton High School.)

"Well, my Dear! I saw this telegram hanging up on my front door when I got out of the car. I thought something had happened to Ralph, so I started running toward the porch, and I fell on the ice and broke my arm!" She was crying again. "Oh, I thought Ralph was dead, I did! I did!"

This was worse than my two clergymen and the black limousine! What sort of Navy "planning" was this? (The telegram was simply a notification of Ralph's new allotment arrangements. The Navy had tried several times to reach Mrs. McClintock by phone.)

"Broke your arm! Oh, you poor, poor dear! What can I do for you, Mae? Let me come over and bring your supper."

"Oh, no, no thank you! Mary, my neighbor, has taken care of me—and I've called the Hickses." (Friends of long standing.)

"But that's not all, Mrs. Harris, dear!" the worried voice continued. "'Sister', Ralph's tiger cat, is very, very bad. She acts as if terrible things are happening to poor Ralph. That cat's always been sort of psychic, she has!"

I hurriedly put together a package for Gilbert to mail to her in the morning, some small feminine luxuries—perfume, dusting powder, nylons, hankies, a bit of costume jewelry. The thieves somehow had overlooked these unopened purchases.

Mae ended the conversation on a happier note, expressing joy at the prospect of meeting me when the *National Observer* man arrived for our mutual interview. ("Ship" was to call me.) "Arm or no arm, I'll bake ye some of my Irish shortbread for the occasion," she promised.

I decided not to add to her fresh burden by telling her about the Saigon situation or my second robbery.[5]

Before I went to sleep, I decided to phone Vuokko's brother in Washington (Dr. Kyosti, whose close friends called him "Gus") in order to ascertain her condition.

The report from Gus (a dental surgeon) was unfavorable, indeed. As with us all, including Ralph's pet, "Sister", Vuokko was mourning for her beloved, losing both weight and sleep. How helpless we all felt, both in our desire to aid Steve—and each other!

---

[5]Nothing came of this second robbery for police, apparently, foiled the attempt. No arrests could be made for either break, however.

Yes, the immediate future seemed anything but scintillating on the home front. How was it across those endless miles of ocean?

(Worse—The Captain [still suffering today from multiple internal injuries] was "beginning to look like an old man." His crewmen, those few who had glimpsed him, were shocked at the change in him.

Dysentery, sores, fever and scurvy were plaguing the crew, in addition to "programmed torture"!

In desperation I'd written the Russian Embassy in Washington, still trying to obtain a North Korean address where the prisoners could be reached. That Ruddy Bear's D.C. Cubs could growl out their whereabouts, I was positive, but would they?[6] I was disheartened, moreover, that I had received no reply from the International Red Cross, ever the one iridescent hope of contact with lost prisoners. That was one organization that could go anywhere, couldn't it? (Not into the North Korean prison, it couldn't!)

The night coming on seemed the darkest to date, and I felt again the relentless hoofs of Chollima, North Korea's mythical stallion, slowly pounding me to pieces as I read the evening headlines, the coup de grâce:

President Johnson reported that the Panmunjom talks *"were failing."* He was *"not hopeful"* of getting the men back *"right away."*

"Right away?" He probably meant *"not ever!"*

The phone broke into the late evening's stillness:

"What would you say to your captive son if you could speak to him tonight?" an enterprising newsman inquired.

(What an easy question to answer, I thought, the easiest one I'd ever been asked—)

(Why, Mr. Reporter, I would simply say—)

"I am endeavoring, with all my heart, to be as brave and mentally alert here at home as I know you are being over there, *wherever you are,* dearest son! For *'I can do all things through Christ, which strengtheneth me!'"*

Was it up to Pueblo parents to save their sons now?

---

[6]They politely suggested I write the Korean Task Force Desk, (at State Department) instead! (Shaggy Bear's brains are as sharp as his claws!)

"To Mae McClintock, a 'POW' mother, who shared my Pueblo vigil in a loving bond which grew out of our working, grieving (and rejoicing?) together," I wrote in my notebook several weeks later.

Friendship is a warm and willing thing—
As welcome as the first fresh scent of spring
From rain-drenched meadows plowed, to soar and sing
Into the soul—new grace to set a-wing.

A friend's firm hand can reach down depths of Hell
And pull the other from her wanton well
Of deep despondency, —what 'er befell
The lost one, and defeat her direst spell.

A friend's wise way or soft consoling call
Can ease the anguish from the mind, install
A brighter vision in the trend, and all
That threatens life and limb, —and tend its fall.

A friendship born of sharing fear and woe—
A special suffering, none the world would know
Except a mother, can a boon bestow
Upon the other, freeing love to flow.

That sons do languish in Korean walls
Behind whose ramparts Torture's Curse bemauls
Our wan and ravaged prisoners,* whose calls
No rescuer rushed forth to answer. . .galls!

A War of Words between the Worlds, indeed
Does little to assuage Chollima's** greed,
While "Gaunt Gray Shadows"*** trust and pray and plead
That Native Land from tyrants sees them freed.

So friend, lift friend! As widows known to sorrow,
We'll teach our lips to taste Hope's sweet tomorrow,
And seek through pray'r our God's age-old prediction:
"A happy issue out of our affliction!"

                                        E. L. V. B. H.

---

*A premonition we both had that proved correct.
**Flying Horse, symbol of North Korea.
****Pueblo's* 82 POW's looked like gray shadows in the photographs sent home.

Entr'acte

SCENE STEALERS

On Stage
  Telephobia
    Ole Sun-of-a-Nation
      Madame Doolittle, Seeress Extraordinaire
        "Dr." Hellion P. Hairstander
          Sign Language
            Pillow Poetry

Secretary of Defense McNamara and Secretary of State Rusk now appeared, via mass media, to be wilting under the barrage of repeated allegations by North Korea, that the stolen ship had intruded into its territorial waters, and the two statesmen wondered quite audibly whether little Miss Pueblo had indeed pushed her prying electronic ear over the watery line. Only the ship's log knew the answer, and it was hardly in a position to tell. (And even that was tampered with by North Korean manipulators.)

In order to cool tension across the truce table at Panmunjom, Uncle Sam dumped a sizeable bucket of seawater over presiding Major General Pak Chung Kuk[1] and his Klucking Klan by ordering our biggest watchdog out to sea, 76,000 tons of oceangoing canine, the *U.S.S.* nuclear-powered *Enterprise,* which steamed to a new position several miles southwest, possibly within or on the western side of the Korean Strait. Our F-4 Phantom jet fighter-bombers would still be within reach of North Korea (however tardy), along with two other fierce barkers, the *Ranger* and *Yorktown,* not to mention cruisers *Canberra* and *Chicago.* This belated act was titled "A show of force, but not a 'provocative' one." To a sensitized audience of *Pueblo* relatives, however, it was an explosive maneuver, a tinder-box test which kept us on the edge of our seats; for if it pushed that extra "knot", the North Koreans would kill our men!

Even South Koreans were perspiring greenishly under their collec-

---

[1]Better known as "Frogface" by his Pyongyang prisoners.

tive tunics at the undivided attention *Pueblo's* men, instead of their
President, Park Hung Chee, were receiving at the conference table.
Were the Orientals learning that the "life of the individual is still
precious" in the U. S. A.? As to the life of their own "individual,"
they did not seem nearly as perturbed over Communist assassination
attempts on their President's life as with the fear that the United
States would bow too readily to North Korean demands for repatri-
ating our Navymen, and thus weaken their own position at the bar-
gaining board.

Next came a strangely familiar mob scene in which onlookers
learned that sign-toting adolescent dissenters are not confined to our
shores alone, evidenced when "over 500 youths," mostly teenaged
girls, demonstrated outside the United States Embassy in Seoul, while
another youthful mob marched on the truce village of Panmunjom to
show "national indignation" over its exclusion from negotiations.
Did they have long, stringy hair, wear owlish spectacles, dreary
clothes, and carry sloppily-lettered placards? Such adolescent theatricals must have caused the wheels of North Korea's propaganda
mills to clunk like crazy.

This dissidence seemed the cue for General Charles H. Bone-
steel, Commander-in-Chief of ground troops in South Korea, to
stride on stage and dish out another cooling draught for all South
Korean doubters, by reiterating assurances that Uncle Samuel would
come a-wingin' and a-sailin' if North Korea seriously challenged
South Korea's freedom. ("Why do the heathen rage so furiously
together?")

Oh my Sainted Foreign-Policy Aunt, what intrigue, what multinational machinations Steve's little ship had spawned! How in the
world did he and Ralph McClintock, two clean-looking, humor-
loving, tall-American types ever get marinated into this mess of
Commie-Oriental pottage?

What scars would be cut into their consciousness—or into their
bodies—if allowed to suffer too long, too far from decency and loving
concern?

> ("It was the screaming of my men [during torture] I
> found hardest of all to bear." Cmdr. Bucher)

Mae McClintock and I were both counting heavily on the Christian upbringing of our sons, as well as their ability to see comedy
in any tight situation, to pull them through whatever ordeals lay
before them.

> (Steve was charitable toward his cruel keepers: "I real-

ized I must find some way to keep from hating them—I tried to feel sorry for them, so I kept saying to myself, 'They have sinned and fallen short of the glory of God!'")

I hoped he might also remember: "I have set the Lord always before me. Because He is at my right hand, I shall not be moved." (Psalm 16:8)

(Both Steve and Ralph were selected by Cmdr. Bucher to assist him in composing his "final Final Confession," a hilarious document. See: *Bucher, My Story* by Cmdr. Bucher and Mark Rascovitz.)

On a smaller screen, TEACHER FINDS DOUBLE TROUBLE IN WAR was playing, via country-wide rewrites from the *Melrose Free Press* and *Melrose Evening News* covering my two housebreaks, as well as Brother Alden's reported brush with death during the siege of the American Embassy ("Bunker's Bunker") in Saigon.

If there was one quality my five brothers shared, it was keeping their comical-cool. Through a diplomatic buddy flying to America, Alden had gotten word through: "Best rest I've had since arriving in Saigon!" (He was confined to his hotel room for days as a precautionary measure, directly following the embassy attack.)

Yes, this faraway war was actually close to me, and brought even closer when I thought lovingly about each of Steve's seventeen cousins and uncles who had served (during his lifetime) or were now serving in the field for the Red, White and Blue.[2]

It was Mae's turn to phone me that evening, and I relayed the great good news of Alden's safety. Feeling exhilarated because of it, I hurried on to present a rather overdrawn portrayal (by way of entertainment) of my smoldering encounter with my bombastic new advisor, Commander No-apology-never Richard Ram-it-down Bordeaux. (It was coded, of course.)

"He won't get any Girl Talk from me, come Tuesday," I promised her. "He didn't tell me one thing I didn't already know—except his views on our State Department's 'never-apologizing-never' to get our men back. And what makes Old Salty an authority on that?"

Mae, as I expected, sympathized with me roundly, and in turn described her own advisor, Lt. Commander Peter Nelson, a dark-eyed Dartmouth grad. As I surmised, he was little older than "her Ralph." Mae liked him, as well as his doll of a Japanese wife named Toi; yet

---

[2]Robert's sons, Alden and Rob; Alden's son, Robert; Bab's sons, Robert and Russell; Ellie's sons, David, Peter and Philip; Uncles Alden, Gilbert, Willard and Edward; Cousins Ted, Lawrence, Alex, Kenneth and Edward.

I sensed beneath her acceptance the dashing of her initial hope, like mine, that he'd be a "seasoned old sea monster." My guy was seasoned, no doubt about it, maybe a bit too salty for my native "freshness."

Mae and I were trying to be resourceful about using our Code Cards for telephone conversations. (See list, page 104.) Our word for advisor was "doctor," for the *U.S.S. Pueblo,* "the Pill," our sons were our "souls," the crewmen, "waiters," apology was "apples" and their nebulous North Korean prison, "the restaurant." Some sentences emerged in rather interesting juxtaposition, as: My *doctor* says to forget the *pill,* and if we want to relieve those *souls* and *waiters* eating (?) in that *restaurant,* we should write and get some *apples* in the bag from *Dullsville Do-Gooders,* i.e. (Solons at the Capitol). Such jargon was plain as day to Mae and me, but confusing, we hoped, to Communists listening to our "line."

Mae's arm seemed to be mending nicely, but "Sister," Ralph's pet cat, was growing progressively worse. Even her white angora playmate was beginning to look askance at her tiger pal, but entertained no second thoughts about finishing off her dinner for her.

Although we never expressed the idea openly, it was evident Mae and I both clung to the hypothesis that keeping "Sister" alive was akin to keeping the 82 crewmen alive, Ralph's feline barometer becoming a symbol of his own welfare, as well as that of his shipmates.

"I've got to get better in a hurry so I can get that cat to the Vet," Mae ruminated. "She's going crazy over that boy. She's a nervous wreck, she is!"

She gushed like a schoolgirl over the package I'd sent her which had arrived, Special Handling, that very afternoon. "I'm sending you something, too, just as soon as I'm able to pack it," she promised happily, "something I've been thinking about sending you ever since that first wonderful phone call from you." (She sent me "something" all right, a perfectly beautiful cerulean mink scarf!)

"Forget it, Mae," I laughed back, "just get those wild Irish roses back in your cheeks so we can keep our blind date with 'Ship' and that Washington news man. I'll be big about it and let you have 'Ship,' mustache and all. He's precious."

It was easy to get a rise out of Mae.

"Oh," she cried back in embarrassment, "never mind about those men, it's *you,* Dear, I want to meet!"

* * * * * *

Yes, Grade Four was, as expected, thrilled that their "famous" instructress was again featured in their Newstime coverage, and news articles in Boston papers: MELROSE TEACHER FINDS DOUBLE TROUBLE IN WAR in all its ramifications took up the entire page alongside PUEBLO MOTHER'S WEEK OF WORRY in the fast-growing scrapbook. "Mother" was ostensibly receiving more than her share of unsolicited attention, and the more traumatic their teacher's involvement on newsfronts, the faster small fingers flew into the paste pot. If I had won some prize of international dimension for literary acumen, peace proposals, Pulitzer, Nobel or whatever, interest would have paled beside such goin's-on as ship-swiping, robberies, guerilla attacks on embassies and the like.

Fourth-graders are at the collecting and hobby-loving level, and my pixies were certainly running true to expectations. . . .

"I don't understand why "Cozy" (Kosygin) didn't assist Prexy Johnson in getting that ship back," I protested to Gilbert at dinner. (I'd better tell him about our code system.)

"The papers claim Russia *(Red-y-Maid)* didn't approve of the North Koreans seizing the Pueblo," he replied. "Remember, Kosygin *(Clarabelle)* got his nose punched when he poked it into negotiations between Hanoi and Washington."

"You mean those Commies are trying to make us believe that relations between the *Bear* and *Chollima* are 'delicate'?" I countered.

"The Bear and Cho-who?" he grimaced.

"Chollima or Chullima, the choice is yours, Buddy. It's the 'national' emblem of the mini-country of North Korea. Seems those scalawags have corralled a fleet-footed flying horse as their trademark, no doubt something on the order of Pegasus, except for the fact one of those Mongolian clunkers would be more symbolic. Well, whatever the thing looks like, it's the same nag that's been pounding its hoofs all over me since those shipsnatchers got their boat hook into history. Most likely they are ramming the critter's hide down the throats of those poor fellows every time they get a lesson on The Cultural Course (Curse) of Communism."

(Old Tomboy was showing through tonight.)

(True, legendary Chollima, winged symbol of "juche" [self-reliance] was no stranger to his "captive audience." Crewmen were obliged to read and be lectured regularly on the spirited beast and the glories of communism in general, attending quiz programs, just as regularly, covering same.)

My Sphinx appeared to be more enamored of his baked sausage and applesauce with candied sweet potatoes than an erudite symposium on soaring stallions. After a nourishing silence, however, he managed a few words:

"Kosygin is goofing off until he can cut his caper backstage. He has no love for us, but getting those guys back home would put him in position to get something out of us that *he* wants—and for Pete's sake, *eat* something!"

"Oh, Mae and I have it all figured out," I reassured him, picking up a fork to pacify him. "We think some spying Commie in Dullsville, that's Washington, D.C., alerted the North Koreans to all those nice sophisticated supersonic surprises hiding in modest-appearing little Miss *Pueblo's* bosom. We give it the Cloak and Dagger angle," and I flourished the fork with the assurance of an expert in such matters.

"I've written to the Russian Embassy for Steve's address," I announced bluntly. "Those Reds know where the men are!"

Brother had his own opinion of my insight into international intrigue:

"Why not use your head for something besides a hat rack? Write directly to Admiral Smith in Seoul and ask him to pass your letter across the truce table at Panmunjom to a responsible carrier."

Gilbert, as usual, hit the jackpot.

Air-mailed by my caustic mentor at the post office opposite his Boston bank, I composed what I considered a reassuring yet innocuous message to Steve. It wasn't easy—there was so much more I wanted to say—so much more love I wanted to pour into his heart!

"To: Lt. Stephen R. Harris, *U.S.S. Pueblo,*" I wrote. I did not use his full title for fear of revealing more than I should about his duties aboard ship.

> My dearest son Stephen:
>
> Through the kindness of Rear Admiral John V. Smith, Senior Member of the U.N. Command Armistice Commission, and Major General[3] Pak Chung Kuk of the People's Democratic Republic of Korea, I am endeavoring to get this letter into your hands. I wish to put your mind at ease about us here at home, and to tell you we are all well and praying unceasingly for the safe return of you and your *Pueblo* shipmates. I keep in touch with your Beloved

---

[3]One U. S. Navy officer informed me these N.K. "generals" were simply phonies costumed to look impressive for their rôle of mediator at the conference table.

frequently, and your affairs are being handled by experts all along the line. Everyone expects a peaceful solution will soon be reached.[4]

Your things are being returned here from overseas, including desk, chair, and car. I'll cover and store everything carefully in the garage for now, the smaller things in the house. A Navy lawyer is handling your financial matters, so put your mind at rest. We all understand what you have had to do,[5] so don't worry about that, either. Thousands upon thousands of prayers are being offered for you and your crewmen, and things are "going for you" in high places, you may be sure.[6]

I have always been proud of you, dear son, particularly of your abiding faith in your Heavenly Father. Whatever pain, anxiety, privation and longing you may have suffered have been borne because of it, I am certain.

How I wish I could take your place, as all other mothers of *Pueblo* sailors must also wish; however we'll pray the time of reunion is not far off.

Your old buddy in the East[7] plans to meet you on that joyful occasion. He keeps in touch constantly, as do all relatives and friends. (My oak tree mailbox is overflowing.)

My cherubic host is keeping a scrapbook for you, too.

If you can manage to speak to Ralph (who hails from a nearby town) tell him I talk with his loved one frequently, and we have become fast friends.

I shall now write to your good captain's wife, and shall correspond with people in authority tirelessly. I do hope you have not been alone all these weeks! I'm sure you are remembering this:—

"The Lord will be a refuge in time of trouble—and has not forgotten them that seek Him." (Psalm 9:9-10)

All the love in the whole wide world!

Mother

It was my turn to phone Mae that evening. Would Steve's letter be returned unopened? I must try to cheer my Milton friend now.

[4]Only wishful thinking!
[5]Make a so-called confession.
[6]Wishful thinking, likewise, I'm afraid.
[7]His Uncle Alden in Saigon.

"Try a little of this on your rice pudding, Mae," I said for openers after we had assessed each other's state of mind, body and news-hoard for the day—all three at ground zero.

"Mae, you know how we Westerners are always claiming we can't fathom the Oriental (it should be *Communist)* mind?—that ever-mysterious,—and in the case of our sons' captors,—that ever-nefarious, devious mentality?"

Mae knew exactly what I meant.

"Well, my girl, I'm about to unfathom it, clear it all up nice 'n tidy, so we won't have to wonder about it ever again! Shall I start your education?"

"Oh do, yes do, Eleanor dear!" she chuckled, ever willing to lend an ear to my corny levity. "I'm just lying here full of painkiller for this old arm."

At this moment, I felt the tiniest flicker of what it *might* be to become a "wonderful person" to someone, although I must say Mae was too generous a subject to be considered a test case!

"Well," I began, "this little newspaper gem was handed to me by Margaret Taylor, a junior high teacher friend. It purports to be a conversation between a Westerner and a Chinese Buddhist. Only trouble is our guy doesn't get to squeak between the lines anywhere, but I suppose that's typical of the way things are going now-a-days; or maybe our Joe became "liquidated" wading too deep into the mysts of mysticism or somp'n. Well, anyway, here's how the Buddhist ball bounces:"

"'Our Empire is woven of the living, the dead and nature. It exists because it sets all things in order. Here everything is part of history. Being so, we seem asleep and are despised.'"

"That last part is no lie, Eleanor. I don't trust them, I don't, not as far as I can throw a—a—"

"A 'cheekful of chicken chowmein,'" I finished for her. (Old Tomboy was squeezing into the conversation.)

Mae hooted.

"Now, now, my dear, 'leave us' be more aesthetically acquiescent to the pearly wisdom of our peers. Kindly remember these saffron sages are our 'brothers,' which reminds me, Mae, do you realize in a few thousand years, or less, when we get all mixed up and melted-down in this multi-hued glorypot known as One World, some Utopian morn we're gonna wake up with complexions of a divine cement color? As we gaze at one another through mouse-tinted eyes, we'll hobnob together in a universal tongue known as Demos, buy our loin cloths with a common currency and—"

"And crown a *Communist* King of the whole Kiboodle," Mae finished for me. "Now, go on about those Chinese—"

"'All things dissolve in our magnificent mass,' the man says," and "'foreign conquerers lose their way in our yellow waters.'"

"I want to know whether the *U.S.S. Pueblo* lost its way in their 'yellow waters,' Eleanor, that's what I want to know!"

"Of course it didn't, Mae. You mark my words, our navigators knew where that vessel was at all times, and our men will prove it the minute they set foot on freedom's soil!"

"Oh, will we ever see them again, do ye suppose?" My listener's voice was on the verge of tears again. "It's been so quiet lately!"

I'd have to try harder.

"You can just bet we'll see them again, Sweetie. Say, here's a nice little tranquilizer for you! I've already written to Admiral Smith asking him to pass my first letter to Steve over the truce table at Panmunjom. If it works, you can send one to Ralph by the same route. I've also wasted a stamp writing to the Russian Embassy in Dullsville for their address, but I'll let you know if I ever dig up that N.K. mailbox, don't you fret!"

Mae was delighted.

"Now let's get this Oriental Brainball rolling—"

"'We look on in scorn while you, in spite of your raging science, dissolve in the deep and fruitful waters of the Land of Tsin!' That's *T*-s-i-n, Mae."

"The way things are going over here, they can leave off the 'T', Eleanor!"

"I'm with you there, kiddo! Remember how the Commies promised we'd 'rot from within' if they pushed pornography, dope, and Godlessness into the heart of America?—divisiveness, as well, of course,—so that just as Lenin promised, we'd 'fall like overripe fruit into their hands'? Well, here's the payoff:

"'You who know so many things, do not know the most ancient and powerful! You rage with desire for what is immediate, and thus destroy your fathers and your sons together!'"

"How's that for a bowl of noodles?"

I hoped our Bugged-in-Bear's ears were ringing with our gracious acceptance of his Dragon-Daddy's philosophy.

"That part about 'destroying our sons together' gives me the creeps," Mae confided.

"Right! That Buddy-the-Buddhist isn't draggin' his brains. The more I think about it, Mae, that part about raging with desire for what is *immediate,* could have 'destroyed our sons together' for sure, if we'd rushed the *Enterprise* into Wonsan Harbor. You have to admit we're impulsive compared to Ole China!"

After we rang off, I dozed for a few minutes. The phone had been so quiet between our calls lately, the silence was oppressive—ominous.

Although the "ham" in me might have nourished Mae, I was hungry myself for some word of assurance that our government was doing something for our lost sailors.

Well, there was a power greater than governments. I put my hand under my pillow and drew out the half-filled notebook I'd kept there since Bob's death, and decided to write a few prayerful lines— something like mailing a loving missive to heaven, and knowing a loving response I might or might not recognize, was bound to return in one guise or another.

Yes, my pen could "keep the lamp burning" for Steve, too! While a POW mother can do little to rescue a son physically, she possesses a hidden power and refuge that centuries, centurions and scimitars have never stricken from her frail being,—the refuge of prayer.

I thought, with affection and sorrow, of the thousands upon thousands of young men who had yielded up their bright young lives for their country. Yet, there was one young man who had yielded up his bright young life to save the world! I would beseech Him to hunt up our lost Lambs and comfort them.

A PRAYER FOR PUEBLO'S MEN

Sweet Prince of Peace, from Realms Above,
    Shake out thy mantle now, of Love;
Let it drift down upon our sons,
    Locked from seas and sound of guns.

On prison quiet let it fall,
    A Shield Divine to light each stall,—
An answer to this silent cry
    That nightly searches foreign sky:—

"Estranged from our Beloved Land,
    Lost captives of this outlaw Band,
Have you, O Country, 'Home of Free'
    Abandoned Us Who Serve by Sea?"

Oh Master's lips, tell each young ear,
    "My Father's love hath entered here!
He knows thy need; He hath decreed
    From Dungeon Death ye shall be freed!"

Hold fast thy faith! Know this, my son,
    Your country's laurels you have won!
The voyage is o'er; the risk is run—
    In Alien Land—your Nightmare Done!

I closed the notebook and lay back on my bed, trying to pull my thoughts through a bulwark of headache pain.

"'The voyage is o'er'? 'The risk is run'?" No, no, the lines sounded like an epitaph! I opened again to the silk marker. I erased the second and third lines of the last quatrain and carefully rewrote them:

> "Hold fast thy faith! Know, this, Brave One,
>   HIS HANDS the Wheels of Justice run.
> Your Hell will die! You'll greet the sun!
>   In Alien Land—your Nightmare Done!"

I tucked the "prayer book" back under the pillow just as the phone rang. News?—or more newsmen?

Surprisingly enough, it was Mae again, and her voice had a new vibrancy:

"Eleanor! Guess what that Chinese Buddhist of yours did to me!"

"Don't tell me—let me guess—you wrote to *Kim Il Sung*!" I simply tossed this back by way of keeping the exchange luminous.

"Better than that. *I sent him a telegram, I did!*"

"What, Mae? You actually sent a telegram to Ole 'Sun-of-a-nation?'" I was wide awake now.

"Son-of-a-what?"

"That's S-*U*-N, Mae," but she hardly heard me in her zeal.

"I dictated it over the telephone, I did, and had it sent to the North Korean Capital, you know, Pyongyang. His palace, or whatever he hangs out in, must be in or near the Capital, don't ye think?"

"I can't think, Mae. I'm too excited. How did you salute the guy, as 'Premier,' 'Excellency' or what-all?"

"I did no such thing. I just called him 'Mr. Sung.' I let him know we *Pueblo* mothers thought it was a pity our two nations couldn't get along together peacefully and had to hold 82 innocent young men as hostages because of it. I told him my son Ralph and his shipmates had been in his country long enough, that they were needed at home, and it was high time he sent them all back! Here, I'll read it to ye just as I wrote it."

Mae's telegram must have reached Kim, for it caused a stir in the Pyongyang prison! Ralph was called on the carpet and interrogated at length by excited "Room Daddies" concerning the message from his mother to their earthbound godling. But, of course, Ralph knew nothing whatsoever about it. He was not punished because of it, and must have been secretly pleased at his mother's bold bid for his freedom. Perhaps he was hoping that her telegram would atone for her references to "that gang in Washington" in her letters to him—a bit sticky even for clever Ralph to explain away! My own letters to Steve leaned so far in the opposite direction, elevating our "superb and brilliant staff at the Capitol" so close to sainthood that the North Koreans, hopefully, became bilious after digesting such tripe!

"Hold on, you Doll of a Diplomat!" I cried. I realize it's past our bedtime (ha!) but I have a tidbit here in my 'library' for the likes of you—wait a minute." I reached under the lacy petticoats of my beruffled bier.

"Here it is, the Life Story of your Teahouse Pen Pal—pardon me —your Teahouse *Telegram* Pal, *Kim the Kimono!*"

Mae hooted happily.

"Are you aware, my pet, that your Ole Sun-of-a-Nation has more adjectives crawling over his kimchi[8] than you could chuck a chopstick at? Like, say, ever-victorious, peerless-patriot, glorious-general, genius-commander etc., etc., etc.? One they forgot to add is Snoreless-sleeper, for when you stop to think of it, Kimzie has to share his royal crib with those two massive and mischievous bedfellows, Burnie Dragon and Borsch, the Bear. As the Good Book would say: His 'soul is among lions' (dragons) 'and he lies even among them that are *set on fire,* whose teeth are spears and arrows, and their tongue a sharp sword.'" (Psalm 57:4)

"Oh, yes, Eleanor!" Mae cried, fully recharged since sending the telegram. "Sung hated the Japanese. You remember how he had to hightail it out of North Korea over to Russia when the Japs took over. That's when he landed in Moscow to be trained in all these political shenanigans; and he's the one that's keeping our poor boys in prison now. Oh, Eleanor, I worry so. Are they warm enough, do ye think? I read during the war about those horrible Korean tortures!"

The Red "Bug" on our Bell System was being ignored tonight!

"Yes,—well it says here," I broke in briskly to stem the threatened tears, "that Sung's poppa was a schoolteacher, no less, and that this obese offspring of his gained control of the Communist Party of Korea in 1946. Besides becoming Premier, he's also Secretary-General of the Korean Workers' Party. Ain't that a coincidence?"

"Do ye suppose he ever married? Probably not," Mae broke in. (We took it for granted Kim kept a castleful of concubines!)

---

[8]Oriental food, the national dish of Korea, a vegetable pickle seasoned with garlic, red pepper and ginger.

"As a matter of fact, Mae, it says here that he married twice. After his first wife died in 1949, in 1950 he married the daughter of the head of the former South Korean National Federation whose job it was to bring left-wing national parties under the Red Wing."

"He didn't lose much time—between wives, I mean," Mae observed. "Ye can be sure he still keeps in close touch with Moscow or sends his flunkies over there to be shown the latest Communist tricks. Probably *they're* the ones who told him to grab the *Pueblo* after some traitor or Red agent in 'Dullsville' let them know how helpless and valuable it was lying out there all alone in the yellow sea!"

"You just read my mind, Mae. Those N.K. gangsters didn't require ultra-brainpower to see it was simpler, cheaper too, to purloin the prize itself, rather than have their Dullsville Red Cubs go to the trouble of stealing the plans and building from scratch—if they had the scratch."

"Yes, Mae when our priceless booty, frail little Miss Pueblo, sailed into their sights in the Sea of Japan on that frigid Tuesday of January 23rd, Ole Teddy Bear sharpened his Red claws (on an icy dock), ordered his flying stooge, Chollima (Mae had read about Chollima), to spread those bronze wings of his so he could climb aboard; then together they swooped down upon the battered maiden and dragged her remains into Wonsan Harbor (her delicate 2½ million dollar entrails mashed beyond recognition, her life blood of interior secrets spilling out her portholes to drown in her wake, or burn to a slow death deep within her bowels in a lone incinerator). Can't you just hear them snorting and growling with glee below-decks, pawing over all that sophisticated up-to-the-second electronic gadgetry they'd been informed by their 'overseas' agents was aboard?"

"—And that our sons were responsible for, Eleanor! Let's hope they were able to destroy everything before they were captured!"

"Let's hope so, Mae, and let's hope, also, that they had those push-button thingamabobs aboard to do the job! Don't you think Gary Powers' U-2 plane was a similar snatch-ploy? He didn't just wander over into Red territory any more than that ship did! One of our famous seers in Dullsville claims that Russian scientists have messed up the magnetic field sufficiently to prevent our pilots from steering their planes where they want 'em to go!"

Mae and I always made a point of giving credit where credit was due, especially to uninvited guests monitoring our communications system. On my line there was a barely perceptible high-pitched singing sound that had suddenly made its debut, and I held Fuzzy-Wuzzy responsible for the solo.

"Gilbert, my own domestic sage, says he thinks your b.f., 'Mr. Sung', may prefer hot Dragon to cold Bear these frosty nights. More than likely the Premier is doing some finger-nail crunching on his royal couch, a-worryin' over whether Boy Scout Kosygin is gonna help Uncle Sam cross *his* street. That's what is known in political circles as bilateral insomnia, Mae!"

"Oh my dear!" Mae broke in, as if she'd just thought of something. "I know it's late, but before we ring off, I must tell you about a new fan of ours!"

In spite of its fervor, her voice had a nervous timbre:

"Most likely ye'll think this is a lot of malarky, Eleanor, but I had a real surprise today. A dear old soul in her eighties (we later dubbed her *'Madame Doolittle')* called me this morning. She's a great pill faddist *(Pueblo* fan) and she claims she has second sight. Take it for what it's worth, but she says those waiters (crewmen) aren't doing nearly as well at that restaurant (prison) as we thought. She 'gets' things or 'sees' them, she says and she 'gets' only a few oily turnips, some dirty rice and rotten fish (the latter called 'sewer trout' by the captives). She claims the 'waiters' get dysentery who work at that awful place. She 'sees' them growing gaunt and thin, she does! Now what do ye think of that?"

What I really thought scared me pink, but I mustn't allow my emotional "ship-mate" to be aware of it.

"Oh, horsefeathers, Mae! You must remember we're bound to have a flock of rare birds coming to roost on our wires now that we're getting to be such 'famous birds' ourselves. You just tell Madame Sees'ngetsall to go peddle her 'pictures' in the Louvre. The only thing I want you to 'see' is Ralph walking into your arms! Our *Men Returning* picture, remember?"

"You're right of course, Eleanor dear. If only I could get that awful flag-draped—"

"Mae! Don't say it! Use Doc Peale's power of positive thinking, of your Ralph *alive!*

"Well, Snooks, here's a sweeter goodnight kiss for you:

"You have your Silly Seeress, but I have my Melodear. Yes, I had a surprise call, too. After school today, the first time the phone rang and I gave out with a happy hello, guess what? I got a barrage of Irish jigs blown into my super-sensitive eardrums. Wow! It was broadcast live by a wild harmonica wielded by one Harry Kevin O'Hara, also a senior citizen. He lives in a home for the aged in Boston, said he just wanted to give me a bit of a boost. It seems his own grandson had been a POW of World War II." (I saw no reason to tell Mae the youngster never returned.)

My patient listener seemed amused at Mr. O'Hara's method of joy-spreading.

"Don't laugh, Mae! Between blows he was asking for *you*, my Wild Irish Rose. He realizes you will be able to identify his repertoire far better than I!"

Yes indeed, many and varied were the fans we were fast amassing; yet at this moment neither of us was in a position to "see" that Madame Doolittle would soon rise to first place, regardless of our "common sense" reservations. For ultimately, this aging prophetess's divinations proved 99% correct, if not always accurate timewise.

Mae and I had already selected Bill Scherle as our Congressional Hero. Through his planning, each morning breakfasting solons at the Capitol were served, via the *Congressional Record*, a daily reminder of the number of days *Pueblo's* sailors had been ignored in their cruel prison. A big box on the front page tabulated this.

A World War II veteran of Rockport, Massachusetts, was our local hero; for at the dawning of each additional day, "Frenchy Hilliard," an articulate "practicing American" climbed up to change the growing total on his own handsome wooden REMEMBER THE PUEBLO sign hanging outside his picture-framing studio at the seaside resort.

Meanwhile, farther north in Manchester, New Hampshire, "controversial" Bill Loeb, owner and publisher of the *Union Leader* likewise tallied the long wait, and proved a great *Pueblo* sympathizer. Mae's long letter of appreciation, which he promptly published, drew reaction from all over the nation.

A huge replica of the lost ship also appeared in the town of Claremont, New Hampshire, home of Robert Hammond, a heroic *Pueblo* marine.

As a friendly offering on the Altar of Motherhood, Betty Rathbun of a Concord, Massachusetts group I still belong to, drove over with her last three pieces of Limoges china that matched the cake set my husband's sister, Elizabeth (Bab) gave me—the color and luster of pale green satin, with crowns of handpainted ivory and sun-colored daisies smiling in a circle at each other inside their gold-encrusted edges.

A tiny minstrel, Victoria Everding of Newton, Massachusetts, also nearing the 80-year mark, put our plight into beautiful verse and mailed it out to us. She has been a cordial friend ever since.

Yes, we were both deluged with kindnesses and mail!

A touching tribute was paid to Steve and his shipmates when another of my adored Ruths and her husband, Ed Mitchell, (both musicians) brought all thirty of their black and white choir members from a Roxbury church to sing in a handholding ring about my big piano,—and later around the table in the party room,—inspirational sacred songs as well as to offer individual prayers for the return of the long-lost prisoners.[9]

Steve's friends, Harvard roommates, Navy associates, former teachers and even a few professors all rallied to soften the blow for "mother." In fact, so gallantly did they persist, that whenever anyone stopped me on the street to inquire what it was that kept me ticking, it was easy to reply: "My *God*—and *His People!*"

Mae, in the meantime was receiving her own share of sympathetic overtures, finding one of them really enchanting (another one equally dis-enchanting).

One newsphoto showed Mae at her kitchen sink preparing lunch for her household pets, Sister and Kitty. Inadvertently, she had left an empty Calo can on the counter beside her, its label clearly showing. Result? One huge shipment of cat food to her front door, compliments of the President of the Calo Cat Food Company.

Episode Number Two was far less rewarding, opening its ugly mouth in the dead of a very cold evening. In fact, Miss New England's Wind Boys were making such a ruckus outside my bedroom windows, I was already half awake when Mae's voice came sobbing over the phone.

I hardly remember picking up the receiver, but that was par for the course now.

While no cranks had as yet swelled the sad tide of our frustrations in solving the riddle of how to rid North Korea of its unwilling guests, there was one gentleman who more than made up for the lack!

In order to refrain from giving this sour seer the publicity, however unfavorable, he'd dote upon, I'll simply christen him "Dr. Hellion P. Hairstander, the First,"—and hopefully, the Last!

"Eleanor! Eleanor!" Mae's voice cried pitifully into my sleepy ears. "Our poor boys are never coming home again, never again. Oh, I'll never see my Ralph again, not ever! You see, I was right all along about that flag-draped casket—it was so clear, so clear!"

---

[9]This same group now comes each Hallowe'en. After the last tiny neighborhood "ghost" has departed (200 or more each year), we hold our own vocal Ghost-in upstairs, with piano and organ accompaniment.

"Mae, stop crying," I commanded gently. "Calm down, dear, and speak clearly. What's all this rubbish about not seeing Ralph?"

I was thoroughly alarmed. Had some bulletin been flashed while I was trying to shut out the windsounds, and sleep? What, in heaven's name, had happened? I felt as if the howling wretches outside my window had forced themselves inside and clasped their icy arms about me in a frigid vise. Yet there was something about Mae's distress that perplexed me. If there was bad news, why hadn't our Navy advisors called us?

Mae wept on: "The radio!—just now—you know, one of those talk programs, it was. This old 'Doctor' (Mae named the culprit) came on to speak. The announcer said he was famous as an ESP expert, and this 'Doctor' said, he said, that our *Pueblo* men—that our boys,"—and she dissolved in paroxysms of weeping again!

My "frozen" emotions rapidly thawed and warmed to the flashing point as Mae reviewed the broadcast. I was furious that some shady character had dared to upset my tender and constant companion lying alone and helpless with a broken arm (and a broken heart, to boot!).

The fighting tomboy lying latent within me awoke to the new challenge. My angel mother would have used a gentler approach.

"Go on, Dear, what did that *stupid faker,* that jackal of a fraud have the nerve to say to you?"

Somewhere in the sleepy recesses of my reasoning, I was convinced that any stargazer who went on the air at this ungodly hour couldn't be worth his salt since most godly people were sound asleep anyway (excluding the two of us, of course).

Just why I was of the opinion rugged language would have an anesthetic effect on my agitated friend, I'll never know, but it seemed to help. Between her wracking sobs I pieced together the radio prophet's epic pronouncement as follows:

"Now, Friends, about the *U.S.S. Pueblo,* we should have gone in after it. Only a few, if any, of *Pueblo's* men will ever get out of North Korea alive! Oh, some may escape their horrendous tortures and be able to withstand the terrible privations of making their long journey to freedom, but—" (He was correct about horrendous tortures, as it turned out, but at this point it was probably only conjecture put in by a glib tongue for traumatic kicks.)

"No, I believe none will ever return," the self-proclaimed diagnostician said in dread conclusion.

This damaging dialogue, according to Mae, was delivered with cruel candor and a sort of jaunty self-assurance, thereby breaking a few more hearts, upsetting a few more fear-ridden minds, tearing down and possibly extinguishing once and for all whatever flicker of hope *Pueblo* relatives listening in might be harboring.

"Doctor" Hellion P. (for Poo-Poo-to-You) Hairstander, in my estimation, was neither an outstanding nor an upstanding "seer," psychiatrist, nor psychologist, whose prognosis in my eyes had no standing at all. In fact, he shouldn't have been standing around any radio station with any standing in the first place—so stand down Hairstander!

To Mae's obvious relief, I ridiculed the whole episode, calling the charlatan every uncomplimentary name I dared employ, until I had Mae more convinced of his chicanery than I was myself.

When I had her wrung dry and ready for Sleepsville, I told her I would call the station in the morning and tell them what I thought of the heartless Blasted Brute, as well as the announcer and backers who had allowed him the wanton privilege of wounding relatives of *Pueblo* captives who might be listening in and just gullible enough to believe him. And our suffering had made us gullible—wide open for the *good* news we were ever hoping would come!

Mae seemed comforted by my brash appraisal, but her last message disturbed me.

"'Sister' is very bad tonight—so restless, on and off Ralph's bed. Eleanor, I do believe she's even worrying about *me* now! She can't last much longer!"

Was Ralph's psycho-cat trying to tell us Hairstander was right!!?

Act V

"THE PEN IS MIGHTIER. . ."

"Blessed be the Lord, my strength, who teacheth
my hands to war, and my fingers to fight." (Psalm 144:1)

Face to Face with a "National Observer"
and Companion-in-Catastrophe
 Belles Lettres
  Pillow Prayers
   Breakfast at Eleanor's
   A Bomb Falls on Dullsville
   "You're Driving Us Crazy"

Three times now I'd bombed into the shining pine kitchen from
the tea table in the shining bow window of the shining family room.
In fact, I'd been burnishing the whole household up to "shining
point" ever since the pink of dawn when I fed my unhibernating
denizens who wandered up from our woods for breakfast under the
porch fir tree.

Yes, three times now I'd taken that "last" critical look at myself
in the kitchen wall mirror, the big one with the triple gold frame, the
middle one of which I had tinted aqua to match the soft pastel wall
behind it.

Something told me Mae McClintock was an ace housekeeper.

I'd polished the beveled plate glass on this and every other glassy
and glossy exposure as diligently as I'd polished myself on this red
letter, this "wicked good" Saturday, for today was the day for personal appearances!

Almost any golden minute now my esteemed, but as yet unseen
telephone friend, Mae McClintock, was due to arrive on her first
visit to Ledgewinds! This was the day, moreover, we were to be
interviewed by a staff writer from *The National Observer,* flying in
from Washington.

After Mr. Davis's snowplow quit the driveway, brother Gilbert
shoveled all paths and entrances, then promptly erased himself to
attend the Boston opening of the New England Home Show.

I hoped Mae was tingling as gleefully as I at the prospect of our
first face-to-face encounter. Just preparing for the happy occasion

127

filled me with sensations I found decidedly preferable to the seeping despair that had dulled my daily outlook and drained my boundless energy ever since Steve's (and Ralph's) brazen capture off Wonsan!

I prayed I could make this meeting as powerful a spirit-lifter for my sensitive fellow-sufferer as it promised to be for me.

Mae's advisor, or Casualty Assistance Calls Officer (CACO), young Lt. Commander Peter Nelson, was driving her over from her home in Milton, on the other side of Boston, no doubt in one of those sleek black Navy limousines. (Why not paint 'em navy, Navy?)

As to what looked back at me from my kitchen mirror at this point of no return, the reflection revealed no "Beast" (Gilbert's term for an unattractive female). I was glad I had borne the cerulean mink fur piece Mae had sent me into the Bellevue Dress Shop downtown and made a happy marriage with a gold wool cocktail dress. The duo whispered sweet things to my figure. With my gold pumps, gold horsie belt and stirrup earrings to match, the total picture, let us just say, had it been tangible, was not one my hard-dying ego would toss into the nearest circular file.

The Powder Puff Beauty Salon downtown played some pretty tricks on the natural curls at the crown and sides of my head; so, yes, I was as ready as I'd ever be to make my bow to Mae.

"Ship," Commander Ross Winship, my picturebook advising officer and the graying, friendly-eyed writer from *The National Observer,* like my clerical "comforters" had arrived simultaneously, and were soon talking together by the family room hearthfire like alumni of the same Alma Mater. They looked up with such interest each time I floated in to fill the tea table that I offered free samples, finally suggesting they might like to tour the house until the guest of honor put in her appearance. Judging by the sounds issuing from the grand piano in the west corner, their sightseeing had ended in the music room. I was grateful for the concert for it left me free to indulge woman's hallowed privilege, that of taking stock before the doorbell rang.

I first added a fresh touch of Afternoon Roses to my lips at the kitchen mirror, then walked into the family room and allowed myself to emote for a few moments over the festive board. The theme from Tchaikowsky's Fifth Symphony floating down the stairwell only heightened the effect, and I hoped my virtuoso would continue the background music throughout Act I of Girl Meets Girl.

Yes, the blue embroidered Madeira cloth Aunt Marcella had brought me from Puerto Rico set off Grandmother Van's cut glass berry dishes with the gold scalloped edges "wicked nice." They

"My bed became my Home Office with Library under the Lace."
(Photo by Roy Hult)

Mother and Dad Van Buskirk

"Send it to Kim Il Sung!"

sparkled in the rays of the late afternoon sun, circling around their
mother bowl housing a rosy heap of powdered fresh strawberries
brother Gilbert had found in the Fanueil Hall Market. Another
matching cut crystal bowl oozed with a billowing cloud of bona fide
whipped cream to party-up the strawberries.

The "green satin" cake plates looked longingly over at Ruthie
Johnson's applesauce butter cake decorating one end of the table,
its luscious goodness smothered under a heavy cap of maple cream
frosting weighted down with fresh-shelled walnut meats. The longest-
cherished of my four Ruths and her husband Carl, had driven over
forty miles to bring it to me last evening, bless 'em!

My own platter of pink-topped lobster rolls, fresh from Franklin
Square's *Lobster Claw* Restaurant gave a gourmet touch of color to
the display.

On second thought, maybe Bab's Limoges lovelies were holding
out for that Irish shortbread (thick butter cookies) Mae had insisted
she would bake with her poor broken arm! In the center of the array,
Dr. Lord's chrysanthemums, hovering like a crown of giant sunbeams,
smiled their approval over all.

Well—and now—what had Steve eaten today?

> ("Once in a blue moon we got an apple. We hid it as a
> special treat—but sometimes vermin, or a guard, found it
> first. The rotten fish was served until it was consumed!
>
> Our drinking water was carried in warm,—while we had
> to break the ice in our wash buckets on winter mornings.
> We were always cold, always hungry, often in pain and
> sick,—and always wondering how long our sentence would
> be—months? years? or forever?")

The piano symphonette was still drifting down the stairwell when
I heard the approach of a heavy car. (That's correct, a big black Navy
limousine!) I watched it come to a halt at the end of the turnaround.

What would dear Phyllis think if she happened to be looking out
her dining room window this time? At least no dour dominie would
alight from it. I must call her after the party.

I plugged in the electric coffee maker, tossed the fur piece, still
fragrant with Mae's own perfume, over my shoulders and slipped out
onto the porch. It was a perfect afternoon weatherwise. Miss New
England Winter must be keeping her February storm-brewers busy
elsewhere (and, hopefully, Funfloating Fate had misplaced her
scythe!).

A pleasingly proportioned woman in her late fifties, dressed in a
black Persian lamb coat with dark fluffy fur collar and chapeau to

match (not completely hiding her becomingly coiffed auburn hair) was stepping out of the limousine. She beamed a motherly face in the direction of the house as she came up the walk and mounted the steps to the porch. A tall, white-hatted officer walked slightly behind her, carrying some packages in one hand and supporting Mae's fur-clad arm in the other. I was glad to see she needed no sling.

I ran to the top of the steps and extended both hands:

"Welcome, dear Mae McClintock, and Commander Nelson!" I cried joyfully, giving a hand to each.

Mae clasped my hand firmly between both her exquisitely gloved palms, her gray-blue eyes crinkling with affection and surprise, while the young Commander took his arm from Mae's and shook my other hand cordially.

"Oh my! Oh my dear!" the familiar expression rang out as she held me off for a second, looking pleasantly down upon me as if appraising her garrulous little telephone friend. "You didn't tell me you were pretty!"

Before I could convey my own pleasant reactions, she took me in her arms and hugged me warmly like the needy child I had suddenly become, my face losing itself in the soft fur of her collar which, like the scarf she had given me, held the same elusive fragrance of an exquisite perfume. Commander Nelson beamed his obvious approval. Like all Navy men, he considered the *U.S.S. Pueblo's* capture a personal tragedy and, accordingly, took a sympathetic interest in the families of its crewmen.

As to Mae McClintock herself, I found her a delightful paradox of down to earth maternalism embellished by the outward sophistication of Park Avenue. It made for a delightful duet. While she was a larger woman than I, she possessed not only style but a sort of becoming "presence", which provided an unexpected complement to the toasty warm heart and lilting brogue I had grown to depend upon for succor.

I surmised at once that my companion-in-catastrophe, like me, believed in maintaining a pleasant façade at all costs; and for some reason, although Mae was a younger woman than the lady who sprang to mind, I was reminded of the dear old soul who used to live near our Maine farms, who, when she lost her husband, kept smiling bravely. "I do my cryin' nights," she explained.

We entered by the porch door, and from the moment Mae stepped inside she seemed honestly delighted with everything she "walked into," from the party room, always set up (this time for Valentine's Day), to Steve's small bedroom on the first floor with its quaint

Boston rocker and hand-turned ship's wheel lamp his cousin Alex Williams, a World War I vet, had made for him.

As I rolled open his closet to hang Mae's coat among the few clothes Steve had left for me to "find a home for," my heart turned over. I ran my hand over his old tweed jacket and squeezed it in a secretive caress—

Mae was fascinated by George Brae's (really great great Grandpa's) seagoing secretary in the family room and I showed her the secret drawer. When she saw the black hole in the floor garden and inquired after Kuan Yin, however, I had some explaining to do. A Black Hole without "Mercy" was too reminiscent of Calcutta, where air-strangled British prisoners had perished! Nevertheless, the bronze lamp overhead was faithfully sending its rosy glow out to the cold February sea,—and Mae loved that!

The second floor musicale had now come to a faltering demise.

I presented Mae and her dark-eyed CACO officer to the two men as they descended the staircase, thanking the pianist for his concert (Ship was the performer), and advising him to be ready with encores after tea.

Ship and the young commander drew up our flower-cushioned metal chairs to the glass-topped table (now covered in blue).

I had brought inside the only garden set vandals had not destroyed. The big party room table was too formal for a *rencontre joyeuse* such as this, and during "teatime" I made it my province to keep the *U.S.S. Pueblo* from sailing into the discussion. We'd be boarding her soon enough.

Conversation, food, and fresh coffee flowed sans gêne in and out of mouths, while Mae and I enjoyed letting the three men carry the verbal ball. We knew our turn would come later. Nevertheless, just as I expected, when she did speak, Mae's brogue and personality captivated the trio.

After tea, Commander Nelson left us to stroll out onto the circular deck to watch, in a dying sunset, the lights of pink crystal cities twinkle beyond snow-feathered hills. Meanwhile Ship and Mr. Newsman had gone over to the bow window seat for a pre-conference conference.

Mae and I hurriedly cleared the table, then went aloft for our own tête-à-tête.

Like me, my companion confessed she went through the necessary social amenities like a sort of Zombie, ever thinking of Ralph and what she could do for him.

"Today is different," she confided cheerfully. She showed an immediate fondness for my bevy of big dolls in their rainbow tutus, posing with their toy instruments (that really played), around the upstairs hallway spinet outside my beruffled bedroom.[1] Like everyone else, she fell in love with the glass-walled music room with its crystal chandelier, and Oriental carpets "lying like a pale blue lake under the windows" as Mae described them later.

Seated at last on the rose velvet divan in the window overlooking the ocean, we spontaneously hugged each other again, swaying back and forth in understanding arms, then hastily shared snapshots and photos of our late husbands and only offspring, chattering all the while like a couple of crones at a quilting party—until we heard a step on the stairs.

Mr. Staff Writer, eager to make his long journey productive, interviewed each of us separately in the same room, while Ship stood apart, pretending to lose himself in the wintry vistas darkening below the great windows.

Just how much editing of our candid answers would Navyboy standing over there have to do? In my own ego-estimation I was becoming a pro in dealing with newsmen, ever mindful of North Korean propaganda-pushers, yet hopeful of keeping the *Pueblo* plight alive. How much to reveal, and how best to reveal it was a constant inner conflict. While policy-makers in Washington encouraged the muffling of *Pueblo's* parental voices, wouldn't a complete news blackout put America to sleep and leave our sons "Orphans of the Storm"?

Did the continuing silence emanating from the N.K. "Task Force" Desk mean it simply did not know what to do next? Perhaps "Rescue, Inc." needed the prodding of an aroused American public! I was convinced brave Rose Bucher shared my anxieties on this point! I must call her soon! She had been bolstering morale the country over by sending handwritten messages to members of her husband's immense *Pueblo* family, as well as speaking for the crew!

Back on the rose divan, our Observer from the Capital seemed intrigued by my mental punch line papers had quoted: "This is where the heroine loses her mind," referring of course to that fearsome Friday housebreak when I had to decide which to call first, the police or the radio station. To help him avoid duplication, I filled him in on all previous press interviews.

"What do you think our country should be doing now that negotiations are no longer in progress to free the men of the Pueblo?" was his first pertinent question. (This in return for a complaint I had made about Stateside Silence?)

---

[1] I arranged them at school in the guise of a miniature orchestra when teaching my unit on musical instruments. Even my Jr. High and summer school pupils enjoyed their smiling countenances in the classroom. . . .a well-travelled and affable, if silent, orchestra!

I decided this called for more than an innocuous answer. I shot my interviewer a frank reply that I knew would never make his column—only it did!

"I believe it is high time President Johnson interceded personally to save the lives of his stranded servicemen, if it isn't already too late! Only a dramatic high-level maneuver such as our President's own intervention, by decree, mandate or even by apology would 'reach' these publicity-mad barbarians, in my opinion," I declared vehemently. "Such a magnanimous gesture by L.B.J. surely would provide Red Propaganda Mills with the oil they crave to soothe their 'system!'" ("Castor Oil, a whole *Pueblo* shipful!" Tomboy silently prescribed.)

"Yes, I'm convinced that if an apology will save their young lives, then our President should offer it, at the same time making sure the North Koreans *guarantee the safe return of the men in exchange for it!* (My teatime calories had risen to the challenge.)

"The world-at-large must first be fully informed, however, as to the reason he is making it! Whether or not there is any basis for such an apology is not the issue here. It's the saving of innocent United States Naval Officers and their crew, illegally detained, and whose only 'crime' was serving their country!"

Mr. National Observer's busy pen appeared to be taking down everything I said.

(Again I knew my principle was cockeyed—probably downright dishonorable by Navy standards—but only by matching our adversary's chicanery and following his conditions for release to the letter could we retrieve our men, I reasoned. After all, they had us over a barrel,—unless we were anxious to embark on World War III, and lose our sons in the bargain!)

The other questions he put to me, oddly enough, were virtually the same ones local papers and TV interviewers had already posed. Was he thinking that the passage of time had altered my views? Questions he asked Mae I knew she would reveal later.

I hoped in my heart that our little tea party had likewise "served" Steve and his men. My guests, at least, seemed to find the afternoon rewarding. I felt better, too, for having given Mae this pleasant interlude. Lesson for Spirit-Lifters: *If you let your grief get lost in a Haystack of Helpfulness, you'll find it lies in a Sunny Field.*

* * * * * *

Like a blow out of the blue, the long silence ended. Newspapers awoke with a loud roar—EXECUTION!

Naturally, our government had chosen to ignore the mass "confession" signed by all captives; but why publicize the fact? We were dealing with an "irresponsible, outlaw regime, whose ideology, views and actions are worlds apart from our American way of life," as Rear Admiral Smith had written me. So why cause them this obvious loss of face?

These "outlaws" who had charge over the destiny of our sons, in my sober assessment, should be handled with extreme caution, not overt ridicule—and certainly with a diplomacy compatible with their ideology! (That is, if we were to stay the hands of the nihilistic murderers!)

I prayed good Admiral Smith was equal to the task of both appraising and exceeding the cunning of such superslick connivers. While to some Americans, Uncle Sam's "big stick" might pose a potent threat, I hoped with all my heart the Admiral would use less deadly persuasion and "speak softly" instead. The "big stick" could kill our sons! (Might the *Enterprise,* had it not stopped short of Wonsan, have been our fatal "big stick?")

I had no trouble remaining sleepless after reading headline after headline that screamed EXECUTION, and only darkness kept me from compulsively counting for the hundredth time the blossoms on the canopy over my head.

At dawn I crept out to the music room for morning prayer. I was, also, most anxious to embark upon my newest brainwave, i.e. Thought Propulsion. I must summon everything in my power to help Steve now. *If our nation wouldn't make a phony apology to save a full ship's complement of young men from certain death—what then?*

As to this thought-propulsion idea, Mae McClintock had given me a first-hand account of a World War II son of a friend of hers, detained for some time in a German prisoner-of-war camp. His mother went into her absent airman's room each day and "projected" thoughts to him at a precise hour, striving to "reach" and invigorate him in his faraway cell. She wasn't even certain he was alive, but forced herself to believe he was. Concentrating on her life-generating task, she beamed her mother's deep love clear into the fainting heart of the prison camp, at least into the one heart that could receive it.

Many months later, after making his escape, a man not much more than a human skeleton fell into the arms of his aunt (in New York City, nearest relative to where his ship docked), and when she had nursed him back to health and he was able to return home, he told his mother "strength-giving sensations" came over him at a certain time each day and these were all that kept him breathing. Fortunately, his young mind was sufficiently receptive to absorb his mother's love and benefit by her fierce protective instinct; and although half-dead himself, he had watched his fellow prisoners die one by one, powerless himself to pass on to them a portion of this implantation of energy that had seeped over and into him all the way from home!

Well, what harm in trying this myself,—extending to Steve in telepathic fashion a full draught from my own fountain of love, pouring warm courage across the frozen miles into the inner sanctum of his thinking!?

Only those 250-odd seagulls on their dawn flight across the big picture windows, from the sea to scenic Spot Pond to lave the heavy salt from their wings (leaving us humans to drink up the dust and feathers) could witness my strange stance on the music room floor—both arms extended stiffly from a lump of pink froth lying face down in abject concentration, thought-waves surging along its two fleshy antennae to tingle out the very tips of fervent fingers aimed toward North Korea!

"Blessed be the Lord, my strength, who teacheth my hands to war and my fingers to fight," my bedside Bible reminded me.

Yes, fingers and a sleep-deprived brain remained the only weapons I possessed to fight the Battle of Anxiety; yet, however obtuse my thinking, I must write Admiral Smith immediately. For was he not God's instrument to stay the hands of Steve's executioners?[2]

I crawled back into bed. The worn notebook was slipped from its hiding place. With fingers struggling to maintain their "fight," I prayed for help in writing to the Admiral:

I NEED THEE

God, touch my lips! From Thee I seek
    The words a Breaking Heart must speak!
God, place Thy wondrous Hand o'er mine,
    And guide my pen with power Divine!

God, breathe new strength into this shell,
    That I may muffle Death's slow knell.
God, reach my Soul and Theirs, as well,—
    Then Lift Us from these Flames of Hell!
    . . . .
In Jesus name, I do both beseech
and thank Thee, dearest Father!
               Amen

---

[2]God's main "instrument" it now appears, for staying the fatal bullets, was the deploying of the Carrier *Enterprise* in the direction of North Korea *after* the capture. Yes, Steve believes this timely maneuver provided the real deterrent to their execution!

My letter seemed to write itself after I replaced my "prayer-book" under my pillow. (Was it God's "wondrous Hand" that carried the prompt personal reply from Admiral Smith?)

Ledgewinds atop Boston Rock # 87
Melrose, Massachusetts, U. S. A.
February 20

Rear Admiral John Victor Smith
Senior Member
United Nations Command Military Armistice Commission
Seoul, South Korea

My dear Admiral,

Eighty-two mothers walk in silence with you to the conference table at Panmunjom. We're truly there with you each time you go.

We sit down with you, and though unseen and unheard, we listen with strained attention, weighing every spoken word and phrase against the life of the imprisoned son we love so desperately.

We have all been apprised of your superior qualifications for your life-saving mission, and of your high sense of duty to your country. We wish with all our hearts we could add our collective strength and wisdom, such as it is, toward the completion of the monumental task assigned you—that of freeing Pueblo's 82 helpless sailors from the hands of their godless keepers—from those master-practitioners in the art of human suffering!

May God place upon your lips the words that will expedite the repatriation of our Navy sons—and ultimately crown your endeavors with joyous fulfillment, good Admiral Smith!

Our gratitude is immeasureable!
Sincerely and prayerfully yours,

Eleanor Van Buskirk Harris (Mrs. Robert S.)
(Mother of Lt. Stephen Robert Harris)
Intelligence Officer, U.S.S. Pueblo—AGER-2)

* * * * * *

Execution! What a gruesome, terrifying prospect! I would not allow my imagination to carry me further—I must picture the men returning, always returning!

I could already hear the questions my eager Fourth Graders would ask me, envision their little faces, grave beyond their years, just as they had looked after the initial excitement of the capture had paled and they were faced with reality:

> "Will your son be executed, Mrs. Harris?"
> "How will they kill all those men? Will they shoot them or hang them?"
> "Why doesn't our country go over there and get them?"
> "Are they (Washington) just going to let them all die?"
> "Why don't we just bomb their whole country?"

Yes, what a pity their teacher had to become a daily reminder of tragedy. Perhaps I should close the Pueblo Scrapbook for keeps.

> *(Pueblo's* captives listened with hungry ears for the sound of U. S. bombers over their prison compound. "Where the hell are the bombers?" they kept repeating, thoughts of their own annihilation completely secondary!)

* * * * * *

On a Saturday, weeks later, I had grown so listless and anemic, despite iron pills and a forced appetite, I had neither the strength nor the desire to carry the load of cheery messages up the drive from the overflowing oak tree mail box. Cheery messages cheered me no longer. If I stacked them up to my chin after filling Ole Raccoon's pockets, I could make it in one haul.

The long press silence following EXECUTION headlines, coupled with the sad result of my first effort to reach Steve (which came to me via the UNCM secretary, Colonel John Lucas), i.e., that the North Koreans had flatly refused my letter across the table at Panmunjom (prior to the negotiations shutdown), left me sickened and thwarted, utterly devoid of any further ideas for making contact with a son threatened with death!

What was happening to our loved ones? No one, not even the U. S. Government was certain they still lived!

To add to my consternation, Vuokko's two devoted brothers during a social call at Ledgewinds, confided in me that they were concerned for the health of their beloved sister.

My frail dove's prospects for survival were worrying me as much as Steve's now![4]

---

[4] I sent her a lovely negligee along with a long newsy letter, entreating her to keep her courage high. She wrote me equally heartening letters, full of charming affection.

Well, time for the Mail Haul. I trudged up the driveway panting like an over-hunted tigress, managing somehow to wedge my load through the porch door. I'd just push it all onto the kitchen counter here for now—oops! One of the heavier letters fell to the floor. How I hated to bend down these days. My head ached so much worse when I did so, but—

A sudden burst of joy almost toppled me to the floor—the handwriting looking up at me was Steve's!

I grasped the letter and stared at it, both elation and deflation boring into my consciousness:

Steve was alive! But how much of it would really be his thinking? How much the "enemy's"? What was he about to tell me?

My heart pounded as my hands fumbled to tear open the envelope. Was he going to plead with me to save his life, my own dear son?

"Dearest Mother and Esther" (Vuokko), the beloved script began:

> I can imagine the suffering you must be going through at the moment wondering about me![4]
>
> It is no news by now that PUEBLO was captured in the act of collecting intelligence in the territorial waters of the Democratic People's Republic of Korea. We are not prisoners of war, but espionage criminals who committed a crime against a foreign state. The penalty for espionage in this country is death. We will not be released unless the government of the United States takes the following action:
>
> 1. Confess to the Democratic People's Republic of Korea that USS PUEBLO did conduct espionage activities in the territorial waters of the D.P.R.K.
>
> 2. Apologize sincerely to the D.P.R.K. for such action.
>
> 3. Assure the D.P.R.K. that such an act will never be repeated. If these conditions are not met, then *we will be executed for the act.* Therefore, you must help me and 81 others of us here.
>
> You must contact our congressmen and senators and plead for proper action by our government.
>
> At the time of our capture we destroyed many classified documents and much sensitive equipment.
>
> As Research Officer, I tried to deny our real purpose in order to preserve security, but the captain fully confessed

---

[4]"Ma, I saw Lieutenant Harris after one of his beatings—he looked awful!" (Ralph McClintock)

to what we did. Therefore, I had no recourse but to confess the truth myself.[5]   However, the U.S. Government
must apologize since it is responsible for the PUEBLO
incident. Otherwise, I repeat, we will face a miserable fate.

Act in our behalf and pray. Esther, have faith in Aiti's
vision[6] that we will have a son, and continue faithfully
doing God's work.

Both of you should keep in close contact with U. S.
Navy authorities and ask for all the help you can get.

We are not in a prison or prison camp, but in a comfortable, clean, and well-heated building.[7] We are served
three nourishing meals a day,[8] and we have been provided with warm clothing. We are in no way abused or
harassed, but are treated humanely. But, we are here and
want very much to come home. Our hearts are torn with
grief and we recognize that our loved ones are experiencing
even greater sorrow.

I love and miss you both so much that even as a grown
man I have broken into tears many times. I hope that I
will be able to hear from you very soon.

With all my love,
Stephen[9]

There was much more to the message, including advice to Vuokko
and me about handling his personal affairs.

I fell into bed after I had called Vuokko long distance and read
Steve's letter to her. Although her voice sounded softer than ever,
the news was eagerly received. I told her Uncle Gilbert would have
the letter xeroxed for her, and a copy made for me, too; for Gilbert
insisted we mail the original to the "North Korean Task Force" Desk,
or preferably, to the Navy Department.

(Ultimately I had well over 100 copies of the cogent sections of

---

[5]They must have half murdered Steve to make him write this lie about the *captain* as
well as *himself!*

[6]"Aiti" (Finnish for [Vuokko's] "Mother") just before the ship was captured had a
vision that a son would be born to the couple.

[7]Really? The radiator held little heat, so little, infact, that the wash water had ice on it.

[8]Nourishing to whom? Even the hungriest rat wouldn't relish "smelly turnips floating
in 'crankcase oil'—three times a day every day." (And speaking of rats, they scuttled
through the building day and night.)

[9]"Stephen?!" Such formality really had me worried! I hoped the North Koreans insisted he enclose the line about breaking into tears! If not, conditions must truly be as bad
as Madame Doolittle "saw" them! (She had already told Mae and me about the icy wash
water and rancid turnips.)

Lieutenant Stephen R. Harris reading his first letter from home. The plant and table were removed as soon as the picture was taken. (Picture was taken in summer during his captivity in North Korea.)

Steve's first letter xeroxed, enclosing one of them in each of my second letters to all Senators and other key legislators. After all, there was no law against pleading for a son's life.)

I had talked with Mr. Vincenzo Strano, father of a *Pueblo* sailor who had *already lost a son in Vietnam the very day the ship was captured.* He was arranging with the State Department to cross the DMZ in an effort to reach his son in North Korea, God help him!

"Cross the DMZ"? I'd suffered through a series of recurring C-movie nightmares about that! Although fired upon by guards, in one of them, I actually *did* get over the line—on foot, of course, leaving behind me a legacy of blood-drenched hopes (and blood, as well) on the snowy trail. I pushed my poor wounded body across miles of icy mountain wastes, arriving at long last (and half alive) at the desolate prison. There, with trembling fingers, I pulled my fragile body up against its dingy bars and, panting with fatigue and hunger, peered through them at the emaciated form of a half-crazed son sitting on a cot in a bare room (with dripping wet stone walls), shivering and staring. When I called his name, he turned toward me, and recognition slowly warmed into the glazed eyes for a moment, then just as slowly, faded out again.

Crying piteously, I extended my arms through the cruel bars that separated us. But, as in all evil dreams, I couldn't quite reach Steve before stone-faced guards raised gun butts high over their heads, bringing them down with all their brute strength to smash my bleeding hands from off the unyielding metal. They flung me, without so much as a chopstickful of kimchi, back into the wilds of North Korea. I crawled back to live on and on, mourning over the memory of a situation I was *powerless to change!*

At this point I usually awoke, writhing in a pool of perspiration, making it necessary to shower, and change both nightwear and bed-linens.

What a pity I must waste so much energy in these nocturnal bouts with my lively imagination! They left me utterly devitalized.

I next phoned Mae, and while she had not heard from Ralph, she knew word must be imminent, and was simply overjoyed to hear Steve's letter, although, like me, she was uneasy over its contents. We were hopeful that the Navy would oblige us with a return address now, even though the letter itself contained none. It was postmarked Marseilles, France. Two identical copies arrived soon after.

("They made me copy that load of garbage twice, Mother!")

In my mind's ear, I could already hear TV sound trucks and newsmen's cars crunching up the driveway. When this news of POW letters to the homefolks broke, I'd better be steeled for a new onslaught of—

The phone rang. Had it started already? I was irritated by the interruption, for I wanted to savor Steve's letter longer and do some analytic deciphering. I'd get rid of this pest in a hurry!

"Hello."

"Uh—my other girls don't usually treat me this way—"

I tried to place the slow, disturbing timbre of the masculine voice. Where had I heard it? Was it some old college flame news of the ship's capture had rekindled? A former classmate, perhaps, back in town and innocent of my connection with the world-shaking crisis? Or—

Abruptly I recalled the voice. It belonged to none other than Commander Richard Bordeaux, my long neglected CACO "advisor." But what a change-over in approach! Was this Ole Smoothie the same self-assured Bomber I'd clashed with in the Naval Reserve Office? I knew he worked late some evenings.

"Oh—I'm sure they don't, Commander. It's just that the news has been so depressing," the artful dodger replied. (And who needs advice about that? But today wasn't Tuesday. It was Friday, wasn't it? I was already three Tuesdays behind!)

"But—well, honestly, Commander, I couldn't possibly drag myself way over there tonight, (I knew he wouldn't "advise" over a tapped phone) even if I welcomed your expertise," I teased.

(How very little I resembled my angel mother!)

He laughed back cordially, "I know—my views about an apology. They still stand." I didn't expect him to enlarge on this. I told him briefly about Steve's letter. He was excited about that, then continued with his "advising":

"I can just imagine the day you've had after recent developments. The papers must have mobbed your place," he went on brightly, referring to execution threats—"And now you'll have more company, —sooo, I'll just add my boots to the crowd and stomp over there, instead. What time do you serve breakfast?" (Was he serious?) "I'm pretty good at kicking out gate-crashers!" (No doubt!)

Yet here was a cautious man, and I liked that. His sense of humor was a pleasant surprise, too. He was probably trying a new tack.

"I'll expect you at nine, Commander, no earlier, please!" I gave him explicit directions for finding "Mother's Mausoleum on the Mountain" and insisted he write them down. He seemed to enjoy obeying my orders. Perhaps it was an amusing switch from commanding "hundreds of men."

"By the way, what you wear on your feet is immaterial, Commander. What you wear in your head is more important. It takes a neat mental curve to 'survey' some of these quiz kids over the side." (over the cliffs?)

The Commander seemed tickled by my use of the Navy term.

Well now, as to breakfast—and the gentleman looked as if he humored a healthy appetite—if he actually turned up hungry at nine a.m., I'd see to it that he earned every mouthful.

Ample portions of Quiz Program would be served with every course, real tasty tidbits, such as:

1. What's the shortest route to Dean Rusk's desk? And what can you, Sir Richard, do to get me there? (fresh fruit juice on ice)

2. Exactly what role is the *Navy* (vs. State Department) playing now in this fast game of rescue? "Fast" before the executioners' bullets, that is. (sizzling scrambled eggs with Bacos sprinkled amidships)

3. Is our illustrious Commander-In-Chief taking tranquilizers (as Mae lamented) or just *dead* as far as the *Pueblo* issue is concerned? (a second cup of fresh-perked coffee if he perked up on this one)

> (Actually L.B.J. was anything but "dead" on the issue; on the contrary, he simply was not reported as doing very much by the press.)
> (A "living corpse," the North Korean negotiators dubbed him. A "putrid corpse," they labeled J.F.K.)

4. Would personal phone calls from North Korea to parents or wives round out the present propaganda barrage? (If I ever heard Steve's voice on the phone begging for his life, it would kill me!) (Strips of Canadian bacon crunched down with the help of neighbor Gertrude Miles's orange-cranberry crush on hot buttered toast should round out this Morning Menu of solid food vs. solid fact.)

* * * * * *

I hadn't had the heart to ask my new breakfast buddy this last one, even though he'd already eaten his reward,—nor the one about the possibility of seeing the prisoners on TV, either. He'd more than earned his keep as it was.

Sure enough, sound trucks crunched up the driveway just as the last bite of hot doughnut swept into the Commander's mouth.

Gilbert, as usual, had eaten lightly and gone out to his shoveling, much as I knew he would have preferred to remain with this man he admired so openly.

"Keep my remarks confidential," my CACO advisor said briskly, picking up his napkin, as he watched from the triple window fronting the table, huge vehicles converging with smaller cars bearing tag-a-long newsmen. Automatically he began carrying dishes toward the washer.

I found myself reluctantly grateful for the presence of this power-fully built protector, and experienced none of the fatigue-and-fear combo that had overcast my earlier screen test. I dashed upstairs for a lightning change and to adjust my hair and makeup. Whether Harry Light-Meter had learned his lesson or not was unimportant now. (Butterfly was dead—well, almost!) A faint hope lingered that Steve might get wind of the fact that his mother looked O.K. and was in there rooting for his deliverance.

> (Back in the desolate prison, in the presence of his crew, when Commander Bucher learned from his captors that "Madame Rose" was making speeches for his repatriation, his head fell onto his chest and he wept. It was the first word he had had of his wife after his many weeks of torture and sickness. He did not need to apologize to ship-mates who were audience to the poignant little drama. They understood only too well—and undoubtedly longed to weep with him!)

"You are about to witness a one-act play entitled *The Anxious Little Mother*," I announced, brushing past the table-clearing commander on my way to the door. "It's the most innocuous route I can dream up to take out of Pressy Pressville. I'm a natural for the role, you'll see!"

"Great! Stick to your lines," he boomed, giving me an admiring glance over the dishwasher. "Look, my boots are already poised for the first kick," and he turned and pointed a toe toward the doorbell.

"By the way," he added with the innate gallantry of a true French-man, "that's a mighty pretty dress you're wearing."

Facts for Flighty Females: There are times when the most fastidious of us, worried, weary or workworn, turn a deaf ear to what the world may think of us—a deaf ear, that is, to all but the masculine voice!

* * * * * *

TWO PUEBLO SAILORS WRITE MOTHERS
MELROSE, MILTON WIDOWS PRAY FOR SONS' SAFETY

Yes, the Boston papers were Pueblowing again:

"A beautiful (!) woman with graying (?)[10] hair stood in the waning sunlight in the living room of her home on the crown of a Melrose hill"—picture of me holding Steve's letter—picture of me playing the organ—picture of Mae holding Ralph's photograph (She'd heard from him.). Quotes from Steve's letter, not given by me, but picked up from a Japanese broadcast, "and although a grown man, I have broken into tears many times." Quotes from Ralph's letter about "missing his Mom's apple pie," and "swimming in Cape Cod Bay."

"Ralph never cared for apple pie, and has never had a swim in Cape Cod Bay that I know of," Mae reported.

"Steve hasn't shed a tear since he was a small child that I know of, either," I replied.

Were our two correspondents trying to tell us something?

> Madame Doolittle was "seeing" crewmen and officers "on stretchers, vomiting, screaming, beaten to a pulp"—! Sores, boils, rashes, and dysentery became minor ailments.
> ("One fellow's head had been pounded so hard it was running with blood and swelled to the size of a pumpkin—we couldn't even tell who it was.")

Old Mr. O'Hara's harmonica was absolutely silent. Even closest friends must be "frozen" by the death threat that swamped us, for scarcely a phonecall broke the strange silence. I hadn't even found the courage to ask Mae if Ralph's cat was still alive!

Was radio "Doctor" Hellraising Hairstander's prophecy gaining a lead?

* * * * * *

Help Me, Heaven!
Now! Pen the spark that fires the minds
Of Statesmen! Pray unceasing,
Thy Wisdom from their lips, compels
Our Tortured Sons' releasing!

I bore in mind those lines I had jotted down at dawn in the sub-pillow notebook; and now with fingers trembling in what I hoped was the end of Miss N.E. Winter's March habit of hurling her frigid epithets across the open recess yard, I removed my mittens and began to formulate ideas on the back of an arithmetic flash card I discovered in one of Ole Raccoon's striped fur pockets.

"Execution!" Time was a precious commodity now, more precious than I cared to estimate, and I dared not wait even until school

---

[10]I've never sprouted a gray hair in my life, nor am I beautiful!

closed to start drafting a letter strong enough to pierce Congressional lethargy.

My pen must be divine-powered and dipped into the milk of human kindness, if decisive action were to prevent Mae's flag-draped casket from multiplying by eighty-two!

The recess bell across the street broke into my scribbling.

By closing time I felt so spent and feverish it was an effort to reach up into my school mailbox; however, when I did, I drew out, not one, but two exquisitely packaged bottles of my favorite flowery perfume (the expensive kind!). Only Irma was aware of this weakness of mine, and her kindness moved me more deeply than the tenderest words of consolation.

Counsel for Comforters: *A personal gift reaches the heart faster than the speed of "sound."*

* * * * * *

After my third battle with influenza, my first hand-written letter was on its way to all 100 Senators. Little did I realize I had dropped a bomb on our nation's Capital!

> Ledgewinds atop Boston Rock, # 87
> Melrose, Massachusetts
> April 17

"The United States will never let pride stand in the way of saving human lives."

(From a speech by President L. B. Johnson)

When is our President going to put "pride" in his pocket and *save the 82 men of the Pueblo?*

(Then followed the main body of the letter)

My dear Senator———(Name was penned in here)

As the distraught mother of the Intelligence Officer captured aboard the *U.S.S. Pueblo,* Lt. Stephen R. Harris, I have waited in vain for nearly twelve weeks for some word of progress by our government. *Pueblo's* 82 men are threatened with *"execution"* as stated in letters home to parents and wives, unless our President *apologizes* and meets certain conditions. What is keeping him? What have you, as U.S. Senator, done to save these men?

While our Navy advisors at the local level right on up through Secretary of the Navy, Paul R. Ignatius, have tried to comfort us anxious parents, we want *progress,* not comfort. "Doing everything possible" seems to boil down to only one avenue of hope, i.e. negotiations at Panmunjom (which must be "carried on in secret" to be effective). While we parents appreciate the need for secrecy, after thirteen such meetings, *where are we?*

What is our sons' captors' price for 82 lives?

What ransom has been offered?

There is only one thing in their letters home these long-suffering prisoners are asking—*an apology!* These 82 highly trained young Navy men love their country well. During these long, anxious weeks of their incarceration, how many times have they asked themselves these agonizing questions:

Is my country about to let me die through sheer neglect of my live-or-die request?

Has my country abandoned me?

Last night on the newscast by Huntley-Brinkley (NBC), documents were shown of the *Pueblo's* records purportedly proving the ship *was* in North Korean territorial waters. Whether or not this eventually proves to be the truth, this entire nation would understand why our President is apologizing—if he so chooses.

I continue to have implicit faith in the power of my great country to resolve this dilemma with honor and dignity. In the case of the *U.S.S. Pueblo,* however, we are dealing with an "outlaw regime" (quotation from Rear Admiral John V. Smith, U.N.M.A.C.).

Even outlaws can lose their patience!

An apology is about as "peaceful" a solution as one could find. Please get busy, Senator (name), before it's too late!

> Sincerely and gratefully yours,
> Eleanor Van Buskirk Harris (Mrs. Robert S.)

* * * * * *

I had Gilbert airmail my plea that same morning from the Post Office opposite his bank.

The phone rang late the following evening at about 11:30 p.m.

"Ye've done it, ye have, Eleanor! Just as I've been saying right along. Ye have a way with words, ye do!" The telephone was scintillating.

"Mae, what in the world are you talking about?" I asked sleepily. I was still shaky after the flu, and the phone had awakened both Gilbert and me. My "nurse" was exhausted, too!

"Why, your letter to Congress! Didn't ye hear the newscast just now? Eric Severeid said, 'A mother from the Cradle-of-Liberty state' had sent a handwritten letter to every Senator, and that it was a 'masterpiece of diplomacy' and had stirred Congressmen to new— Well, right away I knew it was your letter got them all stirred up, I did! There'll be something doing for those poor boys now!"

Fallout from my word-bomb hit at noon the next day:

"Mrs. Harris? Mrs. Robert S. Harris, mother of Lt. Stephen Robert Harris, captured Intelligence Officer of the *U.S.S. Pueblo*?" (I assumed the crisp, female voice belonged to some "wheel's" private secretary.) "This is the State Department in Washington calling, Mrs. Harris. Captain Harwood Wilcox would like a word with you."

The tone was reminiscent of a scolding schoolmarm and made me feel like a little girl who had been caught with her hand in the basket stealing the Sunday School pennies. But why should I feel this way? I had done nothing wrong (except break D.C. pleas for silence).

Lesson for Impulsive Imps: *If you meet a problem head on, your next problem may be mending your head!*

A cool modulated male voice laid it on the line:

"Mrs. Harris? Captain Wilcox calling from the State Department in Washington. I must ask you to write no more letters to Congress. You have created such a run of Senatorial mail and personal calls on the *North Korean Task Force Desk* (that noble tag again!) that they have scarcely had time to work on the *Pueblo* Case. They have done little else since your letter arrived besides answering to the Senators." The voice was appropriately stern.

At first I felt as if Captain Wilcox had sneaked up and whomped the little gal smack on her naughty wrist in the penny basket, but Tomboy surged to her rescue: I had every right as a United States citizen to write any blasted letter I deemed necessary to any United States Senator! Still—

"Oh, I'm terribly sorry, Captain Wilcox, that my letter made such a—"

Yes, I felt humbly ashamed if my valiant efforts to save eighty-two lives had bogged down the very gears of their life-saving machinery! Truthfully, with a temperature of 103° when I wrote it, I had entertained no such confidence in my literary acuity!

In the fever-gutted recesses of my mentality, however, little charred wheels began turning, reminding me that Potentate Winfield Brown and his Brain Trust hadn't been too "forceful" in getting out their "tasks" lately, that is, if one were to judge from overt results.

Their North Korean adversaries had not even allowed them a stage upon which to present their "scenarios," let alone provide them an audience since, how long was it now?

In dealing with men, I'd discovered some priceless precepts: 1. Keep those Tomboy tendencies under wraps. 2. Always allow a little of that "delicate" feminine gullibility to escape from under the net in order to ensnare concrete results. Or, to put it more succinctly: Lesson for a Lass: *Honey catches more "flies" than muscular arms!*

Sympathy for a *Pueblo* parent was completely lacking in the one-sided conversation, yet I apologized humbly and contritely to Captain Wilcox; but, even while I was doing so, my obvious win over Congressional apathy gradually outweighed my pity for poor, poor Mr. Brown's put-upon desk and my naughty "assist" in making it a shambles, or rather, a mecca for mad Congressmen.

I felt no "pity" for my reprimander either, and found myself becoming an opportunist. Well, yes, why waste a "Capitol" opportunity such as this one, even if the Captain's long distance phone-call was intended to be a knockout punch to a distraught mother's powers of persuasion? (Butterfly this time fluttered to the rescue.)

"I'm terribly sorry you found it necessary to phone me, Captain Wilcox! I had no idea my letter would disrupt your efforts so sadly. But now that you've reprimanded me, I'd like to ask you something: *Exactly what has your North Korean Task Force accomplished to date to free our men?* I was purring now, my vocal chords dripping with "flowery perfume," the innocent kind. I disliked no one, but Ole People-Lover might have to stretch her arms 'til they broke to include this gendârme from the Department of State!

My telephone voice has a way of coming over "Naïvely youthful," my male friends insist. Whenever speaking to middle-aged strangers over the phone, they almost invariably call me "Dear."

Captain Wilcox was in no mood to call anyone "dear"; nevertheless, he melted slightly as our conversation ensued, politely inquiring whether I'd read *How Communists Negotiate* by Charles Turner Joy. I knew he would ask me that one, and yes, I'd already read it, for it gave honest answers to the reasons our "task force" found their task a tricky and unpredictable one. The slippery, ideology-bound adversary we faced was schooled in endless ruses for manipulating to his own propaganda-advantage our well-intentioned ideas of talking out the problem man-to-man. He had other ideas for solving problems.

When would this naïve nation of ours ever learn that the only thing our rosy-hued enemy, potential or avowed, respects is strength, *strength of arms!*

(I still cotton to that little pearl of wisdom popped from the prudent lips of one G. Washington back in 1789: "To secure peace, it must be known that we are at all times ready for war!") General George, unbeknown to history, is America's No. I Boy Scout.

As to this latest Dullsville Drama: "The Captain (Wilcox) and the Accused" (me), these opening strains of condemnation were but a shoddy overture to a melodious series of Washington vs. Melrose "Bell Telephone Hours" that promised to wander well into summer. Patient Captain Wilcox, in fact, became my D.C. "contact."

While this State Department attaché did a commendable job of bawling me out for putting a newsworthy dent in D.C. lethargy, fortunately for me, he also turned out to be quite an erudite dispenser of knowledge, answering my countless questions concerning the quandary of being a POW mother, and eventually allowing me glimpses of his own service in our country's armed forces.

Inexorably, however, Mr. Official Stateside Slapper was being steered by this scheming culprit into the sweet spectrum of sympathetic accord:

> "more inexorabl(y) far
> Than empty tigers or the roaring sea."
> Mr. Shakespeare

* * * * * *

How many good people—concerned Americans—there were residing here in New England! For quite naturally that is where the bulk of my "fan mail" came from.

(God, reward these kind writers, for not a crank was ever to croak among them!)

Without benefit of Ole Raccoon's pockets in the warming spring weather, I used a grocery bag to carry the letters up from the oak tree nest.

I had time only to skim the many messages arriving daily, most of them from complete strangers; and I could have employed a full-time secretary to reply to each writer. As it was, I did the only thing possible, composed a form letter. I wanted so much to let them know how much I appreciated their interest—that their continuing support was a "gracious River of Strength from which I drew, each day, the courage to place my feet more firmly upon the paths I must take for the lonely and terrifying Business of Rescue,"—that their words carried with them a "resurgence of pride in the knowledge that the Great Patriotic Pulse of our 'less demonstrative' citizenry was still beating strong here in my beloved New England!"

I further informed these kind people that I believed our *Pueblo* prisoners were already benefitting from the spiritual fallout generated by their multiple prayers (nearly every letter mentioned praying for the men), and that I was deeply grateful for this universal awareness of God's grace and power to save the innocent young sailors from a wanton death.

"Each noon, I wish you could all, for a moment, become little birds in the branches above my oak tree mailbox," I wrote, "watching this small mother carry a Big Bag of Love up her driveway—Love for eighty-two lost navymen—and, hopefully, this heartwarming chore of mine is being repeated daily in eighty-two homes across America!

"'May God bless you and keep you and make His face to shine upon you', particularly upon those of you whose Dear Ones are caught up in the grave misfortunes of war!"

Gilbert promised to xerox hundreds of copies for me, and told me to forget about giving him any money for stamps and stationery.

His face, like mine, was beginning to show the effects of the continuing strain.

* * * * * *

"Why not quit killing yourself over Stephen and his shipmates, Eleanor, and just leave everything in God's Hands?" my gentler Christian friends would ask.

"It *is* in God's Hands,—but I'm not spiritually anemic," I would retort. "Since God gave man a *brain,* I think He expects him to use it. 'Faith without works is dead', and I'm alive!" (well, *half* alive!)

LIFE

> Love prolongs it;
> Hate deforms it;
> But Indifference tolls its early demise!

This business of trying to piece together the splintered fragments of a warm-hued family portrait, smashed by a miniscule wielder of the Hammer and Sickle—as well as the Vietnam War—left me a heritage of doubt. Either our government was doing nothing about its lost crewmen, was keeping us poorly informed, or was afraid that revealing its efforts would fatten the bins of N.K.'s propaganda mills.

Sadly I began taking stock:

First there was Steve. Where was he? Was he alive? Or had he already been executed?

Then there was Vuokko. Would she survive the ordeal at the rate she was suffering?

Next there was nephew Bob, lost in a Vietnam jungle again? Or was he still recuperating from his eighth wound? How safe was his dad, brother Alden, from Saigon rockets and land mines on his cross-country journeying?

What was happening to Steve's other cousins in Vietnam? How soon would Robert's Rob have to be shipped over there? (And how was my once merry plowboy doing in Hue?)

At the end of their partiotic venturings, would all my loved ones return to be pictured in this family keepsake hanging upon the walls of my heart?—Or would some faces be missing—or seared and disfigured by the fires of freedom?

At dinner, Gilbert hit the jackpot:

"Why don't you and Mrs. McClintock quit sobbing yourselves dry up here and take a run down to the Squirrel's Cage and cry into the Main Bucket?"

I phoned Mae immediately and picked up my Code Card.

"Darling, start packing! We're off to Dullsville to visit Dorothy (Dean Rusk) in her tent (office)!" (I had no idea Rose Bucher, bless her, was of the very same mind, and would arrive well ahead of us.)

Mae was ecstatic.

"But Eleanor, dear, (uncoded) how in the world are you and I ever going to finagle an appointment with the United States Secretary of State? I don't know any important people in Washington, do you? Maybe our Congressmen or CACO—"

"No problem, Mae. I'll just give Willie the Wristslapper a buzz in the morning! We're a telephone twosome, now, y'know."

"My dear. Ye can't possibly mean ye'd ask that Captain Wilcox for any such favor, that man in the State Department who scolded ye for sending that letter to—!"

"The same doll. He's our patsy, Sweetie. Never fear. He adores bawling me out. Either he likes my baby voice or—"

"*Or he's afraid ye'll write another letter to Congress,* he is!" Mae laughed.

"*Another letter to Congress!* Mae, my girl, you may not realize it, but you've just rolled out the official red rug! Try this on your carpet sweeper:

> Write! Fight! Put on the bite!
> You'll wake that yawning Task Force yet!
> Bomb, Mom! With more aplomb,
> T'will put you on a Whisperjet!

Act VI

CONFRONTATION

Bomb II Brings the Whisperjet
  Mother Tiger Goes to "Dullsville"
    Sales Daze
      Letters from Lawmakers
        So Nice to Meet You, Gentlemen!
          Lost in the Sea of Japan!

My opening salvo in my second word-bomb to Congress, dated the Fourth-of-July must have punctured the apathy of the most lethargic lawmaker, judging by the avalanche of replies received—a factual description of North Korean torture. I sent all one hundred Senators the letter in my own handwriting, as before.

Bomb II went as follows:

> Ledgewinds atop Boston Rock, # 87
> Melrose, Massachusetts
> July 4th—

1. "They use a fishline about 3/16 of an inch in diameter, cutting off the blood supply to your limbs, forcing you to kneel on a cement floor. They jam your hands up behind your back in a position higher than you can hold them yourself, then tie the same cord around your neck. Whenever your hands come down, you choke yourself. Your arms and legs become grotesquely swollen until you can't stand. Your neck is a mass of sores. You can't breathe.

2. They knot a loop of stout cord, put it around your forehead and slowly twist it with a hard stick until it all but cracks your skull—the pain is unbearable."[1]

3. They leave you tied up all night with an electric light bulb close to your eyes—the bugs do the rest—by morning

---

[1]The fine-looking brother of a *Pueblo* mother underwent this torture as a prisoner of World War II. He is now in a veteran's hospital, a human vegetable, recognizing no one.

155

your eyes are eaten out, or if not, you are all but blind.[2]

This is North Korean torture, the true story of it, as told by former prisoners.

Pueblo's men are silently pleading for their lives! Let's stop kidding ourselves that they're "being humanely treated" and get to work on their release!

(Then followed as before, the main body of the letter:)

My Dear Senator ——— (name added)

"As the now sickened and completely disillusioned mother of the Intelligence Officer formerly aboard the *U.S.S. Pueblo,* (Lt. Stephen Robert Harris, a six-month captive of the North Koreans), may I first thank you for your courteous and detailed replies to my letter of April 17th. As you recall, I implored you to consider that all-important face-saving request of *Pueblo's* captors, i.e., an apology!

Although the tragic matter of the *Pueblo* and her 82 survivors has been neatly kicked under the Congressional rug for the State Department to sweep up, I beg you to consider yourselves not exonerated from further responsibility in saving the lives of these tormented and forsaken Navy men! *It was you, their Senators, they asked for help.*[3]

Please examine the enclosed letter carefully. It has been mailed to me three times in my son's handwriting. Are the North Koreans trying to tell us they really mean business?

(Each Senator received a xeroxed copy of the plea in Steve's own handwriting.)

I am keeping a scrapbook for my son. In it I have written the name of each Senator and will note beside it what he has done for *Pueblo's* crew. Many of you went to great lengths to report your initial reactions and recommendations following the *U.S.S. Pueblo's* brazen seizure; however, other than writing the State Department in my behalf, what have you done recently and personally to save these men?

Your silence has been noticeable, Mr. Senator! If your own son were among these neglected prisoners, would the

---

[2]*Pueblo's* Charles Law's eyes are permanently damaged, not by insects, but by two by four inch wooden clubs used in the bludgeoning of his stalwart young body.

[3]Famous last words!

snail's pace and lack of progress by their "rescuers" be tolerated by you? Why not send your personal solutions to the State Department for scrutiny? I pray you would not suggest the use of force, as that would surely mean a swift end to the very lives we are striving to save!

Isn't it possible to use the "language of diplomacy" in forging an 'apology' which would guarantee the safe return of our men—alive? Above all, such an "apology" (deserved or not) must not provide crafty North Koreans with the proof of guilt required by them to annihilate their captives! Be wary of its wording!

Our country saved the lives of two men, Captain Carleton Voltz, and Captain Ben Stutts, by offering false apologies. Is it any more "dishonorable" to save the lives of 82 handpicked, highly trained, valorous men, Mr. Senator?

May I repeat the quotation by our President:

"The United States will never let pride stand in the way of saving human lives."

Is this an empty echo?

Unless *Pueblo* mothers see some semblance of progress very soon, we may resort to desperate measures: (Mother love is a thing to be reckoned with!)

I could go on and on, Mr. Senator, but all that has been asked for—that I've heard about—is an apology! That is our ultimate course, I believe.

Pueblo mothers cannot, and do not intend, to stand idly by and watch their beloved sons die a slow and tortured death as sacrificial lambs upon the altar of political expediency!

> Prayerfully yours,
> Eleanor Van Buskirk Harris
> (Mrs. Robert S.)

* * * * * *

Just as my crazy jingle had predicted to Mae, Bomb II put me aboard a Whisperjet to Washington. Or, at least, very soon after my "torture letter" had made its impact, Captain Wilcox proved exceedingly agile in obtaining an appointment for me to see Mr. Rusk, making plane and motel reservations, and even planning to conduct me himself to the Secretary of State's inner sanctum (and remain with me during the entire visit).

That my Stateside Attaché was not still angry with me about ignoring his plea for "no more letters to Congress, please!" was evident in his parting directive: "When you arrive at the State Department front entrance, Mrs. Harris, just start looking around for a very handsome guy." (He was 100% accurate on that point!)

I was terribly disappointed that Mae had decided against joining me:

"Ye know what an emotional person I am, Eleanor. I'd either break down and bawl during the interview, or tell Mr. Rusk where all those Heads of the U. S. Navy ought to go!"

Mae's views and mine had never quite meshed on the matter of U. S. Navy appraisal.

"But ye'll have Vuokko right beside ye, and I'm ever so glad of that, I am!"

Yes, I was delighted that my sad little Windflower was able to meet me for the confrontation. At Logan Airport Mae kissed me fondly and handed me a pretty beribboned package. (How like her to see me off!)

"Just a little something for ye to read on the plane," she said. I put it into my handbag.

* * * * * *

In preparation for this "historic" flight, on a warm August 8th after the closing of Summer School classes, I worried down a miniscule breakfast, turned up the screws on my Navy button earrings that Ruthie Mitchell (another of my four Ruths) had sent me to go with my spanking new navy and white "sailor suit," and walked by the planter wheel into the family room.

The morning sun from the sea window bathed in gold the polished wood of the family crest hanging above the fireplace. I'd never paid much attention to its ancient motto, and never intended to put it on any wall of mine—until teacher-artist Janet Oberg Stark and her husband, Leslie, friends of long standing, fashioned this handsome replica of the faded original and presented it to me as a housewarming present. It looked rather elegant against the pine walls.

Amor Patriae Exitat it said beneath the green trees and gray castle. *"Love of Country Moves Me"* (or excites me) I translated it.

I never realized how boldly the old motto would one day reach out and *move* my own serene little life!

When Steve saw the antique emblem hanging on the walls of his grandmother's library, had he ever given it any consideration? (I had. I'd considered throwing it in the trash barrel when we cleared out the old homestead on Wyoming Hill after my mother's death.)

The hands of my warring ancestors must have choked off my

incendiary intentions—for I had to admit over the centuries its ex-hortation certainly had inspired its quota of familial service to God and Country, i.e. what I could remember of it.

By the by, how much of this militant blood was bubbling about in my own veins? If none, then I'd better get a transfusion for this D.C. flight! Perhaps I should take stock. I looked up again at the handsome replica—

Let's see now—there was Grandpa Westman. With the heavy silver medal those blasted thieves had stolen, Queen Victoria had decor-ated this senior officer for long service in her Canadian regiments. And just back of him galloped a Civil War general,—and even before him there was Colonel Abram Van Buskirk (only he happened to be a Royalist and galloped north in the service of his king). General Washington had taken care of that oversight rather neatly, however, by billeting his men on the broad acreage of the colonel's abandoned New Jersey farm. The family was still ahead patriotically, regardless of the Royalist, however, for three of mine and three of Steve's ancestors were already toting muskets for George in the Continental Army—

Further back in the 1600's, Steve's Thomas Harris had first set foot in the New World at Jamestown, Virginia and my own John and Priscilla were making history here in Plymouth, Mass. at the time of the fashioning of the original crest. (Brother Alden, two nephews, and Alden's daughter, Priscilla, bear the ancestral names.)

Modern Warriors had left their footprints, or wingprints, on the soft patinas, as well—for Steve, his cousin Bob, and three of my brothers had been decorated for jobs well done on sea, soil or in the air for Old Uncle Sam.

A Vermont grandma had put us six youngsters to sleep (really kept us wide awake) with stories of the ancestral motto-minders, their long-buried bones bleached white by the suns of heroism (ac-cording to our raconteur, at least). If there were any "amnesty" skeletons hanging in the family gun closet, their bones were never found.

Well, so much for the past. For the present, "Love of Country" was moving other bones to its banners—or was it love of a *son* whose country appeared to be abandoning him? Well, be that as history decides, whatever a Funflowering Fate had potted for me in Capitol gardens, I was "moving" there to pick, whether or not it had bloomed to fruition. Harvest time for the Prisoners was *now!*

Lesson in Parental Concern: *If "necessity is the mother of inven-tion," then desperation is the daddy of deeds!*

As Mrs. Hayes, mother of *Pueblo's* Radioman, Lee Hayes from Columbus, Ohio, declared on a TV broadcast: "This is a time for anger!" I couldn't agree more.

I picked up the packet of little white cards lying on the kitchen table, stashed them in my new handbag and started for the door.

Just what would Grandma's heroes of the crest say, if anything, to their latest "warrior," Brunnhilde of Boston Rock? Something like—maybe—

> "We sende Thee Freshened to the Fraye,
>   Thy Forebeare's Blood imploring:
>   'Pull Mars' Mailed Fist from out Ye Breast!'"
>   (Plunge in a Tigress Roaring!)

The last line was mine. I hoped I could live up to my lineage.

* * * * * *

The flight out of Logan was a moderate one passengerwise, and with the seat beside me remaining empty, I settled back with nothing but my thoughts for company. While home responsibilities winged away behind me, memories of the past moved up and rode beside me.

On my last flight home from Washington after visiting Stephen, Senator Ted Kennedy had started to drop down beside me, then spotted a friend beckoning to him. He retrieved his briefcase from aloft and left me with a smile, only to be replaced by a Republican, Congressman Bradford Morse from Massachusetts,—who had moved over to be near my twin brothers seated behind me. The three had been classmates at Boston University. Brad's letter to me, like those of all "Capitolists" was courteous and highly sympathetic, but devoid of any new ideas for rescue.

"Your letters and calls have top priority here," he'd written. "I tried to reach you by phone, have contacted numerous officials knowledgeable about the *Pueblo*—cannot confirm or deny these North Korean reports—ready to do all that I possibly can to help you" etc., etc.

My first "bomb" on Washington had brought varied responses:

Bobby Kennedy's reply held sad overtones now: "I hope the delay in my response will not deter you from writing to me in the future, for I hope that I may have the benefit of your views on other important matters of mutual concern facing us in the coming months." The "coming months" never materialized for Bobby!

Yes, so much had happened since the *Pueblo* capture, young Bobby murdered, Dr. King murdered—Commie Bear could scarcely wait, no doubt, to lumber across the world clear into North Korea's prison compound to growl out this grand news!

("The killer of Senator Robert Kennedy," Steve's strutting captors blurted, "was hired by President Johnson, who also engineered the killing of John F. Kennedy." *Kill* was one English word his keepers had all mastered. They also claimed President Johnson "has all the cars in America." Pathetic?

When asked where the men of U. S. Tank Divisions stored their vehicles, crewmen soberly replied, "Oh, the fellows take them home each night and put them in their own garages.")

Brother Robert's friend, Vermont Congressman Bob Stafford, wrote him to be sure and tell his sister that he and two other Congressmen had introduced a bill "providing hostile pay" to the crew of the *Pueblo*. (Noble gesture. Now, how about getting the men home so they could claim it?)

Winthrop G. Brown, Deputy Assistant Secretary, Bureau of East Asian and Pacific Affairs, wrote that he had "supplemented the direct dealings with the North Koreans by seeking the good offices of a number of third countries." His statement provided me with a sweeter view of the N.K. Task Force "Desk."

One Senator said that "in the bluntest terms we should tell the North Korean Government that unless they release the *Pueblo* with its crew and all its equipment intact, our naval forces will be instructed to seize all vessels of North Korean registry wherever they may be found on the high seas." Many Senators' letters, in fact, voiced the same idea.

Shades of President Jefferson! I lifted my eyes from the sheaf of letters I had taken from the briefcase under the plane seat and watched the silent sea of whipped eggwhites glide away beneath me. I remembered reading a chapter in my high school history textbook where Tripoli began seizing our ships and Prexy Jefferson used his most syrupy powers of persuasion in his correspondence to his "great and good friend, the Bashaw of Tripoli," also mentioning in passing that he had been "induced" to send a squadron into the Mediterranean for the protection of our right to navigate the ocean freely. Such dewy diplomacy! It worked, too!

Lesson for Lawmakers: *A polite phrase, adroitly aimed, can shatter the glass wall of a man's greed.*

Had freedom of the high seas, or at least North Korean interpreta-

tion of it, proved Little Miss Pueblo's nemesis? (It had, indeed!)
Navigators relied on all countries to respect that one!

Historic reminders of other sea-nappings crept into my thinking as
I tried to locate Virginia's tobacco farms down through a rift in the
eggwhite puffs. They looked like huge empty parking lots.

When the *U.S.S. Chesapeake* was attacked by a British frigate off
Norfolk in 1809 and American seamen were captured, Jefferson
dispatched, not negotiators, but *gunboats* and got the men released.
I must have had a good history teacher that year, for I even remembered the case of the United States Steamer *Water Witch* surveying
the Parana River in 1855 which was fired upon. President Madison
sent—negotiators? Nix on that! He dispatched a large expedition-
ary force to South America, receiving both apology and *ransom*
($10,000 worth) for his trouble. (Those were the days!)

Lesson for Today's Trouble Shooters: *Next to force and prayer,
nothing succeeds like—money!*

I was bold enough to suggest in my second letter to Congress that
we "cut off trade with all Communist countries until the men of the
Pueblo were released." (One Congressman took my suggestion, but
the bill was turned down. No one explained why. Did Ruddy lob-
byists get their Pinkies on it?)

Most Senators went to the State Department for ideas. Where
were theirs?

I shuffled quickly through the remaining letters. Many Senators
found Steve's letter "moving," in my First Bomb; even more found
my disclosures in "Bomb II" "shocking." But, again, no new plans
for repatriation were brought to light on senatorial stationery.

Both the diversity of thinking and the utter lack of workable
suggestions contained in my mass of mail from Dullsville made my
own thinking inconclusive. Gilbert had the words for it:

A Capitol Idea: *"Listening to letters from lawmakers is like holding a bee's nest in a bucket of H_2O. Lots of buzzing—but no real
sting!"*

I suddenly remembered Mae's parcel containing "something to
read on the plane." I reached into my handbag and quickly divested
the package of its gold paper and rainbow ribbons, so pretty I could
not destroy them, so tucked them back into my purse for safekeep-
ing. In my hand I was holding a charming little volume: *Friendship,
A Selection,* by Louise Batchelder. One section of the book felt a
bit bulky, so I opened it to that page. There, clipped to it, was
another of Mae's "little somethings"—a check for fifty dollars! There
was also a brief note:

"Eleanor, I want you to have this. After all, it would have cost me this much to go with you. If you dare return it, you'll lose me as a friend. Good luck, Dear, and God go with you on this errand for our poor boys.

Love,
Mae"

The selection on the marked page read: "Friendship renders prosperity more brilliant, while it lightens adversity by sharing it and making its burden common." (Cicero)

"How true, Dearest Friend!"

I unfastened my seat belt and reached up for my "Navy" jacket with the gold buttons. There was no time now to savor the generosity of my devoted co-sufferer, for we had touched down in the Great White City and people were already heading for the exit. What a darling Mae was! And how I longed for her companionship at this moment!

Inside the gate of the waiting room in this city of strangers I felt a depressing surge of helplessness coupled with loneliness that even Mae's magnanimous gesture failed to dispel. Steve had always been waiting for me at National Airport before.

I watched fellow passengers bring engulfed in the embraces of loved ones; and for a moment forgot to be lonesome at the familiar and "loving" sight of those tender reunited twosomes one always finds at airports in wartime. Now it was little mini-skirted doves cooing up into the adoring eyes of young servicemen in neat uniforms. Subconsciously my eyes began searching among them for Steve and Vuokko—and I became lonely again.

Over against the side wall I noticed two good-looking gentlemen standing with faces alerted towards the gate entrance. They were awaiting someone from this same flight, apparently; one, a fortyish Navy officer in impeccable blues, the other, older, clad in a summer-weight business suit.

Lucky Lady to have two such men waiting for her, the romantic in me thought briefly—"briefly," because they turned and after a swift appraisal, approached me!

"Mrs. Harris?" the older man smiled, as if certain of his identification. "We're to escort you to the Marriott by Navy limousine."

They introduced themselves cordially, mentioning my forthcoming interview with the Secretary of State by way of identifying themselves, and the younger man took my overnight case, my only luggage. Man! What a groovy kidnapping! "Wicked nice!"

"The reason we hesitated to speak to you, Mrs. Harris was—well—

may I say quite frankly, we were looking for an older woman," the man in mufti explained, glancing down on my crown of curls. It was even nicer than if he had said "older-looking" woman.

I was sure Mr. X was a security man for the Navy, but whatever his reason for meeting me, his remark brought with it a silent appreciation for the services of my hairdresser and dress shop proprietor.

Woman's intuition seldom slumbers, and as I stepped into the chauffeured Navy car, it told me my rescuers might have official reasons for their chivalry. Was I their Open Sesame to State Department doors? Papers had intimated that Navy noses were put out of joint when the State Department took over *Pueblo's* case. Well, if I could help these gentleman slide a foot or two over the Secretary's threshold, I'd do it, for they (Navy) must be as baffled as the rest of us by the prodigious silence issuing from under the doorsills of Stateside chambers. Yes, unlike Mae, I harbored more than a slight penchant for navymen, even the handsome ones.

As Navy wheels rolled under me over the broad avenues of our nation's stately Capital, they sang a spritely song:
  "Take my heart, you dolls, you Men-o'-the-Sea,
  Your Salty Spray's my cup o' tea!"

* * * * * *

At the Marriott, after showering and awaiting the return of my luxury taxi (Vuokko was meeting me outside Mr. Rusk's chambers), I removed Mae's rainbow ribbons and gold wrappings and laid them in a drawer, then checked to make sure the little packet of cards was still in my purse. I'd purloined a dozen of them before school closed, from Grade Four's ample stock over in the Arithmetic Counting Corner, choosing white cards, only, upon which to write my "Rescue" questions for Mr. Rusk. The children preferred the colored ones for their arithmetic drill games. On second thought, I'd added a few *yellow* cards for those dreadful posers I really wanted answers to, but didn't have the nerve to ask the Head of State. The "yellow questions," of course, I'd left at home on the kitchen table. Next, I checked to make sure a certain letter and paper Mae had insisted I include, were also in my handbag.

This journey was not to be a mere dabbling in histrionics, but a Command Performance for which the diva, herself, had composed the lyrics, long before she was fitted for her costumes.

And now—at long last—the curtain was rising on what I presume to my august audience was just another of those trivial little dramas unfolding daily in Dullsville's strategic sanctuaries.

* * * * * *

In spite of my good intentions, unfortunately, Navy toes did not even get to touch the threshold of Pope Rusk's Pontifical Privacy, although how the rebuff was executed, I'm still in ignorance. Vuokko and I simply found ourselves *sans Navy* being introduced to a tall, magnificently-built, impeccably-turned-out man with a totally relaxed expression, well-schooled, no doubt, in the art of revealing nothing of the personal reactions taking place beneath its framework. (You've heard the term "restrained elegance"? It's what he had, man!)

TV made Dean Rusk appear smaller and rounder than he is. He actually possessed a sort of massive dignity and I sensed I was in the presence of extraordinary intelligence—equal, I trusted, to that of his predecessors in the fine oil portraits lining the polished wood-panelled walls of the spacious sanctum we had entered.

My thoughts flew back to the Wakefield Baptist Church choirloft: "Thou hast set my feet in a large room." Now "Send out thy light and thy truth, let them lead me." I was not nervous, only alert. Vuokko, too, seemed completely at ease in the "large room." I felt the delicate aura of her beauty as we were shown to a large leather divan. I was lonely no longer.

The scene opened with the Leading Man's well-rehearsed monologue on the various and sundry duties of the Head of State, among them being the release of prisoners of war. Somewhere in his lines Mr. Rusk stated that in this latter respect the "batting average of the Department had been extremely good."

The Secretary's statement fell like a cooling cloudburst on my parched Desert of Hope. If I had expected to find him the nervous chainsmoker Rose Bucher described, I was pleasantly disappointed. Mr. Rusk was superbly calm. But, after all, I was not the wife of the ship's captain; nevertheless, I *was* the mother of the guy in charge of the multi-million dollar reason for *Pueblo's* sailing orders, as well as its thirty skilled technicians and operators. Perhaps, too, I was more relaxed than Rose describes herself as being, although I don't quite know why, unless it was simply that God was doing His thing, "sending out his light"—and, hopefully, about to "guard the door of my lips"!

Just as I anticipated, this statesman was "canny," but I also found my host articulate, patient, and at times quite charming. He and his wife had visited Finland recently, he informed Vuokko, after she had inquired briefly about obtaining clearance papers for her intended visit to her mother there. She had met Mr. Rusk on several state occasions because of the top-drawer aspect of her former Washington job which evidently called for special authorization for departing the country. His manner indicated he might have remembered the girl sitting opposite him,—or was it because she always drew this kind of attention?

When it seemed my cue to speak, I first reached into the smart navy leather pocketbook Vuokko and Steve had presented me on that memorable October visit, and drew out the nicest photo I owned of Steve, his framed Harvard R.O.T.C. picture, as charismatic and flattering as such photos are. If they didn't simply yearn to rescue this good-looking guy, they were crazy!

I placed it on the end table beside our divan in full view of the assemblage: Mr. Rusk, Captain Harwood Wilcox,[4] Ambassador Godley,[5] Mr. Leonard,[6] the Task Force Man and the two who loved him most—not to mention a young man hovering in the doorway of the outer office. The "office dick" (for a private detective he surely was), shuffled his important papers convincingly beside the pretty blond secretary we had met on the way in.

I next reached into my purse for the packet of white question cards executed in my most painstaking script. A good thing I had left those "yellow" questions back home on the kitchen table. Mr. Rusk would "rupture"[7] if he ever saw those!

"Mr. Secretary," I commenced in a voice that must have been steadied by prayer. "This is the young officer for whose life I am here to plead—his life and those of his eighty-one shipmates." All eyes turned politely toward the photo. The big hands offered to take the cards from me, and began sorting them slowly. The bland expression and heavy-lidded gaze remained unchanged—but mine

---

[4]My handsome wrist-slapper who shadowed Vuokko and me constantly and courteously during our entire visit to the Department of State. (Code name, Panda.)

[5]G. McMurtrie Godley, Deputy Asst. Sec., Bureau of East Asian Affairs, whose brown eyes, keen intellect and affability captivated Vuokko and me. After my Task Force berating of Mr. Leonard, Vuokko and I had enjoyed a brief conference in his own quarters before entering the Inner Temple. Mr. Godley, alone, seemed to appreciate the lonely struggle of two fragile and vulnerable "frails" for the return of their beleagured loved one. He assured us Steve was "not a forgotten man", and on the way to his boss's office, threw a big powerful arm about each of us, and by way of further comforting, assured us it was a most welcome surprise to discover two such charming ladies invading sacrosanct corridors of the State Department—(the type of serum that injects womanhood with new respect for mankind). How very much we both needed Mr. Godley's kindness!

[6]One of the most "forceful" of the N.K. Task Force "forces", whose brain I'd already bitten before the interview. He ended up doing a mighty good job, incidentally.

[7]Grade Four "verb"-iage.

"I placed Steve's photo where Mr. Rusk's Brain Trust could see it. If they didn't simply yearn to rescue this good-looking guy, they were crazy!"

didn't! I simply couldn't believe what I was seeing! Vuokko seemed to sense my surprise.

As the famous Clement Moore Christmas jingle puts it: "when what to my wondering eyes should appear, but—a jolly old elf and eight tiny reindeer?" Nope!—a jolly old *yellow card!* Worse yet, two, three, or even *four* jolly old yellow cards! Ye Cats! How did those awful questions ever sneak in there? Had Gilbert thought I'd forgotten the yellow cards and tucked them into the pack?[8]

The words of a tiny poet of my summer school's Creative Writing Class waltzed across my chagrin:

> "Here lies the body of Polly Page,
> Or what was left in the lion's cage!"

Oh brother! Which "yellow" question was the Head of State peering down at now? Was it:

"If your own son (only he had daughters) *had been aboard the Pueblo, Mr. Secretary, and was now a six-months captive of cruel barbarians, wouldn't you be doing more than you're doing now to secure his release?"* Or was it that nifty:

"My friends keep telling me: 'You just wait 'til ex-Navyman Dick Nixon gets his grip on the wheel! He'll get those guys out in a hurry!' *What's the matter with this administration's doing the job? Don't the North Koreans trust you?"*

I could think of worse ones:

(1) What United States traitor in Washington, or Red Spy of their own ilk, spilled the beans to Moscow that the lonely little *Pueblo* was really a floating treasure house?

(2) What "Red"-eyed Agent, watching from our Defense Towers, *advised the Enterprise to stop steaming just short of Wonsan Harbor?* (Second thoughts had me believing this was the wisest decision, however.)

(3) Why the *delay* in arousing Prexy J.?

Ole Tiger's teeth had turned to foam rubber—but I hadn't intended to bite the Secretary of State, only scratch him a little, maybe. What other awful posers had I put on the yellow cards? Oh yes, *whatever happened to our "intelligence" in North Korea? Are we afraid to go in there?* (Ugh! I'd better not try to recall the others. There was a doozy about Walt Rostow, too!) The Secretary's voice broke into my trauma:

"How many of these questions have you already answered, Mr. Godley?" (Blast it! I wanted to compare their answers. Vaguely I

---

[8]Exactly!

wondered how he knew I'd tested the Ambassador's thinking at all!)

The two questions Mr. Godley had answered were put aside, but I could recall them well enough to insert them on "redirect" later on. (I was a Perry Mason fan.) Maybe I was canny, too. I intended to see that Mae, at least, got her fifty dollars worth.

Lesson for Fact Finders: *If you wish to ask a question of a superior, don't be obnoxiously humble about it. Take heart. Ask it! If he can't answer it, then he's not your superior—he's your equal.* (Well, isn't he?)

Mr. Rusk chose as his first card:

(1) *"Approximately when can we expect to see our sons* (alive) *again?"* The answer here, after multiple words, approximated a *"Heaven only knows."*

(2) *What concrete evidence do we have that our men are still alive?* The answer, for all its elegant deviations, added up to one word, *"None!"*

(3) *Don't we maintain a contact of any sort at all in North Korea that can keep tabs on the condition of the prisoners?* (I now knew the National Red Cross was not allowed to go near the prison in North Korea.)

Gist of reply: (My considerate host must have seen my "yellow" question on intelligence!) "Intelligence cannot function in a country that checks every moving body, their coming and going from village to village for any reason whatsoever. A stranger coming into their midst would be immediately suspect."[9]

In spite of Mr. Rusk's courtesy and patience, there didn't seem to be any enlightening or encouraging answers forthcoming at all, even after the one about the possibility of North Korea's honoring the crews' Geneva Convention Cards (North Korea didn't), intervention by neutral nations (inspection and persuasion), and some lesser ones I've simply forgotten. A slight ray of sunshine warmed the bleak horizon at the prospect of our ambassadors abroad and their underlings doing their patriotic thing "innocently" at social teas, by sweetening (via suggestion) the drinks of sympathetic sippers in strategic positions of power. I, for one, was happy to assume that nibbling with the right people might prove nourishing to *Pueblo's* plight. Bon appetit!

(4) *Why not send a South Korean to the conference table, one schooled in Oriental strategem?* (i.e., North Korean deception!)

---

[9]The answer, as with all of them, is as accurate as memory can reconstruct it. Wish I'd had a tape recorder, if allowed. Gilbert said I should have known better than to ask this one—that Mr. Rusk's answer would have been negative, anyway.

Answer, in effect: No dice—*lose face on both sides.* No love lost between conferees to begin with.

(5) *How much Ivory Tower thinking has gone into our negotiating procedures?* Answer, in brief: *Oh, lots!* (Sources listed proudly.)

Doctor Nurhan Adrian, my ex-Navy-officer dentist, donated this last question.

I did not inform Mr. Rusk of Professor Rieschauer's "one year" projection for repatriation of the prisoners, for I was hopeful his "own forces" could sweep to the gates of victory in less time than the professor estimated. (Fat chance!)

"Has anyone written Kim Il Sung?" the Secretary of State suddenly asked, looking up from the cards and over at his Brain Trust.

Well—no—no one had—uh—no—

Ye cats! Hadn't these Bridge-Builders even contacted the *Chief Engineer?* I nearly fell off the divan, mentally. Well, here's where my good friend Mae would start earning some interest on her fifty dollars:

"I know someone who has!" I piped up blithely. Everyone looked my way. Here was my opportunity to write both Mae and Ralph into the script. Although my august audience did not utter a syllable, their faces registered expectancy.

"I am referring to Mrs. Mae McClintock, widowed mother of a *Pueblo* communications technician, Ralph McClintock, her only child, who served in the ship's monitoring detachment under my son." (They were all aware of Steve's grave responsibilities aboard the ill-fated vessel.) "She lives in a city not far from my own, and because of this tragedy has become a close friend."

Their undivided attention urged me on:

"A few weeks after the ship's piracy, she *sent a telegram to Kim Il Sung"* ("'Kimchi', that Ole Sun-of-a-Nation," I thought dimly.)

"Did she receive an answer?" Mr. Rusk asked pointedly, though he didn't look surprised at my negative answer. He probably made it a habit not to look surprised at anything.

"Just what did she say in her telegram?" naturally followed. The Brain Trust picked up its collective ears as I repeated the gist of the telegram.

"The message is simply stated, to be sure, but it's as forthright and honest as Mrs. McClintock herself," I insisted. Then, since I held the stage, added, "and if at all like his mother, her son must be a splendid young man." Lesson in Living Richly: *The Bank of Life holds many generous words within its vaults. Withdraw them cheerfully and give them to the needy. They cost you nothing—bring interest—and may make an unworthy "receiver" indebted to you.*

If my listeners were amused by the homey informality of Mae's message to the Premier of the pilfering Minipower, they gave no sign; in fact, their facial expressions inspired continuation. Vuokko's shy smile of gratitude seemed to welcome my taking over the major burden of the parleying, as she had previously begged me to do.

"Mrs. McClintock originally planned to accompany me here today; however, she is extremely upset at this time. ("extremely upset at your blasted silence," I wanted to say.) She asked me to represent her beloved Ralph, as well as my own son, Stephen, Vuokko's husband,"—and I smiled over at her,—"in this plea for their release. In fact, the dear lady enclosed a check for fifty dollars to cover my traveling expenses, which she tucked inside a little gift book she presented me this morning at Logan Airport!"

Vuokko's tropic-sea eyes lost their sadness at the unexpected disclosure. She appreciated the value of Mae's friendship to my morale. Her smile proved contagious, for my small audience warmed outwardly at my little touch of spontaneity.

Mr. Rusk decided to have a cigarette. My glance stole over to the glorious big grandfather's clock guarding the entrance. Nearly one hour and twenty minutes had elapsed since curtain time!

"You might send *me* to your conference table," I tossed out lightly, taking advantage of the relaxed atmosphere. (Butterfly was sneaking out of her shroud.) "Mother Love has been known to conjure up miracles."

> *Love,* thy name is *Woman*
> *Conflict,* thy name is *Man*
>
> *Protection,* thy name is *Mother*
> *Hate,* thy name is *War!*

Surprisingly enough, someone did take me seriously and resorted to the old saw about a parent being "too emotionally involved." Perhaps *right there* lay the crux of our lack of progress—that we needed to be *more* emotionally involved!

My listeners, naturally, could not appreciate all that my emotions had been "involved" in over a lifetime of teaching, nor could they, unless they had been long-term cultivators of young minds, know that teaching itself schools one in self-control as in no other Field of Combat in Christendom! Personally, I'd probably profited more from the distaff side of my profession than from the more rewarding one—i.e., wit battles, tight situations, personality conflicts, deadlines to meet, new strategy and new ideas to incorporate, and all such educational challenges.

Right now I was answering a challenge, too, one that involved eighty-two lives. And since Abject Silence seemed to be clouding the sum total of the "Task Force's" accomplishments to date, my undying ego said even if *I* could be more "forceful" than that!

I decided that since Mr. Rusk had seen the yellow cards anyway, I might as well ring down the curtain with the clincher of them all. ("Awake, my soul, stretch every nerve, and press with vigor on.") This question should stretch everyone's nerves, especially those of my host.

"Mr. Secretary, I realize I am being outrageously candid,—probably the correct phrase is 'unpardonably rude',—but I cannot return home until, as a mother, I ask you this. It might give your thinking a fresh angle: Seriously, if your very own son had been aboard that ship and was now a six-months captive of these cruel, unpredictable barbarians, wouldn't you be doing something—I don't know quite what—but something more than you're doing now?" (My "forebeares" should be pleased. Their tigress was "roaring.")

"What more can we do?" Mr. Rusk countered just as candidly as if he would relish some answers himself. *"Can you suggest anything more yourself, Mrs. Harris?"*

Rose Bucher had warned me on the phone that the Secretary often answered one question with another. (I thought that habit was reserved for us Yankees!)

"Sure, send a *woman,* preferably a *mother, someone who loves those men* to your blasted next meeting," was what I wanted to say, but I'd played the egotist sufficiently for one performance. Then it popped out, the best "yellow" question of them all:

"Why not apologize, Mr. Secretary?" (The "door" of my lips was wide open.) "Even if we're innocent of their accusations!"

("The Navy will never apologize—never—!")

"Apology's no problem," Mr. Rusk answered. "It's these other conditions they're demanding now—"

(*"Apology* no *problem?"* Wow! I could hardly wait to deflate Sure-Thing Richard with this one!)

But these *"other conditions"*?

* * * * * *

A few moments later Captain Wilcox was standing, and Vuokko and I needed no further signal that the curtain was going down, even if the plot had not resolved the heroes' fate. The villains had gone unscathed, the dialogue, save for the last line, was dull, and in truth the whole scene would have to be rewritten—if only we could uncover just the right author!

I removed Steve's photo from the end table and looked into his young eyes with overwhelming sadness. ("How long, O Lord, how long?") At the same time I replaced the photo in my ample pocket-book, I pulled my "ace from the deck" as Mae had dubbed it.

"Mr. Secretary, one final request," I pleaded pleasantly, after Vuokko and I had expressed profound gratitude to the placid giant smiling down on our handclasps, "I wonder if you would be kind enough to keep this letter in view here on your desk as a daily re-minder of the men who are utterly dependent on you for their — their future," I managed, uncertain of my words for the first time.

I felt a sudden weariness as I handed him the newsphoto of the *Pueblo* with a small picture of Steve superimposed upon it. (I wished I had a picture of the entire crew.) Below it in my hand-writing, was a letter which reviewed the solemn reason for my visit. Beneath the letter, as I had promised Mae, hid the page with the poem she had insisted I copy: *A Prayer For Pueblo's Men.* (She'd even mailed one to Ralph.)

The big hands took the papers from me and studied them assid-uously for a moment.

"I certainly will, Mrs. Harris," he smiled warmly.

("Again I thank Thee, Dear Father" who teacheth my *fingers to fight!*)

But now, these "other conditions they want us to meet"—how could one "fight" those?

* * * * * *

Despite the outcome of our tête-à-tête topside, a few hours later Vuokko and I were not doing too badly with two orders of medium-rare roast beef and related viands, downstairs in the motel's posh dining room. We had begged off the invitation to dine with our Seagoing Saviours as politely as we knew how, preferring the solace of our own company. We'd given our all for the cause and did not think a return engagement during dinner would serve it further.

"I never dreamed I'd turn down a dinner date with two such charmers," I said, trying to sound cheerful as I sampled the tossed salad. "They waited so long at the stage door for us."

"I'm sure they understood, Mother," she answered softly. "After all, I thought you gave them a pretty thorough résumé on the ride back here to the motel."

"I consider it brutal that they weren't allowed seats for the per-formance, just the same, and I trust I made my regrets sound sincere. Do you remember Mr. X's pointed question as to whether I had 'learned something' today?"

"Yes, I knew what he was referring to, Mother. I've been aware of the friction between the two departments for sometime (State and Navy) but actually, there's a remote possibility this schism could work to the benefit of Steve and the crew." The pretty voice faltered on the last phrase.

"Let's hope so, Dear. My big worry now is this Sea of Japan condition. If Mr. Rusk hadn't classified it, I would have liked to have gotten our two Navymen's reactions to it. Let's hope they'd have given our prospects a lift."

But now I felt I had reviewed the Stateside visit sufficiently. Vuokko looked so disheartened, I must try to administer some cheerful medicine.

"I really hated to say goodbye to two such delightful gentlemen; they were so intensely concerned. Like ships that pass in the night, I suppose our sealanes will never cross again."

"Don't count on that, Mother," she smiled sagely. "Someday you may be pleasantly surprised."

What my wise-in-the-ways-of-Washington daughter-in-law meant by her reply was lost to me, for one question crowded my thoughts: "Vuokko, who do you think sent those two dolls to meet my plane, and how did they recognize me? I've never described myself to anyone."

"Oh, undoubtedly your CACO (Advising) Officer described you to them," she returned unhesitatingly.

"You mean "Sure-Thing"—that is—Commander Bordeaux? Why, of course! He was rather miffed because I hadn't told him of my traveling plans sooner—said he might have been able to get leave or something." The idea of Sir Richard as a bodyguard here in the Capital, didn't seem too distasteful. Maybe he needed a vacation from his 'hundreds of men.'"

"This is a beautiful place with beautiful food, and beautiful bric-a-brac on its shelves," I said by way of "getting out of uniform." "Look at that adorable little china lady playing the lighted grand piano over there. Her costume reminds me of my light opera days.

My music-minded daughter-in-law admitted the lovely piece was the first thing that had caught her eye when we came in, and she pressed me to tell her about my early operatic indulgences.

"Oh, my yes! And a beautiful people, too!" I continued, looking toward a certain table, after briefing her on my brush with the music theatre world. "By the by, do you see whom I see?" Excitement was bouncing on the rim of my sarcasm.

"Oh, he's been here for some time," replied my supper companion, not even looking up from her coffee, "was probably here before we arrived—just a quaint custom we have in these parts."

It was the young security man, the "office detective" from Mr. Rusk's inner sanctum.

"Is he suspecting or protecting?" I queried.

"Just ex-checking, I'd say, or possibly not interested in us at all. Maybe it's his night off."

"I wonder why he didn't check our handbags? I'm pretty good at dropping bombs."

Vuokko smiled knowingly.

There was so much of a serious nature we could have discussed had we known just where to commence, or had had the stomach for it,—so many unanswered questions we could not bring ourselves to ask, heartbreaking thoughts we knew we were sharing—yet we numbly chose to keep them all unspoken. Were we, at long last "putting all in the Hands of God?"

My thoughts returned to the letter I had requested Mr. Rusk to keep before him on his desk. Vuokko had begged for a copy. I hoped it would do some good.

> Ledgewinds atop Boston Rock, # 87
> Melrose, Massachusetts
> August 8

To the Honorable Dean Rusk
Secretary of State
Department of State
Washington, D.C.

My dear Mr. Secretary,

As the distraught mother of the fine young officer in charge of the *U.S.S. Pueblo's* Intelligence Detachment, Lt. Stephen R. Harris, I am certain I voice the silent directive of all anxious relatives of *Pueblo* crewmen when I urge you to continue bending mind, heart and soul to the monumental task of freeing these young Navymen from their cruel prison in North Korea!

While we continue to pray steadfastly to our Heavenly Father for the return of our dear ones alive, we realize you, as Head of State, are our earthly representative, chosen to carry out God's plan for them.

We, therefore, vest full confidence in your personal powers of persuasion, trusting you to bring every mortal force to bear on the resolving of this sad dilemma—lest these eighty-two meet a slow and cruel end—abandoned by the country they loved and served so well!

> Gratefully and prayerfully yours,
> Eleanor Van Buskirk Harris
> (Mrs. Robert S.)

Vuokko insisted on taking the dinner checks to the cashier, so I sauntered out into a sort of latticed walkway to wait for her. I had invited her to spend the night with me here at the *Marriott,* and I'd see to it she didn't pay for *that!*

Mr. Office Dick's table was so close to my new location, I couldn't resist the impulse to play detective with the detective. I stole a few sidelong glances through the doorway laced with a smile of sweetest recognition.

Lesson to Lady Loiterers: *Keep smiling. Your laugh-lines look "smooth" that way!*

Each time I reached into my purse for something during the interview, cards, photo, etc., had Mr. Detective panicked for fear I was about to liquidate his top-drawer boss? Evidently he didn't hold this against me, for he smiled cordially in return. Either he liked accordian-pleated, sea-blue silk dresses with sparkling necklines, or he sensed with some degree of empathy that while my lonely little game of Twenty Questions was over and done with, no one, not even his top-drawer boss, seemed quite certain of the answers.

Vuokko joined me presently and handed me a be-ribboned white box. In it sat the little china lady playing the (un) lighted grand piano!

* * * * * *

"—It's these other conditions they have imposed upon us now— they want us to promise we'll keep out of the Sea of Japan!"

The motel shower replayed these lines in a relentless tattoo on my bathing cap just before bedtime. I had insisted Vuokko shower first, for I had some unhurried thinking to do. Nevertheless, when my turn came, and I felt the cubicle close me in with my thoughts, the sound of the water, like that other shower that rained down the words of Steve's phony confession, poured this latest threat from North Korea into my consciousness, until it became a potpourri of anxiety.

"Keep out of the Sea of Japan—you must promise us"—(if you ever want to see your sons again)—*"It's these conditions they want us to meet!"* They want us to promise—apology no problem—promise!

—the Sea of Japan—(is so large, we could never promise that!) Our country would "put pride in its pocket"—and a lot more, too, in order to apologize, bless it—but what country would "promise" to stay out of the vast Sea of Japan in order to save eighty-two lives? Would ours? (I could already hear Sir Richard's reaction to this one!)

The steamy air was stifling—if you ever want to see your sons again—you must promise to—"use *slingshots, slingshots, slingshorts! Keep the lamp burning, Mother!*" I began to feel faint—"keep the lamp burning?" Dear God—how?

I turned off the shower and hurriedly patted myself dry. I must have air—right now!

Vuokko lay motionless in the double bed beside mine. Was she simply pretending to sleep for my sake? Even with her hair in fat gold curlers under a sun-colored be-petalled night bonnet, she looked adorable.

"Keep out of the Sea of Japan." "If you ever want to see your—" No. There'd be no sleeping for me this stifling August night!

I put on my negligee and moved soundlessly out of the motel bedroom, leaving the door ajar in hopes of cooling the room, stepping across to the railing of the high balcony. My mind sought fresher fields, and I began thinking of Robert and Doris, and their handsome, unspoiled children way up there in the cool mountains of Vermont. There'd be no apple-picking forays for Gilbert and me *this* fall!

"Just close your eyes and drink," Doris had laughed as we crowded inside the mountainside Rube Goldberg Cider-making shack. She'd seen me looking askance at unsanitary-appearing pipes, crushers, belts, bottles, bellows, apple mash, moving-gears-and-gadgets above and alongside the huge sagging "ceiling" of burlap, whose underbelly resembled a sodden sea of brown applesauce! "Just close your eyes and drink?" *This* coming from my hospital lab supervisor, that super-sterile housekeeper sister-in-law? But, truly,—one swallow, poured from the dew-covered jug of liquid gold orchard nectar the hard-browned farmer took out of the little corner refrigerator inside the mountain mill, made me forget its humble origin!

Oh, that like closing my eyes on the weird cider-making contraption, I could shut out now these more sophisticated moving belts of unproductive verbiage (brown applesauce), the claptrap of the presses, the sludge of intermeshing bureaucracy—and just close my eyes and drink as coolly of God's golden wisdom, and feel as refreshed as I had on the green mountainside!

My serenity-seeking mood swung me next to Gordon, Martha and dimpled Robin riding her horses and tending her twenty-six cats on the farm in Maine. "Hurry and get up here, Battlebrain," Brother Bill had urged, "so we can put you out to pasture. After you've hit the hay for awhile, we'll go to every antique shop and barn on the coast!" (What was my former Maine barn-purchase, Kuan Yin, up to now? Was she clearing up her dusty eyes by swimming in the Sea of Japan?) —And Alden in Saigon? How many times had his Green Beret Bobby been wounded now? Had he gotten out of the jungle alive? (How long, O Lord—?")

I looked down at the floodlights that gave the motel trees and plantings their ethereal emerald glow beneath the night softness of a summer sky. I felt suddenly grateful that I could still thrill to the beauty of this modern fairyland scene,[10] with its luminous bridges, welding structures that went on and on like a multi-lighted city of the future, finally losing its dazzling smile in the vast dome of darkness above.

But now as I looked up into the black velvet above me, gratitude gave way to that all-too-familiar loneliness, a loneliness as vast as the dome above me, and I felt like a miniscule lamb lost in the endless meadows of night.

While I had "wilted" steadily within the painful vacuum created by Steve's absence, it was the absence of my beloved husband I felt more keenly at this moment. "Keep out of the Sea of Japan," indeed! Oh, how I needed my dear one now, the unerring correctness of his thinking—Bob was never indecisive—(Mr. Godley had jogged my memory all too well)—I needed the hard comfort of Bob's arms about me, too, the closeness of his voice lavishing upon me those little compliments that keep a wife in love.

Yes, what would my Darling have done, knowing his only child was stolen from him, and abandoned to the whims of hate-filled barbarians? What would *he* have suggested at this impasse, *now that his country's rescue-power lay hanging upon the threads of enemy "conditions"?*

Sad lines I had penned nine years before, the first in my pillow notebook, drifted down to me out of the summer night. They seemed surprisingly fitting now.

---

[10]Lesson in Learning: *If, after prolonged anxiety and stress, you are still able to identify with beauty, your gray matter is probably continuing to acquire creases.* (You're still able to *think,* Man!)

BELOVED HUSBAND

For you, Dear One, the Journey's done,
    There's no more Earth can teach you—
        Now, standing on this Lonely Isle,
            I lift my arms to reach you!

It's empty here. Life's Hall is drear,
    With strangers at its portals;
        I know them not, nor do they me—
            I'm lost among these mortals.

A hunger yearns, a mem'ry burns
    Within my heart to foment.
        My lips long for your Wealth of Love,
            And not for cry of moment.

You played your part, then took my heart
    And left but dreams to cherish.
        O steer my ship this starless trip,
            Lest in dark seas I perish—!
            (The Sea of Japan—?)

Dear One, reach down, and lift this "crown
    Of thorns" that pierce my sorrow;
        And kiss me now on wounded brow;
            Anoint me for the morrow!

Then pluck the strings across my heart;
    Though no voice sings beside me,
        Send me the will with song to fill
            This empty void inside me.

I'll chant the strains you loved to hear,
    Strike full the bright chords only!
        (But way down deep while thou dost sleep,
            My soul will still be lonely!)

* * * * * *

I returned to the motel room, closed the door, and looked down once more on Steve's young bride whose sleeping face was slightly illuminated by the outside lights. What a bleak outlook for both young people! If only *I alone* could have borne the burden for them! What insidious damage would time bring to their minds and bodies, by the slow eroding of the ordeal?

Vuokko's overnight bag lay partly open beside the dressing table. I reached into my own travel case and removed the sealed gold box containing the flowery perfume, "the expensive kind,"—the last of the two generous packages my school principal had tucked into my mailbox that last dark day in March. I was glad I hadn't opened it and had been resourceful enough to save the gold gift wrappings and multi-colored ribbons from Mae's little book on Friendship.

Carefully, with the touch of a would-be artist, I packaged for my sleeping roommate the glorious fragrance. In my frenetic departure, I had given little thought to gifts, and had intended to take Vuokko out to dinner, at least (but she'd gotten ahead of me there!)

I dropped the pretty package into her night case and slipped into bed. I knew my generous "Boss" back in Melrose would approve wholeheartedly.

* * * * * *

After I had paid my Logan Airport taxi driver and given him a fat tip for this trouble, (I was a people-lover, remember?) I went directly to the family room phone and put my travel case down beside the red easy chair.

"Hello, Mae? This is your Dullsville Emissary reporting in." Mae was all ears.

I tried to sound cheerful, and was almost relieved that Mr. Rusk had "classified" the Sea of Japan! Mae knew I would not discuss, but write any important details of my visit.

"I guess I must have put on some of God's armor, as you suggested, for I'm not too badly wounded, Mae, but frankly, my dear, I am little better informed than when I left you." (Mae wasn't exactly astounded to hear this). "But this trip did one thing for me. It demonstrated *again* something very charming and dear to me—about *you!*"

"And what's that?" Mae laughed, knowing exactly what I was going to say next!

After a short hassle over my returning her bountiful gift—which hassle I lost—I gave her a full account of my visit with Vuokko, as well as a general idea of the one with "Dorothy" (Dean Rusk) and "her" court. (The high singing sound on the phone was still perceptible.)

"Mae, dear friend, one more thing before I ring off," (my voice sounded strained to my ears), "there is something I've been meaning to ask you for some time, yet I simply haven't had the courage to do so!"

"Ye haven't?" Mae replied, surprised. "Well, now! Go ahead and ask—whatever I have is yours."

How like the dear soul, I thought! This coming on top of a gift of fifty dollars! Although I was maintaining a cheerful tone, my spirits were at a pathetic low. The Washington trip had nearly "finalized" my fears for Steve's future. Whether it was a case of misery loves company, or the frustration of simply not knowing the answer, I cannot say, but curiosity had reached a peak concerning Mae's psycho-cat, and I just had to know right that very minute what had become of poor little "Sister," our mutual symbol of the welfare of our sons "abroad."

"Mae, you darling doll! As if you hadn't already been superbly generous, all too generous, in fact! No, what I want to ask has nothing to do with *things*—it's *animals,*—specifically your tiger cat! Mae, do tell me whatever became of sick little 'Sister'? You must tell me—now!"

"Oh—poor Sister! Didn't I tell you about her?" she asked in disbelief.

(My "armor" was slipping a little. I wished Mae hadn't used the term "poor" Sister.)

"You may as well tell me," I sighed, trying not to sound as forlorn as I felt.

"Well," Mae went on, "ye know she got so bad I finally had to take her down to the Vet's. I hated to do it, and it wasn't easy because that cat is smart. She knew I was upset and up to something strange. Besides, my arm was still giving me some trouble and I couldn't carry her too well."

"The doctor shook his head when he looked at that poor scrawny thing," (My "armor" was sliding to a heap at my feet)—"but ye know what he said?"

"What?" I shot back, almost afraid to acknowledge the lift in her voice—

"He said to me, 'Put this cat to sleep,' ye say? Put Ralph's pet to sleep? I'll do no such thing, Mrs. McClintock! Ye take this cat back home! Then ye go hunt up something of Ralph's that he's worn, something ye haven't laundered. Put the cat on it and see what happens! Then go and fetch her a good meal.'"

"Yes? Yes? Go on, Mae! What happened then?" (I felt as if I were back on Wyoming Hill asking my dear father to go on with his bedtime story.)

"Well, Eleanor, ye just won't believe this, but I scurried around—

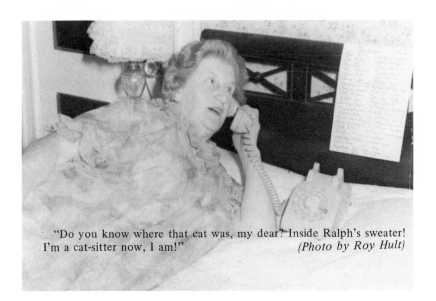

"Do you know where that cat was, my dear? Inside Ralph's sweater! I'm a cat-sitter now, I am!"   *(Photo by Roy Hult)*

I keep Ralph's things cleaned and in good repair, ye know! That's what worried me."

"I know, Mae. You're a marvelous mother and an ace house-keeper!" I was getting goosebumps all over. "Now, for Pete's sake, hurry up and tell me what happened. I've broken two fingernails on this telephone already!"

Mae laughed, but she appreciated the importance of extrasensory Sister's behavior to both of us.

"Well, all of a sudden I thought of the attic bedroom where Ralph has his ham radio equipment set up. Sometimes he went up there to read, but it gets cold up there sometimes—"

"Sure enough, in a drawer of the dresser up there I found his old brown sweater, I did! I was looking for it to send to the cleaners but couldn't find it—thank heaven!"

"I went downstairs and put it on Ralph's bed. Poor ole tiger was jumping on and off, as usual, and nearly half-dead while she was doing it, she was. Well, Eleanor, when I put her on that sweater of Ralph's, the poor little thing began to sniff and sniff and sniff! She was still sniffing when I went downstairs to get her a good fish dinner, with a saucer of cream to go with it, mind you!"

"But, Eleanor! When I came back upstairs, there was no cat!"

"No cat?" I broke in, horrified. (My divine armor, or what was

"Mae, you'll never know what that feline barometer of yours has done for me!"
(Photo by Roy Hult)

left of it, was about to sink through the floor and out of sight! Had Sister crawled off and expired?)

"Do you know where that cat was, my dear?—Inside the sweater! She crawled inside and refused to come out, she did! She's slept inside Ralph's sweater ever since! I had to put a bit of fish on the end of my finger to get her to stick her head out and eat her supper!"

I felt like howling for joy! "Oh, Mae! You'll never know what your marvelous story has done for me!"

"Look what it's done to me!" she laughed happily. "I'm a cat-sitter now, I am. Like a fool, I carry her meals upstairs to her every day, and she sticks her head out and eats, then goes back to sleep. I put her box of kitty litter beside the bed."

"She just eats and sleeps all the time now, she does. The white angora can't figure this foolishness out; just follows me when I go upstairs and watches and watches. Now I ask you—which one of us is crazy—that cat, or *me?*"

"*Me,* Mae! I'm crazy with *joy!* Because that little ole tiger cat of Ralph's, in spite of my wasted, dreary old trip to Dullsville,—in spite of every blasted thing—well—*you* know!"

Mae knew![11]

---

[11]"Sister" waxed strong again, (that is, strong for a cat of precarious vintage) and lived to purr mightily at Ralph's return. Two years later she quietly slept her life away—on Ralph's sweater!

Act VII

"WITH ALL POSSIBLE LOVE"

Detour
> *The Red Curtain Rises on: "Movie Stars of a North Korean Prison"*
> *Mail Call*
> > *Seeing Is Believing*
> > > *Phantom of the Foam*

Observing those "wonderful people" I once longed to emulate emphasized one Biblical truth: That God tests those he loves, severely indeed. And for what purpose? To become His shepherds in the Fields Beyond?

I enclosed Hebrews 12:5-7 in my next letter to Steve, certain that he would, like his mother, be evaluating our common ordeal as a supreme test of faith:[1]

> "My son, despise not thou the chastening of the Lord —
> For whom the Lord loveth He chasteneth — If you endure
> chastening, God dealeth with you as with sons; — "

By mid-August I had descended to such a low ebb physically that Gilbert persuaded me to abandon my telephone vigil (I never liked to be far from the home phone) and join him on his annual vacation. Breathing in the rejuvenating vapors of a seaside farm didn't seem too revolting an idea, at that!

If I felt strong enough for the safari, we'd first drive to Quebec to pick up Cousin Doris, (not to be confused with Robert's wife) who had just lost her husband. We could make a detour on the way up to Island Pond, Vermont, home of Bradley Crowe, one of the youngest and most personable of the crew, and perhaps drop a word of encouragement to his parents.

We turned off the main highway into God's country, rolling slowly along in order to observe at first hand the "Beneficent Intelligence behind nature." (Henry Thoreau?)

---

[1] As indeed he was, to a superb degree! *My Anchor Held* by Lt. Cmdr. Stephen R. Harris and Rev. Jim Hefley (Fleming Revell Pub., Old Tappan, N. J.) tells it best.

Lying like a patch of spilt sky on the floor of a lush green valley, the Pond, really a lovely lake, sparkled below the Crowe family farmhouse on the hill. In proper New England tradition, a single church spire rose from its verdant nest like a freshly sharpened pencil, pointing out the sapphire serenity of a summer sky. How sorely the young prisoner, locked in his stifling, flyridden room with seven other perspiring young bodies, must long for this airy vista!

(Crewmen called the clouds of buzzing flies the National Bird of Korea and were given "fly flappers" to rid themselves of the pests. One energetic flapper-flipper bagged 75 flies in a single hour.

Piles of turnips rotting in the blazing sun of the reeking courtyard below them, along with the fresh excrement dropped upon them by passing dogs, did nothing to enhance the purity of the ozone!

Some sailors were given charge over small green plants, "to be kept watered at all times." This was done faithfully — by nature's most convenient means — which swiftly strangled each struggling bloom.)

After a most cordial visit with Mother and Father Crowe, plus the older daughters and husbands they had hurriedly assembled for our visit, Gilbert and I prepared to depart the idyllic landscape. To my avid listeners in the pleasant farm sitting room, I had revealed only the more encouraging aspects of my D. C. Quiz Crusade, especially Mr. Rusk's remark concerning the State Department's "good batting average" in retrieving its POWS (but I did no dipping into the Sea of Japan).

Gilbert reminded them of the work Veteran's organizations across the country were doing for *Pueblo's* cause, and told them about Mr. Hilliard's *Remember the Pueblo* sign down in Rockport.

I brought them up to date on Rose Bucher's lone fight and her bumper sticker idea, quoted uplifting phrases from my fan letters as well as senatorial replies,—and reminded them of the millions of prayers ascending from homes and churches for our two sons.

Mae's clairvoyant cat, Mme. Doolittle and the "Cool" Caller to Room 12, with all due respect to their powers of discernment, were cut from the scene. My ego mustn't appear "teched" to these good Vermonters.

Yes, the devoted New England family seemed delighted that this "mother of an officer had gone out of her way to bring them news" (which their rural location might have denied them)—and their gratitude positively glowed. The host of snapshots and photographs placed in my hands told me Brad was the beloved baby of the family, and I answered their many questions as well as conjecture would allow —

As I often wondered during my bolstering of Mae, had I gone overboard and given false hope in my zeal to bring comfort to those whose hearts were as heavy as my own? I must ask for Guidance here.

Gilbert and I were sorry to refuse Mrs. Crowe's kind invitation to stay to supper, but we had over two hundred more miles to go. "I'll see you in California!" I called cheerily from the car.

As my wheels turned northward, I prayed silently into the windshield: "Dear God—'let the words of my mouth and the meditations of my heart be acceptable in Thy sight'!"

(Would my Angel Mother have been pleased with her tomboy today?)

* * * * * *

Bronzed brother Bill, tall and sleek as his twin, and also a bachelor, couldn't keep the happy smile off his face at the prospect of the three of us breaking into the quiet rhythm of his fabled corner of Maine's seaside country. Busy as he was with his many responsibilities, (besides working on Gordon's building projects, he made clever artifacts for gift shops), Bill loved having company, especially if there was a good cook amongst them — and Cousin Doris was a second Julia Child! The generous boxes and covered tins of goodies from her Lennoxville kitchen proved it. Cousin Kathleen, her sister, had sent a batch of homemade raspberry preserves and jellies from her Quebec farm, too. With Bill's big vegetable garden up in back of the weathered barn, we'd—oh, if only I could send some of this to Steve—poor guy!

How he loved bringing his college roommates up to Holly Farm! (Would he ever come again?)

Holiday Magazine (and more recently *Down East* Magazine) had recorded a dozen photogenic angles of this white-gabled, tall-chimneyed little beauty as well as of Big Beauty, Gordon's farm next door,—both circa 1750,—including some charming photos of his twenty-one-year-old dimpled daughter, Robin—most beautiful of all. John Stage had posed her looking out of Bill's shuttered barn window, smiling down at her *twenty-six* cats. A fistful of hamburg hidden in her hand on the weathered sill had pulled them into a perfect circle below her rustic perch.

And "up the rud a piece" in historic Old Harrington Meeting House

Churchyard, Captain Ebenezer Blount, who had built this homestead and added on its wing, has been slumbering soundly—since 1757. *Holiday* Magazine had failed to wake him, even when they had me standing on top of him posing beside his lichen-etched tombstone, wearing my flattering straw skimmer. ("It figures," Gilbert said.)

Bill had barely settled the last of our luggage on the pegged and polished floorboards beside our bedroom fireplace when I caught a distant sound that immediately took on significance. I pushed aside crisp ruffled curtains to open a window as speedily as I dared, for its lavender-tinted glass nestled in fragile frames that had to be propped open with a stick.

Yes, the big bell housed in the cupola on Gordon and Martha's stables across the side meadow was pealing steadily. It signaled phone calls to workers in barn, field or woodlands.

"That call's for me, Doris! I know that call's for me," and I bolted out the screen door.

"Tell Bill and Bert not to wait (they were planning to go clamming in the cove) — tell 'em supper's at seven, that I brought up a roast — be right back — make yourself comfortable."

The last directive had me out and under the peach tree, already heavy with fall's luscious promise, and I almost collided with a wooden prop Bill had placed under one of its gold-laden branches. I raced across a neatly mowed field, by the willows on the duck pond, and past contented horses munching behind white-fenced enclosures. How dare they look so unperturbed! One or two started for the railing in hopes of being handed a green apple.

A few surprised swallows swept out over my head as I puffed into the open door of the spacious horse barn, momentarily revived by the fragrance of new-mown hay mingling with the pungent essence of saddle and harness. The groom's phone in the harness room was nearer than the ones in the big house, and I prayed the heavenly gong up there would keep on sounding until —

"This is the Naval Reserve Training Station calling, — Bowen here. Has a Mrs. Robert Harris arrived?"

"Speaking," I gasped.

Where was everyone? Not a living thing was in sight except two long rows of sleek but indifferent Morgan horses, Martha's prize babies, chomping and twisting their ears, only their heads visible behind the garnet doors of half-shuttered compartments bearing their proud names — Corisor, Corisham, Reata's Supreme Lady —

"Commander Bordeaux will speak with you."

Holly Farm Cottage (1757)

Author with Ruth Johnson (above) and
Gilbert and Carl Johnson (lower deck)

Martha with Morgan Colt

Even though my meadow sprint was keeping it busy enough, my heart managed a leap. This bit must be important if No-Apology-Never was reaching clear into Maine for me!

"Eleanor!" the voice boomed out splendidly, "How would you like to see your son this very afternoon — in a movie, that is? How far are you now from the New Hampshire Naval Base?"

See my son?? See him after all these months of — !! (Mme. Doolittle's dire descriptions drifted in to mar my picturization.)

The Commander's question brought with it a weird combo of joy intermingled with nausea. Oh yes! I wanted to see Steve — but dare I? Could I bear to look upon the sad reality of his condition? ("This is probably the way I'll react when I'm about to meet my Saviour," I thought incongruously — Joy at the prospect of greeting my Lord and Master face-to-face — Nausea at the remembrance of my sins! Only now it was nausea at the awful images Madame Doolittle's psychic imagery had conjured up!)

Commander B, on the contrary, was bursting with bliss, obviously overjoyed to be able to offer something graphic in the way of progress, if indeed that's what it was. A Commander Hill was to project some propaganda movies showing the men in their prison compound "this very afternoon" at the Portsmouth, New Hampshire Naval Base — and my advisor gave me explicit directions which I strove heroically to absorb. When he hung up, I began to feel faint.

I rolled my face into the harnesses hanging neatly beside Martha's handsome saddles, and pressed my pounding forehead against the barn wall. Would that *Pueblo* headache ever vacate my psyche!

A friendly arm was encircling my waist — Robin's? No, Martha's! The gesture seemed out of character, for my quiet-spoken sister-in-law, in spite of the fact I knew she was fond of me, like my Vermont and Canadian Dorises, was not given to tender overtures, and most assuredly not to those wide-open demonstrations of boundless affection this hammy relative of theirs was always bringing off.

I blurted out the news dizzily.

"I'll be under the peach tree with my car at 12:30," she smiled, after I had refused her offer to come into the house for coffee. She studied my face for a second. "I'm sure the Navy wouldn't show those movies if the men didn't look presentable." We drifted out into the sun. After I told her I could make it back to Bill's O.K., she waved and disappeared into the barn,—and the swallows came soaring out again.

I began to feel as if I might survive after all, and on the way back across the meadow, I tossed a few green apples from under the early tree to the horses awaiting my return, grouped against the white railings like a Rosa Bonheur painting.

* * * * * *

While apprehension may be preferable to realization in most calamities, both leveled off to the point of being equally harrowing in viewing the movies of *Pueblo* captives taken behind the carmine curtain of North Korea. The rewarding facet of the afternoon for me, other than the prime one of seeing for ourselves that the bodies of our sons were alive and moving, was, of course, the loving presence of Mae McClintock — as well as the meeting of other relatives of *Pueblo* captives.

Three or four (CACO) advising officers sat apart and visited together while "mourners" were seated along two sides of a long rectangular table in one of the rooms of a large red brick building on the New Hampshire Base.

Captain Hill's movie projector took up the far end of the table, and it was a slightly nervous hand that moved forward to operate it. The Captain had already shown this film to *Pueblo* relatives the country over, so the unsteady hand spoke volumes. Was he already anticipating the dismayed reactions of his viewers? Martha's comment that "the Navy wouldn't show the movies unless the men were presentable" lost its aura of assurance.

The question uppermost in my mind was not one concerning the condition of Steve's body, but of his spirit: Would — or could a flat movie screen convey to me some confirmation that Steve had sought out and been comforted by the presence of God within him? This had become extremely important to me.[2]

Captain Hill, during his introduction, did caution us that the men would look thinner as a result of the Asian diet, which was virtually devoid of starches, but that the men "appeared well".

Mae had arrived with Commander Nelson earlier and now sat opposite me, stunning in a white starched lace that set off her fine figure and auburn-gold hair. I was wearing my D. C. "sailor suit" (a pleated white skirt with striped pullover under a navy jacket) which Mae told me she wanted to see, after hearing about the eventful time I had buying it.

---

[3]Had he also remembered a childhood Harrisism: *Ride the Horse! Don't Let the Horse Ride You!?).* Steve had been a shy little guy as a boy. Just how much of an impression did parental counseling make? Had I done a good enough job in preparing him for the rigors of a Communist prison?—

(The salesgirls in the Malden dress shop had recognized me from TV and newsphotos. They must have spread the word, for when I stepped out of the dressing room to view my finery in the triple mirror out front, a small audience awaited me, with questions and all good wishes for Steve's repatriation. Was I buying these outfits for the grand homecoming? (How I wished that I were!)

Even the store proprietor had appeared and pronounced me "damned attractive", 'though I noticed his eyes never left his merchandise. He even helped to select my wardrobe and later carried it out to my car. I was a sort of pseudo-celebrity now!

Catching my act through the store windows were three small boys who stole into the shop and asked for my autograph. ([They knew all about the *Pueblo*.] Mme. Doolittle told Mae these three courageous lads would "come back into my life."—And sure enough, they did.)

Well, I was the spectator at this show, and today's apprehension was even greater than that which I used to experience each Saturday when I teased an older brother into taking me to see Pearl White in *The Perils of Pauline*. Today I was Pauline, tied to the railroad tracks. Would the onrushing train cut me to pieces?

Norman Spear's grandmother from Portland, Maine, with whom I had talked by phone, was present at the long table, also Irmgard Shepherd, James's wife from Williamstown, Massachusetts. Unfortunately John Grant's parents from Maine, Hazel Hammond, (Marine Bob's wife from New Hampshire), and the Crowes of Vermont[3] were not at the showing, although there was a handful of in-laws and cousins of New England crewmen present.

The lights went out, and I had a feeling everyone in the room, regardless of the closeness of relationship, was saying a silent prayer as the reel began to turn.

Large printed Oriental characters in vertical rows were first to appear on the screen. These were translated by a running dialogue in Oriental-English in a flat, vituperative voice which spelled HATE and ANTI-YANKEE in every syllable.

The voice, divorced of its venom, might easily have come out of an

---

[3]For some reason the Crowes had not received an invitation – a Navy slip-up somewhere? How glad I was I had stopped in to see them! I would write and tell them about seeing Bradley.

old Charlie Chan movie with Charlie Chan (Warner Oland?) himself speaking, until the familiar names of the ship's officers jarred one back to the present as they were interpolated into the all-too-familiar diatribe, accusing our "heavily armed imperialist U. S. Spy Ship" of "intruding deep into their territorial waters," naming various offshore islands in order to polarize the vessel's position at the time of capture.[4]

Next followed a proud narration of the boarding and daring seizure of these warring imperialist monsters and of their subsequent incarceration.

Naturally in the bombastic account, the captives were soon softening, relenting their "atrocities" and even writing countless pages of "sincere" confessions as a result of their "repentance", induced, no doubt, by the "humane" treatment by their kind masters in this model prison in the "Socialist Paradise". (called *Korea,* by the by, not *North* Korea, my deah!)

And certainly, when our war-loving land got ready to "go to its knees" in apology for its malevolent crime, these same (same?) enlightened and contrite pawns would be allowed to depart for homeland and kiddies, not one whit the worse for wear after their short vacation as house guests of the "Peoples' Democratic Republic of Korea!" (not *North* Korea — *Korea,* my deah, they *are* Korea!")

The opening harangue, despite its abuse, held no surprises.

And now, in stalked the moment of truth — eighty-two young screen stars about to premiere — and indeed, no Hollywood audience was more engrossed, more desperately desirous of a successful screen test for the young actors than this one!

I was terribly sorry that "official selectivity" did not allow Martha and Doris past security guards, but left them to wile away the afternoon in an anteroom off the main gate. They were ever so understanding about it—a couple of those "wonderful people".

Against a barren background of prison walls, a long line of slow-moving, haggard-looking, unshaven men comprised the grand opener, a "silent study" in black and white. As each thin expressionless automaton moved toward a table to lean down and sign a document, (the combined "confession" of the 82), his loved one watching him from the Naval Base table longingly called his name, doing the same whenever any familiar face was spotted. Newsphotos had acquainted us with many of the men.

---

[4]Lies, lies, lies, later proved to be lies. As a clever retaliation later on, Executive Officer Ed Murphy fudged the navigational charts so that the ship was placed several hundred miles inland!

"Eleanor! Eleanor, there's Steve!" Mae cried with tears in her voice, but of course, I'd already seen him, and could not utter a syllable in return, for my heart was choking me. He simply leaned down over a table, scratched his name, then moved on wordlessly with the others.

"Oh, there's Normie, my Normie!" Grandmother Spear called next; but there was always a pained pause after the first joyous cry, for they did look "changed" to say the least. Mae found Ralph in due time and reacted bravely.

Mae and I were on the lookout for Bradley Crowe and Bob Hammond, so we could write a word of encouragement to their relatives.

As Steve stepped forward, I must admit I was impressed with his calm dignity and precision of movement. He seemed to have the situation under control — and I sensed instantly that my question on his spiritual status was partially answered. His white, unshaven face and thin frame were a shock to me, however, and my spirits wilted as I watched him herded off into obscurity like a lost wanderer, merely a link in the nightmarish chain gang.

As I described Steve to Gilbert later on, "He looked 'dug up',— as if he'd been buried for weeks."

> (In a way he had been — locked alone in a small room with covered window, cracked walls, crudest of furniture, and only a dreary hanging lightbulb burning day and night for company.
>
> A sack of rice hulls was his mattress, and one thin blanket his entire bedding.)

Though the movie was in black and white, I was quite aware of a striking paleness and a certain lack of natural vibrancy in all prisoners.

Yes, Steve's bearded face, angular look and absence of his usual high color were a sad bartering for the genial, apple-cheeked, 200-pounder Vuokko and I had said goodbye to! "Keep the lamp burning"? Steve's own lamp of joy seemed all but extinguished! If only I could have looked into his eyes. But the eyes of all prisoners were perpetually lowered. Was this attitude the demand of Oriental captors for obeisance? Or was the sudden sunlight a strain on the "dug-up", "solitary" prisoner? (Both, we learned later.)

I was relieved that Mae was reasonably satisfied with Ralph's appearance. She had not shed a tear in spite of her emotional reactions. Ralph's hair looked a trifle thinner than that in the charming photo on Mae's living room coffee table; he was by nature tall and lanky anyway and had suffered from hepatitis just before sailing from Japan. We were relieved to find, in comparing notes, that we both thought the entire crew, — or as many as were shown in the movie — appeared from their relaxed manner to be taking the whole raw deal rather philosophically.

Commander Bucher's image showed the worst ravages of all. By comparison to photos in the *Pueblo Colorado Journal* I had held in my hand the October before, the ship's captain appeared to have aged more than ten years. The bones in his face were almost fleshless, his hair, gray and dull-looking.

The two youngest officers, Skip Schumacher and Timothy Harris (no relation) looked so woebegone, I wanted to reach out and pull them to my breast, yet each of the six leaders in the drab procession maintained a dignity of bearing becoming an American officer. Not one captive behaved in any way to discredit his country, and those about the table spoke openly of the game deportment and composure of the men.

We next viewed crewmen "at play" in a pathetic attempt at being lively and skillful in a game of volleyball.[5] The obvious strain they were under, clad in their drab, ill-fitting prison garb, tore at our hearts,—and the table grew silent.

A horrid little Harrisism began forming in my brain: Lesson in Trauma: *While anticipation may be preferable to realization,—in the event of tragedy, it is participation that pushes up daisies!*

Seeing the gaunt figures struggling to please the eye of their deadly camera forced my memory back to Coleridge's *Ancient Mariner* — to the scene where in the relentless, baking moonlight, after weeks of sitting becalmed on a southern sea, a thudding, searing wind whistles through the rotted sails of the eerie ghost ship, and the bony corpses of the dead crew rise up like automated skeletons from the heat-shriveled boards of the deck—and start manning their stations!

Pueblo's captain, Commander "Pete" Bucher, was next shown behind a crude wooden barricade "enjoying" the luxury of a shower. Not a smile passed his lips as a high pail of water dribbled down over his pate and he soaped himself briskly, looking out hollow-eyed at his audience all the while.

Another luxury shot showed a youngster giving himself a shave with a straight-edged razor, after which he beamed obligingly and

---

[5] The men had attempted to elongate the only round ball provided them into the shape of a football so they could play that game, but were refused the privilege. Their captors failed to comprehend this mad desire for malformation.

rubbed his face. His smile proved contagious as he made some remark which his shipmates appeared to enjoy. We were positive this was Bradley Crowe.

"All it takes is one clown to keep them from cracking," Norm Spear's Grandmother observed. "Look at him now! *He* knows, *we* know this is just a put-on, and he's making the most of it." The young actor was not her Normie, but she had found him several times, too.[6]

Grandma Spear's observation set my gears to meshing again. Lesson for Forlorn Fighters: *The prancing feet of a clown, a real "heavy" on life's Fragile Mirror, may be all that keeps it from cracking.*

Thank you, Grandmother Spear!

"I'm gonna send a lush picture of myself to Premier Pig-Jowls and ask him for a fair exchange of warm bodies," I suggested gloomily to Gilbert in reviewing the sad condition of the captives. "There's that voluptuous one in the short nightie Steve took two Christmases ago you told me I should send to *Playboy* Mag for laughs—Besides, I like rice!"

(Let us hope my angel mother was not listening from aloft.)

"Oh, he'd welcome that with open palms," Gilbert returned. However, I gathered he inferred the "palms" would be open toward my throat, not my dainty waistline!

The big reels were patiently rewound and shown a second time. We would have stayed all night seeing them over and over again, had we had our secret wish, for our terrible hunger for these glimpses of our dear ones could hardly be satisfied in two meager showings. But movietime was over.

I found Sir Richard standing at my elbow. "Well, how do you feel now that you've seen your son, Eleanor?" he asked indulgently.

"Clobbered,—if you must know, Commander," I replied honestly. "The trouble with you Navy people is, you really don't know how to evaluate what you've just seen as well as we do. While those men may 'appear well' to you, they looked like mere bearded shadows of the great guys we sent away. You couldn't possibly appreciate the catastrophic reactions going on inside us when we first saw that ghostly line of 'confession' signers! All I can say is, Commander, I am happy to see that Steve can still move. I am indebted to the

---

[6]Remarked Norman after his release, "When I saw the way those armed North Koreans beat up a guy with their gun butts when they first stepped aboard ship, I said to myself 'Normie, you're dead!'"

Pueblo's men were nearly all clowns at heart; both their humor and resurgence of faith sustained them in their captivity. Despite bestial torture, not one of them cracked.

United States Navy for showing me that, at least, I really am!''

Before we left the table, there was a noticeable silence. Was everyone trying to recover from the shock of what they had just seen? I took advantage of the lull by electing myself spokesman for the group, heartily thanking Captain Hill on behalf of all present.

This fine, sensitive man showed his own relief in both his smile and his now-steady handclasp as each one approached.

We stood around for some time discussing the film and its pathetic stars, also exchanging bits of news we thought others might have missed. There seemed, unfortunately, to be a paucity of encouragement in any of it.

Mae set a tentative date for Doris and me to drive out to her pretty home in Milton to have dinner with her on the first cool day after our return from Holly Farm. We hugged each other affectionately on leaving. She promised to phone me at the farm (and keep the phone ringing until I could race across the meadow), if any good news came from her CACO.

I could see both Martha and Doris were mightily impressed by my spit-and-polish Navy Nannie when I introduced them to him outside the main gate. Sir Richard (Ree-charr) was positively pristine in his summer whites, and French courtesy rose to the occasion as he invited us all to join him for a bite to eat at a favorite restaurant only a short ride away. It wounded me to refuse him, for he had not quite forgiven me for excluding him from that possible leave he might have gotten to accompany me to Washington. However, as graciously as a sick heart could do so, I declined. I knew Martha had to get back to her blue-ribbon beasts, and Cousin Doris to her vacationing.

I shook hands with my White Knight and climbed in beside Martha and Doris. The Commander looked a little lonely when I turned and waved back to him. Had the movie made him thoughtful, too?

Yes, at the rate they were declining, how long could the 82 Navy men hold out?

* * * * * *

In Washington, in late August, Representative William L. Dickinson of Alabama was saying the men might be released to coincide with North Korea's Independence Day.[7] (October) Should we build our hopes up once again?

---

[7]Pure speculation, Mr. Representative! Don't get our hopes up like Senator Young did. (Young had stated the men would be ransomed and released.)

* * * * * *

On the very same day the Alabaman congressman made his assumption, I received a second letter from Steve:

28 August

My dearest, most precious Mother and Esther:[8]

Let me say first of all, Mother, your letters are getting to me. I was delighted to receive Jack's wedding pictures, both photos, and the Easter thoughts.[9] The six letters I've received and enclosures are much more meaningful to me now than you could possibly imagine. In future letters please send many more snapshots of yourselves.

The Democratic People's Republic of Korea once again made clear its firm and unchangeable stand in the Pueblo case, that is, that the PUEBLO crew will be repatriated only when the U. S. Government admits and apologizes for the crimes committed and gives assurances that such crimes will never be committed in the future . . .

We are not content to remain here forever nor to answer to the Korean law for crimes organized by others. Furthermore, the government of the Democratic People's Republic of Korea will not wait indefinitely for the solution to this problem.

We are appealing to our loved ones to continue doing all they can to elicit swift and just action to secure our immediate release. I am not aware of your specific activities Mother, but I've heard that you are working energetically for us,[10] so keep up the good work. I trust the wisdom of both of you.

I'm sound of mind and body and full of hope and optimism. Although I am detained here, the Lord never

---

[8] Steve must have suffered unbearably to be this affectionate! I was worried, but his letter sounded rational, except for the obvious propaganda.

[9] My Easter photo, a glamorous one taken before Steve left — (I was attired in a rose red satin dress standing before the fireplace in the music room)—had the "Room Daddies" (surly guards) all agog. They couldn't believe I was the same age as their demi-god, Kim Il Sung — and deemed it a triumph of the first water that I'd attained it. (After all, in North Korea, who does, if they "live" on the diet imposed upon their prisoners?) They took away my photo and kept it for themselves. Steve said I would have blushed at their remarks.

They always asked Steve for my letters. The reason is unbelievable. (See end of story for this.)

[10] "Heard" from whom? Ruddy Bear, our Home Communications Kibitzer? Or from one of those five-Koreans-in-a-car?

fails to give continuing comfort. My faith has never wavered, but is only stronger than it has ever been . . .

Well, Mom, it looks as though you are bearing up admirably under all this. According to Ralph's letters, Mrs. McClintock has described you as a "tower of strength". I guess if you ever needed to be one, now is the time.

Esther, my dear, I know that the present situation is extremely hard on you, but you know better than most where to turn for help in times such as these. When this is over, we will have endured the greatest crisis we will ever know in our lives. Remember the prophecy of one spiritually gifted: Our first child will be a son, and we will live together in a foreign land. Has God ever broken a promise? . . .

I can think of no precedent to our situation in recent history. We are like prisoners with no term of sentence established. Will we go home tomorrow, next month, years from now, or never?

Mail from home has been most wonderful to receive. The local news of the town is great to hear. Keep it coming!

If you have not already seen us on T. V., you soon may, as we have had a press conference and film coverage about our lives here and our earnest appeal for quick repatriation.

In closing, my beloved ones, may I say: Mother, *keep that light burning!* Esther, dearest, be brave and remember I love you very, very much — both of you — and if it be God's will, I hope to be with you again.

With all possible love,

Steve

* * * * * *

Famous last words from the N. K. Task Force Desk in Washington had it that "outlook for early release does not appear promising."

The summer ended in sad frustration.

* * * * * *

On an unseasonably warm morning in late Indian Summer, I awoke at dawn. Some silent urge was luring me into the music room. In any other year I would have awakened to the delicious realization that it was Saturday, turned over and drifted into sleep again; but I would have forfeited one of autumn's rare phenomena hanging at this very moment in the skies just below our cliffs.

I had been lying abed, wondering about Steve — watching the fat pink fingers of dawn steal into the heavens to the East and point accusingly at a lazy sea. The morning was a bit sultry, and heavy cloudbanks crept across the accusing fingers, threatening to blot out Aurora's roseate tints as if jealous of her artistry.

I slipped on my lacy pink cloud and tiptoed out to the music room window that looked out to sea. Under the slow smile of the morning sun, I watched the same sea gorge itself upon the fat fingers of dawn, then lie back surfeited, its swollen belly rolling contentedly in the fluorescence of a fresh new day.

It was the center window I felt drawn to, however, and I found myself looking again into the same painted valley my two dear ones had looked down into almost a whole sad year ago.

Oh, if only they could see it now! For now its hues were softly fused into a muted dream-tapestry. But in order to see it all, I had to peer down through a gossamer mist lying in enormous silvery sheets across the sky. Like a cloud-cradle hung out to catch the stars, it stretched the full length of the valley, clinging from hill to hill like a massive spider web whose edges were fringed in gold. Down beneath its eerie translucence, the Fells woodlands melted into a miniature forest, the city-patches into toy villages of golden gauze, the hills before Boston towering over all like shrouded guardians of a forgotten fairytale.

I must rouse Gilbert at once. For all his acidity, he was a skilled artist. The diaramas, wall hangings, and woodworkings he fashioned in his subterranean hobby-workshop attested to the fact. He must come upstairs and see this rock-top marvel.

I whirled toward the turn in the staircase just as the phone rang. My initial annoyance did a quick reversal and my heart leapt. Was this my CACO officer wanting to be first with the good news? I dashed back and fell on my bedside phone.

"Eleanor! Eleanor! Oh, I hope I didn't wake ye — Forgive me, Dear, for phoning at this early hour — but I just had to call and tell ye what happened to me yesterday! Ye weren't home last night? I kept trying to — "

"No, Mae, it was PTA night at Beebe. We usually hold it on Monday, but — well, never mind. What happened, Mae?"

I stretched the cord to the snapping point by dragging the telephone to the top of my grand piano, even standing on tiptoe to see it — but the giant web hung just below my eye-line. How long would such fragile beauty last — ?

"Well, Eleanor! I must be going daft or something because, my Dear, yesterday *I saw Ralph!*

"You *saw* Ralph?" Somehow I could almost anticipate what Mae would tell me next. There were no surprises any longer concerning the nature of our vigil — it had a continuing mystical movement to it, as if propelling us to the core of some secret truth.

"Yes, I *saw* him, I did! I don't know whether all this N. K. Founders' Day or Independence Day business the papers are talking about had anything to do with it or not — I just can't afford to get my hopes up anymore — but late yesterday afternoon, just before dark, I was feeling very blue, and I happened to look out the dining room window — the one facing the garage — and there, plain as day, I saw Ralph walking into the driveway! He just came walking up the driveway and turned the corner out of sight. I saw him plain as day, I did, Eleanor!" she repeated.

"What was he wearing?" I asked, mists of autumnal magic completely forgotten.

"He was wearing his white summer uniform. But, Eleanor — wait, — that isn't all!

"Go on, Mae. This is astounding!" I was getting so cold and goose-bumpy I crawled back into bed and snapped on the electric blanket.

"Well, Eleanor — I was so taken by surprise — so upset really — I was afraid Ralph might be coming home to say goodbye or something — I didn't know — I was nearly out of my mind. I had to tell somebody, so I went over to Mrs. McVitty's next door. I was wondering what she'd think of me and my visions, but do ye know what she said to me?"

"Go ahead. I'm insulated for shock."

"Well, my dear, she wasn't as surprised as I thought she'd be, for she said to me, 'Mae', she said, 'I wasn't going to tell ye this, because I didn't know what ye'd think of me; but now ye've told me what ye saw, I'll tell ye what *I* saw.' "

" 'I woke up early one morning a few weeks ago and I distinctly heard your front door bang, so I went over to the window. 'That sounds like Ralph', I said to myself, and sure enough, I distinctly saw him — Ralph — run down your front steps, get into a car and drive off. I tell you, Mae, I always know when someone is leaving your house because I can hear your front door, and sure enough there he was!' "

"Mrs. McVitty also said he was wearing his white uniform. Now what do ye think of that? Maybe we're both crazy. I just can't take much more, Eleanor! Do ye think I'm going daft?"

"Mae, I think it's wonderful! I believe it's a good omen! Ralph was probably projecting those very thoughts of home so vehemently, you and Mrs. McVitty actually saw them in the flesh, so to speak."

"Ask Gilbert what he thinks about my seeing Ralph, Eleanor!" Mae asked pointedly. Like me, Mae regarded my household Sphinx as all-knowing.

"Oh, he'd probably say it was time for 'white uniforms' to nab us both for the comforts of a padded cell. I'll tell him as soon as he wakes up — But, Mae, if you think you're crazy, move over, kiddo! I've seen a few things in my day, too!"

"Ye have? Ye mean about the ship being captured? I've never forgotten that—or that "Thing" that walked into ye're schoolroom the morning the ship was boarded—but, of course, ye didn't really see that—"

"No, it has nothing to do with the *Pueblo* at all. Mae, listen— go downstairs and brew yourself a cup of coffee. You're going to need it. Ring me up when you're ready." I ran into the music room.

Mae was excited enough to carry out my suggestion, and a few moments later the phone rang, and there she was, all ears for my "sighting" story, and about to be internally bathed and buttressed as a supportive measure.

My heavenly web still hung suspended over the valley —

"Fact is, Mae, I've revealed this eerie episode only to Gilbert and my minister, so consider yourself privileged, Kiddo," I commenced.

Mae promised to keep my secret, then urged me on.

"Seven years ago I spent my first night alone in my brand new house up here on the ledges. As I've told you before, my vantage point here is a historic landmark, one of the high 'reference points' listed on the United States Coast and Geodetic Survey maps."

"Oh, yes! And I remember ye're telling me about ye're rock being a signaling station for the Wampanoag Indians and Gilbert's finding the arrowheads when ye were digging those garden pools. From ye're rock to Wayte's Mount to the Blue Hills here in Milton, they probably signaled. I can see big Blue Hill from the end of my street."

"Yes, Gilbert has those arrowheads under glass. Your Blue Hills must have been great Indian territory, Mae, but there's a more romantic story connected with our rock here. It boasts its own private lady ghost, mind you! When I was little, my father read accounts of her from a copy of a very early newspaper, *The Melrose Chronicle,* I think it was called. She has been seen wandering about up here, after an especially wild Nor'easter drives its heavy mists across the cliffs — in a shroud, no less, Dearie! But for some strange reason I'd completely forgotten about the Phantom of Boston Rock when I decided to build my house here — uh — how's your blood pressure, Mae?"

"Oh — ha! ha! — I'm getting so carried away, I didn't notice. I'm even forgetting to drink my coffee!"

"I chanced upon some domestic bushes growing against the cliff wall before we started construction and asked Gilbert about them. Like his brother Bill, he's a history buff as well as a pretty fair horticulturist.

" 'Oh, those were planted by old J. Wesley Dodge, the hermit who built himself a small house up here,' he explained. 'Don't you remember reading about him in *Goss's History of Melrose?*' The name rang a faint bell, is all.

"Well, in August I insisted Gilbert depart for his vacation in Maine with Bill, at Holly Farm Cottage, as scheduled, and leave me here to play house in the new domicile. Summer School was over, and I was anxious to put up curtains and drapes, and do all the things one does to a new home. Bert told me I was crazy not to accompany him, since I'd never slept alone in any house in my life before (which was true). At nightfall I did get a bit edgy, even with all the downstairs lights blazing. The neighbors were all away on vacation, and to make things even more interesting, a noisy wind arose and it started to pour cats and dogs—which, of course, dimmed down the lights of Boston and other cities lying below. I turned on the Gay Nineties bedside lamp Gilbert had bought me for the new house, but that only served to keep me awake.

Well, after I'd read all sorts of eerie things into every creak, crick and crack I heard, from sheer exhaustion I finally clicked off my little lamp, turned over and copped out into oblivion."

"Grab a pencil, Mae. We don't want these modern psycho writers getting the jump on us. This bedtime story could be worth a bundle."

"How can I write anything? My hand is shaking so now I can hardly drink my coffee," Mae chortled happily. "Go on! Go on! What happened next?" (I could see my ghost therapy was helping my sensitive companion.)

"Well, according to my little clock later, I must have been asleep for over an hour. Anyway, the next thing I remember was thinking someone had turned my lamp back on, for I had the sensation of light on my face, even before I opened my baby blue eyes. It seemed to be a sort of signal. And, brother, when I did open them, guess what, Palsy? I found myself *looking straight up into the face of a woman I'd never in my life seen before—a complete stranger!* She was leaning over the same side of the bed as the lamp, her eyes staring down into mine as if to say, 'What the blazes are *you* doing here?—here in *my* house! Get out—the short cut is over the cliff!'"

"Although she held nothing lethal in her hand, her expression was angry and accusing enough to indicate to Yours-Trembling-Truly that she was about to strike me, or at least to shake me! But ole Tomboy's early training snapped back like a reflex — and almost instantaneously I leapt up and struck out with both fists. My female apparition, nevertheless, exercised her nether-world prerogative and disappeared just as quickly!

"Now ordinarily, I'm a most friendly little beast, (Mae agreed) loving little paws ever stretching forth in beneficent brotherhood and all that jazz, but this dame was no friendly 'brother',—brotherhood or sisterhood being farthest from her dusty little phantom mind — nor was she any long-lost relative either, for nowhere in my lineage had any lady of Spanish(?) blood — if lady she be — put in an appearance!"

"I can see I'm going to need another cup of coffee!" Mae quipped. "What happened next? Hurry!"

"Well, I flopped back onto my furbelows in a cold sweat, my heart racing so rapidly my whole chest pained me — so intense was the pain, in fact, I dared not stretch out my arm to put on the lamp. I honestly believed I had seen my first and last phantom.

"What a disgraceful way to depart this fair world, I kept thinking, — *being scared to death!* While it might be novel and rather original, it seemed to me quite unacceptable by modern mores for meeting immortality.

"I envisioned good Brother rushing home from Maine and coming in upon my moldering corpse—wondering what in tunket had caused this dead-eyed stare of glazed terror. What had I seen in this pretty bedroom in a brand new house that had caused my awesome demise? After all, only *old* houses were haunted, weren't they? Ghosting was always practiced in dank cellars, cob-webbed attics, on abandoned castle staircases, aboard derelict ships, in cemeteries or darkened museums, wasn't it?—so what the—?

"Hold that pencil steady, Chum. This should make the *Twilight Zone,* or *One Step Beyond!*"

"What did she look like — the ghost, Eleanor, — besides being Spanish? I mean, how was she dressed?" Mae hadn't even heard my phony prophecy.

"She was olive-skinned of course, with black glossy hair, parted in the center and puffed out a bit over the ears in a sort of Jenny Lind hairdo — Ye cats! I can see those jet earrings swinging and sparkling now. Frankly, Mae, if she hadn't worn such an accusing look on her face, I would have said she was pretty — very pretty — a trifle buxom though, and not terribly young — about in her mid-thirties I'd place her. Her dress was rich-looking, — satin, I believe — but for the life of me I couldn't tell you the color. It had lace at the neck and sleeves — not as early as a Martha Washington mode — but resembling one of those old Godey's Ladies' Book types,[11] about mid-1800's, I'd say.

"Well, there I lay quivering on my couch of pain, wondering if what I was feeling constituted a heart attack. It should have — but what in the name of credulity would I tell a doctor? Eventually I simmered down to the point where I got the lamp back on, got my shuddering anatomy off the bed and did some thorough ghost-searching, greeting at long last the welcome dawn. I could scarcely wait for a decent hour to arrive so I could rouse my writer friend, Mary Stetson Clarke, a Melrosian who has enjoyed marked success turning out novels with both local and more extensive historical backgrounds.

"While I knew my angry apparition was no returning ancestor, I had a hunch that Mary could relate her to local history, — and sure enough, she did."

"'I feel quite strongly that it was "Zeta" who visited you,' she said calmly. 'Why Eleanor, I'm surprised at you! I thought all long-resident Melrosians knew the story of the romance and tragedy of J. Wesley Dodge and Zeta, his beautiful Cuban bride!'

"Well, Mae, it seems young Dodge was a seafaring gentleman, a Merchant Mariner who fell in love with a sugar magnate's daughter, married her on the island plantation in Cuba, and arranged to have her rejoin him in the spring, at which time he would have a home ready for her here below our rocks. The lovely Zeta, dressed in her trousseau finery—not in a shroud as the old write-ups had it—prepared to meet her young husband as her four-masted schooner sighted Boston's far shores. As history relates it, a fierce Northeaster suddenly arose, sending the vessel foundering on a shallow reef. All hands on the ill-fated sailing ship were lost.

"Young Wesley, broken-hearted and partially demented with grief, climbed our cliffs, built himself a small abode and refused to leave his lofty perch because it commanded an unobstructed view of the faraway scene of the tragedy. He used to stand on a certain rock (I know the very one), stare out to sea and call her name, 'Zeta!

---

[11]I used to collect original pages from this fashion magazine of the 1800's.

Zeta!'—until, emaciated and too sick to leave his bed, he was nursed back to health by the good women of the little village standing below us here—and eventually enticed off the rock.

"His beloved, according to historians, however, continues to come and search the heights for her young husband, in the mists that drift over our rocks following a major storm at sea."

"Okay, Scribe, got it all down? Now I ask you, do you feel so 'crazy' now, Mae? *I saw that woman just as clearly as you saw your dear Ralph!"*

We rang off just as I heard the downstairs shower go on. Time to start breakfast; but first I ran to the window to see what had happened to my angel-hung cloud cradle.—But, oh, there it was, hanging in tatters, long wisps of it blowing listlessly as tired ribbons across the floor of the sunless valley. As with the ill-conceived news of the imminent release of the captives, it had no solid foundation in fact,—soon to be ripped apart by the winds of time and truth,—once more leaving our emotions shredded and hanging in uncertain bewilderment.

Act VIII

IN "FULNESS OF JOY"[1]

"He heard my voice out of his temple and my cry came before Him, even unto His ears." (Psalm 10)

Party of the First Part — Party of the Second Part
  Cool Cats
    Voice in the Void
      Flood Tide
        "Knock and It Shall be Opened"

Autumn sloughed away into winter and by mid-December, hope of retrieving a son fully alive became only a hungry hope. There had been no contact whatsoever with the prisoners themselves since their early September letters. Even if Christmas miraculously brought us our most cherished "present", would it be in the form of a human vegetable? An incurable invalid?

The mass media was revealing nothing but reiterated hope these days, which, when analyzed, was almost as nervewracking as bad news.

It seemed to Mae and me that our prayers were the only link with our sons now, and I am ashamed to confess that while my "whole being" went into my supplications, I was secretly disappointed that I could feel no reciprocal warmth other than what I found in the golden assurances of the Good Book. Nevertheless, I would bear in mind God's promises and remain constant in my faith:

"What things soever ye desire when ye pray, *believe that ye shall receive them and ye shall have them.*" (Mark 11:24)

Such words would be my supporting staff in the days to come.

While the crew had appeared on television intermittently during the final weeks of summer and on into the fall, there had been no further developments along visual lines for weeks now. In one TV closeup, Steve solemnly announced to the world that he would leave the U. S. Navy!

---

[1] "Thou wilt show me the path of life: *In Thy Presence is fulness of joy;* at Thy right Hand there are pleasures forevermore." (Psalm 16:11)

At first I wondered just how much of his young life had been kicked away in order to force this lie out of him; however, second thoughts found me hoping he was simply obliging his keepers, knowing no listener would accept such a hatful of trash, anyway. There was always that steady calmness about him, and while his eyes were perpetually lowered,—obviously *de rigueur* for captives,—I got the feeling that had he been allowed to raise them, he would have winked!

In one of these North Korean "News Conferences", Steve sat so close to the camera, I longed to reach in and pluck him from his sty; and I found myself moving my bedroom chair right up beside him to study his condition more closely and listen to the well-rehearsed antics of North Korea's sober marionettes. So near — yet, so very, very far away!

Mme. Doolittle was doing nothing to brighten the yuletide season, either; in fact, her breakthrough was bloodier than before — "unrecognizable pulpy bodies on stretchers—screaming—retching—the two symbolic *pails* again![2] (Madame's "gettings", unfortunately, proved correct. The already frail bodies of our loved ones were at this moment being subjected to their *"Hell Week"*[3] Torture, i.e. programmed persecution on a 'round the clock' basis!)

As if signalling their doom, the lovely bronze lamp above the floor garden flickered, and winked out. As I reached up to relight it with the last rosy bulb I had in the house, an ominous premonition had me beseeching the assembled Hosts of Heaven that this final beacon I was holding in my hand would be the one to guide our shadowy mariner to home port. It simply *had* to be! I must *"keep the lamp burning!"*

* * * * * *

"—And *why should the poor kids in your Fourth Grade be cut out of their Christmas party just because I'm over here 'in stir'?—(and just think, Ma, you won't have to get me a present this year!")*

Oh, I could just hear Steve saying it, if his sense of humor hadn't been kicked, starved, bludgeoned, or bled out of him!

Yes, perhaps I should make an effort to "keep" Christmas for his sake, keep it as we had in happier years. He might need this comfort-

---

[2]There were reportedly several attempts at drowning in pails of water (specifically, two pails of water). The cruel keepers wore "heavy" boots and were especially adept at kicking their emaciated victims in all the sensitive regions. Karate? The North Korean version emphasizes the vicious use of feet (tae kwon do) rather than hands.

[3]Captives' own label.

ing assurance, this picturization of all the bustling preparations at home as he lay on his — well, whatever he had to lie on (a sack of rice hulls).

I could at least write and tell him what we were trying to do — even if it was only a one-way communication. Yes, my very next letter must describe all we were doing "in expectation" of his returning to share it!

At school, I told Irma what I believed Steve's wishes would be concerning the keeping of Christmas on all fronts. In her generous fashion she, herself, insisted upon arranging for the faculty dinner to be provided by our excellent Chinese restaurant, *The Golden Gate,* downtown just off Main Street. I wasn't to lift a hand if the staff came to the house.

What new reservoir of energy could I tap now for all that "keeping Christmas" at both home and school entailed? There were those Heavenly Choristers in Grade Four still to groom (18 angels, the Holy Family, kings and shepherds) as well as selections from *The Messiah* to memorize for our annual Christmas presentation in the school auditorium. (I must send Mae an invitation.)[4]

> (Even before the Christmas season got underway on these shores, in the empty hours of his incarceration — often after a cruel beating — Steve found comfort in recalling happier scenes, many of his childhood — of Christmases at home or over on Wyoming Hill with his grandparents, uncles and other assorted relatives. Most healing of all memories were those of sailing in summer breezes across Cape Cod Bay with his dad.
>
> Sometimes he "projected home movies" such as these on the cracked walls of his virtually unheated, barren cubicle.)

First Steve would be thinking — if he was still alive to think — about his Uncle Bill tramping the snows of Maine's sea-scented woodlands to select a well-formed balsam, then lopping off the sweet boughs of other evergreens, some with cone clusters still clinging, to

---

[4]We sang two selections from Handel's *Messiah: Come Unto Him* and *He Shall Feed His Flock,* done in unison — with an echo chorus out of sight — rather than as solo arias. The effect was indeed "heavenly." Angels bore no wings, but had long flowing sleeves on their white or pastel gowns. Glitter-covered halos took on a celestial iridescence under careful stage lighting; and since all but two or three of the schools' pupils were Christians, our Christmas Musicale, an annual Melrose school custom, flowed on undisturbed.

pile into his truck for the annual Christmas pilgrimage to Ledgewinds. I must not fail to attend the midnight service at church. I could forego the bell-ringing and carol singing on Beacon Hill in Boston this year. And of course, I'd invite the only two great aunts Steve still possessed (Eula and Ida) over for the festivities. After Steve (?) played Santa, we'd stack the presents under the big tree in the center window upstairs, pick up the wrappings and ribbons and sing a few carols to the drifting-up essences of browning turkey and spicy pumpkin pie. Steve would gladly welcome an exchange of organists, and as Vuokko took over, I could slip down and organize the feast.

Hoping to submerge harrowing thoughts of continuing damage being done to torture-wracked bodies, I strove to do what I believed Steve would wish me to do—"Keep the Home Fires Burning",—and "pray unceasingly" as the Apostle Paul directed.

Indeed, I prayed into the windshield while driving, prayed into the school chalkboard while writing, prayed under the Reading Tree, or over the heads of my busy fourth graders as I walked among varying formations of chairs and tables. I even prayed to fences and hedgerows as I walked my hand-clinging chicks over to the recess yard up across West Foster Street. I clung to my Heavenly Father as tenaciously as my pupils clung to me.

"O turn unto me, and have mercy upon me; *give Thy strength unto thy servant* and save the son of Thine handmaiden." (Psalm 16)

"Yes, dear Lord, if it be Thy will, *'SAVE THE SON OF THY HANDMAIDEN'!*" (My ego was over-exposed, I realized, in considering myself God's "handmaiden"—yet, for this contingency I chose to think of myself as such!)

* * * * * *

Several snowy evenings later, Mae's voice broke the long pre-Christmas silence.

"Eleanor, take this for what it's worth, but Madame Doolittle's 'getting' a new picture now, she is!"

"Well, Mae," I replied listlessly, "what has the old girl dredged up out of her dreamworld this time?"

"My dear! She has the entire *Pueblo* crew out of North Korea recuperating in the tropics on a grand big estate! She thinks it may be Hawaii.

"In her 'picture' they're lined up in neat rows with a big palm tree in back of them, dressed in brand new Navy uniforms. She sees Steve and Commander Bucher in the front row, she does — and there's more!"

"Go on, Mae," my dull voice managed. "I'll hang in there."

"Yes, Eleanor, they're standing at attention in a big courtyard with wonderful green grass under them and a fountain sparkling in the center of it. I think she said the courtyard had three sides to it with pink walls."

"Oh, yes, the 'Pink Palace.'— Really, Mae! She pulled that Pink Palace out of her hat months ago!"

"Yes, but the Pink Palace has balconies on it now, with people on them lounging around in white. They're looking down at our men being decorated at some ceremony or other. Doesn't Henry Kaiser have an estate in Hawaii?" Mae seemed in indestructible good spirits.

"I don't know and I don't care, Mae. All I can say is this is quite a switch from the scream scene. Balconies and a fountain, yet! Green grass and pink walls! Madame D. herself must be losing her buttons! When, may I ask, is this green grass picture being hung on the wall?"

"Oh, Madame Doolittle says they're out of North Korea already and being cared for right now on this big estate, so they won't look too badly when we see them!"

"Mae, for once let's check out this newest vignette of Madame's mind. I'm going to call the State Department first thing in the morning and get Willie (Capt. Howie Wilcox) on the wire. I'm going to find out if Madame is right. If so, Washington shouldn't be holding out on us. This news blackout has really gotten me down!"

* * * * * *

Just as I feared, Captain Wilcox informed me that the men were "still in their North Korean prison." They had not moved an inch. There were absolutely "no definite plans for their imminent release", and I was "very foolish" to place so much confidence in a demented old fortune teller — or words to that effect. Willie had spanked me again — however, he did say it was "so nice to hear my voice."

* * * * * *

Steve's Uncle Bill was only too happy when I phoned him, to do his tree-chopping stint for Steve, as well as for my own hopes of successfully staging this facsimile of a gala holiday season.

Shouldering his axe with Gordon's hired man, from his own acreage he cut the ten-foot balsam, adding a truckload of fragrant fir branches for fashioning into outdoor wreaths and indoor bowers back here in Gilbert's cellar hobby room,—the final touch being to entwine them all with little electric stars and flowers. Along with the dozens of red and white tapers burning in the sconces of upstairs mantlepieces, on tables, in planters and niches, these small twinklers provided our only indoor lighting. Outside, the top of the deck was strewn with colored lights, which from below resembled a huge crown glowing in the sky.

There were always those party-comers who worried about my burning the house down, but I always told them we could postpone that for another year. This was the way Steve liked it, so this was the way it was going to be! The soft glow gave the rooms an aura of magic that I prayed would sparkle its way clear into North Korea!

Having read in some woman's magazine that to push a party to swooning success, the hostess must see to it that each of the five senses gets its fair shake, I often hired a professional organist, violinist or instrumental trio, friends of mine, whom I insisted on paying. To this balm for the eardrums, I added an olfactory offering: the woodsy fumes of a special balsam incense my guests always believed was escaping from the very fir bowers themselves! (I've given away whole trees of it.)

Party One of the trying season was destined for success even before it started, for each teacher, bless her, went out of her way to keep only genial conversation bubbling about me—while I, in turn, summoned the last vestiges of ham, butterfly, tomboy, tiger and God-leaning energy to shore me up as hostess. Gilbert, as usual, made his escape to a "mod movie"[5] —or so he declared!

While I ate scarcely anything myself, there was one heartbreaking enigma which made its awful arrival upon the scene at the very height of the festivities — one which, thankfully, only *I* possessed the power to see, to feel—but tragically enough, to do nothing—absolutely nothing about!

While the flickering light of multiple white candles played over the Christmas party table, laden with its heaped-up platters of delicious fare, a gaunt, unshaven face silently came into focus, facing me at the opposite end of the room! Hollow-eyed, it gazed mutely upon the disappearing viands — at times raising its eyes in slow bewilderment, as if trying to recall the reasons behind these half-forgotten sounds of laughter. The misty face was Steve's!

Looking more closely over the heads of my guests, I was aware of a host of other faces surrounding the table with the same hungry-eyed fixation. Had my thought propulsion pulled the crewmen to my very table? Dear God, how could I ever live through another visitation such as this?

---

[5]His idea of a joke. Actually he spent my party-evening browsing Boston's interesting shops. He must have, judging by the unique and multiple purchases he lugged home.

* * * * * *

As Christmas edged closer, morale slumped lower. No news whatsoever was oozing from the slack mouth of a faceless Washington. Newscarriers were doing nothing but wishful conjecturing, and I could do better than they at that!

Even the portents of nature promised a winter of unusual severity, leaving their traces on Ledgewinds' snowy grounds. Pheasant couples from the woods below put fire on the white horizon as they wandered closer and closer to the house for feeding. Our rockbound woodchuck, skunk, raccoon family and rabbits, some of whom should have been sleeping, were still on the forage trail, and Gilbert kept them well supplied lest they raid his bird-feeding station. Squirrels, having discovered an ultra-heavy autumn harvest of acorns, now dug in vain to recover their buried treasure from under the oaks—so we fed them, too.

Mae and I rarely called each other now. What was there to say? We had both been busy composing and mailing out Christmas form letters imploring friends and relatives to trade their customary greeting cards for personal pleas to the State Department or key personnel at the Capital for the immediate release of the crewmen.

Probably the heaviest blow to date descended when a special courier from the Boston Postal District arrived at our doors to gather up our five-pound Christmas parcels for the prisoners — *to be mailed to North Korea!*

Mae broke the silence first — with tears.

"Eleanor! Eleanor! Ye'll be ashamed of me when I tell ye,—when I tell ye what I almost did! I swear I'm going daft, I am!"

"Relax, Mae—I'm 'identifying' with you, Kiddo. Not only do I have to impale notes to myself on my school desk,—when I leave the building to go uptown, I can't even remember where I parked the car. Vuokko writes that she is having similar trouble. What's yours?"

"Oh, it's much worse than that—much worse! Eleanor, I've cried so much I'm just a wreck, and now that Christmas is so near and those poor boys being beaten all over again"—The tears were inundating her words—

"Well, Eleanor! I simply couldn't stand it any longer, this dreadful silence — too long — just as if they were all dead — so I decided — I decided — well, I couldn't bear to think of Ralph coming home in a flag-draped — "

I bristled at last, but only to prevent my good friend from further self-torture.

"Mae! *Will you please forget once and for all that blasted 'flag-*

draped coffin!' Madame Doolittle, even that 'hood', 'Hellraising Hairstander' in their most brutal brain-rides *never ever saw any flag-draped coffins, caskets, catafalques, corpses or cadavers!* So as Steve would say, 'Come off it, Mother!' "

"Well, maybe *they* didn't see any, but *I did,* I tell ye! Anyway, I just didn't think I could survive a minute longer without poor Ralph—and meanwhile 'Sister's' begun acting up something terrible!"

"Sister?!", I broke in alarmed. (Oh, this was bad, really bad! What did this behavior on the part of our feline barometer signify?) Above the clunking of my heart, I felt a lump swelling in my throat, yet I summoned what small ration of ham there was left in my system:

"Well, after all, Mae dear, 'Sister's' only a cat! I don't know why either of us puts so much stock in her kooky capers. If we ever told outsiders about it, they'd put us down as a couple of goofballs. But tell me now, Kiddo, what were you planning to do, jump in the Blue Hills Reservoir?"

"Well, no—but ye know, Eleanor, sending those Christmas packages to North Korea was the last straw. It proved one thing for sure to me — that our poor boys would not be coming home — and maybe not even be alive to receive our gifts — they couldn't possibly live through any more torturing—

"So there I was, sitting at the kitchen table just crying to die — But I happened to notice that the living room was in complete darkness, and for some reason I wanted to leave the house looking occupied, so I dragged myself into the living room, all the while crying my heart out for Ralph.

"As I put my hand on that pretty Italian lamp in the front window and the light broke the darkness, it was just as if my poor heart broke right along with it!

"But ye know, Eleanor, the strangest thing happened! — Just the moment I thought my heart would burst into a thousand pieces, a voice as clear as the light filled the whole room. It said, 'Ralph will be with you at Christmas.' That's what it said, Eleanor, *'Ralph will be with you at Christmas!'* Now, what do ye think of that?"

There were two lumps in my throat now, but after a few painful seconds, I managed a grateful "Mae! It's the very sweetest message that ever came over my phone! I hope you went to your knees in gratitude to your Maker!"

(Neither of us gave a rip in Redsville at this point whether Old Furry Ears was listening or not. He simply couldn't "relate" to celestial conversation, anyhow. A "Russian rocket" had already "shot God out of the sky" — remember?)

"Yes, yes!" she answered in a faraway voice, as if she hadn't heard me. "And I will say of the Lord he is my refuge and my fortress; my God: in Him will I trust — *He shall give his angels charge over me,* to keep me in all my ways — Eleanor, that's the part of the 91st Psalm I mailed to Ralph. I tore the page right out of my Bible, I did!"

> (This was the page that was worn to shreds from passing it from hand to hand among the Scripture-Starved prisoners. Steve often speaks of it in his talks around the country. How grateful the men were to Mae McClintock! They sought her out to tell her so when they returned to San Diego. *Who says God is dead?*)

We discussed the Miracle Voice at length, and I finally convinced Mae her experience was something we should both cherish and believe in. "What's been happening at school lately?" Mae suddenly asked, as if seeking another cheerful turn in the dark road. Mae never tired of hearing about the goin's-on in Grade Four. I told her about our Christmas program and asked her to attend.

"This year's class has its quota of good singers, and, in general, is every bit as loving and helpful as last year's; but they're tired, too exhausted even to be naughty. The coming holidays will look good — to them, at least. They did so enjoy fashioning Christmas stars in 3-D, dowsing them in glitter, and climbing up onto the table to tie them onto the Reading Tree!"

"Yes, the poor little tykes must be tired — Oh, Eleanor, I'll never forget them in that wonderful Memorial Day pageant! My friend often speaks of it, too! — such singing! — and those proud little boy flag-bearers wearing those shiny ribbons across their breasts and those sweet-faced little girls in their long party dresses carrying the garland of red, white and blue flowers on their shoulders down through the big center aisle of the auditorium! If every teacher made patriotism live for their children as ye do, Eleanor, there'd be better citizens coming out of our schools today!

"I just don't know what I'd do if it weren't for those youngsters in Milton High School! When they come into the cafeteria they always ask for Ralph, and how I'm getting along. They're the best morale-builders I've found anywhere, and they keep me from feeling old!"

Lesson in Rejuvenation: *Looking for the Fountain of Youth?*

Any happy classroom will splash it all over you, if teacher keeps the water refreshing enough!

> (Each little fourth grader volunteered as many qualities that make for a good American as he could dream up, and we added them to the board list for a whole week. Gold letters were cut during art class and pasted onto white satin (for girls) and red satin (for boys) ribbons to be worn from shoulder to opposite hip. Language lessons found us defining, and applying these qualities to present-day situations, to be used as part of the pageant dialogue. *The Garden of Memory* had a cute youngster visiting it in a dream sequence, meeting such noble characters as LOYALTY, DEVOTION, VALOR, BROTHERHOOD, TOLERANCE, HONOR, OBEDIENCE, FAITH, LOVE, REVERENCE, SACRIFICE, DUTY, INTEGRITY et al. Most patriotic songs were sung in three parts.)

* * * * * *

Even the weather worsened as dark December inched forward, and Gilbert and I put out food for our growing cordon of ravenous two- and four-footed hunters, both at dawn and again at dusk. "Oh, if only I could be feeding *you,* dearest son!" I mourned. Hope was growing fainter now — Perhaps I had been rowing the life boat too long. I began to question whether I'd recognize the rescue ship even if I saw it!

> (Survivors of war disasters at sea have demonstrated superhuman endurance in rowing their life boats right up to the very moment a vessel is sighted. Only then does their strength abandon them, rendering them powerless to make the final haul to safety. One Christian survivor tells of this sudden dwindling of strength in the very face of rescue — and while powerless to move himself, he felt *"strong unseen Hands cover his own, grasp the oars, and row him straight to the hull of the great warship!"*)

* * * * * *

Gilbert, at my suggestion, had left at 4:00 a.m. to ride back to Holly Farm Cottage in the truck with Bill and get a day's change of scene. It was too early for Bill to stay on through Christmas and, although both were reluctant to leave me, Gilbert insisted he'd take the 6:00 p.m. bus right back and return home about midnight (Was he afraid my Godey Girl Ghost would make a return visit?)

My tireless twin brothers had left me a house not only firred and festooned, but completely dirt-free and filled with all the party fixin's they'd collected for me from local bakeries and groceries—to which they'd added their own ideas of what kids should eat at a Christmas party, i.e., candy canes for the tree and individual boxes of ribbon candy. I was ordered not to meet Gilbert's returning bus or train, but to "hit the sack as soon as I got the last kid out the door."

And tonight was the party! Tonight! I had borne up nobly during Bill's brief stay, probably due to watching both of them transform the place into a Yuletide story-book. Even the dozen or so big dolls I had standing around the ancient melodeon in the upstairs hallway were holding little lights now. I'd already dressed them in the pastel angel costumes—pinned down to size—and placed on eighteen smiling heads, the sparkling halos from Grade Four's Christmas program. Children and parents alike always hovered over this doll collection, which, as I stated, I sometimes transported to classrooms, complete with tiny instruments of the orchestra.

The withdrawal of Bill's truck down the driveway was akin to the rescue ship leaving the scene. And as it was with Mae when she put her hand on her living room lamp, my strength was winking out. I had been rowing too long—and an empty sea stretched before me.

Dejectedly, like a rerun of Mae's own description of herself, I sat at the kitchen table in my dressing gown, feeling like a lost spirit in a deserted cemetery. Oh, I was dead all right, and the huge piles of oven-fresh bread, for all their delicious aroma, rose like miniature tombstones on the table before me, as if to mark my oncoming demise!

Platters of home-cooked chicken and assorted cold cuts lost all interest for me, especially the big plastic bag of lettuce, whose very crispness seemed to rebuke my own wilted state. The melted butter was ready to assemble all this into the man-sized sandwiches Room 12 drooled to, but there were only two lifeless hands to apply it. (My pupils always appeared in spanking new party attire, so I couldn't ask their assistance, much as they'd adore wallowing in all this edible unpreparedness!)

It was dark now. A gentle snow had been falling all afternoon, awaiting the touch of my new plowman (down with the flu!) Neighborhood shovelers were busy with their own customers, believing, no doubt, that my regular "snow-remover" would soon be on the job.

In exactly one hour and twenty minutes, twenty-eight bustling, bubbling, hungry refugees from Beebe Beehive—avec parents—

would be ascending the snowy slopes of an unshoveled driveway to discover an "undressed" hostess confronting an unprepared feast.

Despite my rugged determination to keep on keeping on, I must face facts at long last:

More torture to already lacerated, pounded, bruised, sick, kicked, starved, pummelled and pain-wracked bodies, à la Madame's "gettings," clearly spelled one objective — MURDER! Yes, Steve must be dead by now — Mae, poor soul, was right — even her cat knew it! Well, in that case, to heck with this whole silly show!

I would push myself over to the door, lock it, put out the lights, hang out an emergency sign of some sort, then, like Mae, just sit down at the kitchen table here and "cry 'til I die!"

First, with my sobs, I'd soak every one of these blasted bread tombstones rearing up at me; I'd drown every platter of meat in tears, ("just add water to make its own gravy" — ha!) — let loose the flood that had been building steadily up to bursting point during these eleven months (of hell!)

Then, when "No-Apology-Never" purred up in his pretty Navy limousine to break the bad news, he'd have to *wade* to the front door!

My depressed state brought equally depressing phrases hurtling down into the silence as my head dropped onto the only bare spot left on the holly-berry tablecloth:

"See yon Mother bowed in anguish, behold her, so woeful and forlorn for the Lord hath dealt bitterly with her. Oh Lord, My God, why hast Thou forsaken me? It is finish-ed, finish-ed, finish-ed!"

Dubois' *Seven Last Words* I had sung so often in Lenten season was hardly befitting this one, but it "befit" me.

The sad phrases continued washing through my brain — "And it was about the sixth hour. And the sun was darkened — And darkness covered the earth — "

With sluggish indifference I pushed up my head and regarded the wall clock with the little elfman laughing at me as he sprawled on its wooden roof. "Sixth hour"? Yes, that's when my guests were due. Fifteen minutes to five now — who cared? My whole body throbbed with fatigue, and my swollen eyelids burned with desire to spring the gushers that promised to drown the past. What a stupid goon I had been to pay out the last of my power to endeavors not directly concerned with Steve. And for that I was "finish-ed," "finish-ed," "finish-ed!"

I arose with great effort, turned around to the pine cupboard behind me and placed my hand on a fresh box of facial tissues, the initial step to total inundation — just as the door chime sounded!

Oh, wouldn't you know some little rascal would want to be "first!" Over an hour "first!"

Well, I'd send him straight back down the driveway. How had he gotten up, anyway? The snow must be quite deep by this time, and it always drifted higher. No, better still, I'd send him back down to greet everyone and tell them there'd be no —

I held back the tears long enough to slide back the steel bar on the porch door, but in so doing, through its glass panels I was greeted by a most astonishing sight, a sight which forced my "broken" heart to start clunking again.

A round-faced Oriental stood outside, his gaze intently upon me. Now the almond eyes were crinkling into a warm smile, (much more genuine than that on the face of Kuan Yin).

"Peter! Peter Tai!" I cried in disbelief as I threw wide the storm door onto the snowy porch. "Come in! Come in! You, my dear lad, after — how many years is it — seven? Well, Peter, you are an answer to a prayer! You really are!"

"I am?" he grinned, obviously both surprised and flattered by my demonstrative welcome.

Automatically I shook out his coat and storm hood and hung them in the guest closet which took up the entire west wall of the party room.

"Golly, Mrs. Harris, I haven't seen much of you since I was in your sixth grade at Beebe," he beamed. "I'm a sophomore at Northeastern University now — Say, you know, Mrs. Harris, it's a funny thing, your saying that to me—"

"Saying what, Peter?" I was feverishly removing the frozen fresh fruit ring and punch syrup from the refrigerator, for now that rescue was present in human form, I had miraculously returned to life —

"Why, about my being 'an answer to a prayer'—uh—oh—Wow! What's going on here? Looks like a big celebration!" And he whistled softly as his eyes traveled over the glittering party table with Christmas streamers criss-crossing in back of a two-foot Santa, whose white fur mittens clasped the ladle of the crystal punch bowl.

"Well, let's just say we *hope* there'll be a celebration — and that's where you come in, Peter, my angel! My fourth graders and parents are due at six!"

Peter needed no further explanation: "Just give me an apron," he smiled serenely as he sniffed and fingered the balsam boughs entwined above the window frames.

Peter would know exactly what to do with those "tombstones"

on the kitchen table, for it was his father and mother who owned and operated the Golden Gate Restaurant down on Foster Street. Peter had spent a good part of his young life in its kitchen.

"Why yes, Mrs. Harris. I was just walking along Main Street, minding my own business," he chattered on, returning to the kitchen after washing up,—"when Something said to me, 'Why don't you go up and make a call on Mrs. Harris?'"

"Honestly, I thought it was a good idea. After all, the other kids are always coming up here, and I knew you'd have the place all decked out for Christmas — as you do for every other season, I hear — and — uh, say, — why don't you go and get ready? Just tell me again what time you expect the kids, and I'll be all set for them. I can find everything I need in the drawers here, don't worry. You can leave that punch stuff here on the counter and I'll put that together for you, too. Have you got plenty of ice?"

Peter, while he was talking, had already buttered half the first "tombstone" for the sandwiches. He worked with a lightning speed which proved contagious, for I found myself speeding upstairs, although for a different reason. The flood was threatening to brim over again, but this time from pure joy and relief. *"For by grace you have been saved through faith; and this is not of your own doing, it is the Gift of God."*

Was this newness of life I felt seeping through me due solely to God's answering my need so graphically? For in spite of my desire to "feel some reciprocal warmth," my need *had* been met! ("Commit thy way unto the Lord and put thy trust in Him, and He shall bring it to pass.")

Was there a second reason for my revival, as well? Something happening thousands of miles away beyond a Yellow Sea?

> (Yes. The torture abruptly ended. Prisoners, although still quivering with pain, allowed themselves to believe something was afoot. Gashes were mysteriously bandaged, swollen, beaten faces covered with hot wax to cover the scars, bruises soothed in egg poultices. Even the vile food began to taste better, and was served in greater quantity.)

I felt the crushing weight of eleven months being lifted from my shoulders by some invisible Force, rendering me a fresh lucidity for the first time. Was tender-hearted Mae, likewise, being treated to this metamorphosis?

I was suddenly glad I had taken the time to have Carlo contrive a pretty upswing for my hair, even if traces of childhood curls slipped out and clung to the nape of my neck. Having showered earlier, and put on some makeup, it took only minutes to freshen up, step into my deep-red velvet gown and matching satin pumps, add the twinkling gold corsage Bob's sister had sent me, as well as clip on the dangling gold Christmas-tree-ornament earrings guaranteed to fascinate fourth graders. I held the pink, cut crystal container over Carlo's creation, drenching it in the flowery stuff, then moved swiftly into the music room to light the candles in their crystal sconces.

The big bell on the front porch (not the door chimes) suddenly clanged into my endeavors. This was used only to summon Gilbert up from "down under" the cliffs or from "up under" the front terraces. Only children swung it to announce their arrival. Oh, why must there always be an early bird!

Peter came to the foot of the staircase: "Mrs. Harris, there are three boys here who want to see you." Then he lowered his voice. "They're too big for your fourth grade. They said you'd know who they were, and they want to know if they can shovel the driveway."

Shovel the driveway! Oh brother — could they! Peter's dramatic appearance had completely erased from my memory this necessary phase of preparations.

I hung up my robe, tossed my scuffs into the closet, closed the louvered doors and clicked downstairs. Peter met me with approving eyes.

There was still a three-quarters of an hour leeway. Three conscientious workers should be able to hew out a navigable footpath in that time. Parents had already been requested to park at street level, so no one should run down the shovelers. Floodlights and post lanterns told me it had stopped snowing, and the lights of Boston were already winking out of their white shrouds. For once Miss N. E. Winter (or was it Funstorming Fate?) was being considerate.

I walked in on a red-cheeked, mittened trio standing wide-eyed around the party table, obviously relieved to get in out of the cold.

"Boys, I'm so glad you — "

"Hi, Mrs. Harris!" they broke in cheerily. "Remember us? You know, the three kids that snuck into the dress shop in Malden last summer to hear about the *Pueblo*? Huh?"

"Why, of course I do — now that I get a good look at you! You're the boys who asked for my autograph. How wonderful to see you again!" Their grins were enormous.

"Gee, but it takes a long time to find this place," the tiny one said. "We were gonna climb your mountain, but it was too icy — (his eyes fell on the Christmas gown) — is that there one a' the dresses you bought?"

"Well — "

"Yeah, that's why we're so wicked late. We been all afternoon gettin' here," his heavier chum added, not waiting for me to answer what he obviously considered a silly question. His eyes roamed over the food. "This guy (meaning Peter) says you're havin' a big bash here tonight—so maybe we better be moseyin'!"

There was no time to lose, not even time to thank God for this second miracle. *Would there be a third ——— by Christmas?*

"Listen, boys," I broke in quickly, "how would you like to earn some money, then stay on and have supper with the party youngsters? They're only fourth graders, but — " (A foolish question, indeed!)[6]

I explained the emergency briefly and told each one to take a shovel of some sort from the garage and get busy on the driveway. I snatched six buttered slices from the first tombstone, slapped three fat slabs of roast beef between them and pushed the munching trio out the door.

In half an hour flat they were back in the warm family room phoning their parents for permission to remain, with a promise of a ride home from their hostess. I talked briefly with each mother, having no trouble obtaining their permission after identifying myself, although I did find it difficult to retreat graciously from lengthy discourses on the *Pueblo*. I hung up and turned to the partyroom.

I lifted the glorious red, white and blue floral centerpiece, a gift from Grade Four parents and my principal, from the cool floor of the west wall closet and set it on the party table amid wows and oohs. When I finished lighting the upstairs tapers and switched on tree and window-bower twinklers, the Christmas stage would be set. How glad I was that I had managed to finish sewing the new gold overdrapes for the music room as I watched the mantlepiece candelabra turn them into gleaming columns of fire, the tree glowing like a white goddess.

About all I had to do now besides turning on the electric coffee urn, for which Peter's lackeys had filled three sets of sugars and creamers, one for upstairs, was to remove Florence Cheney's three trayloads of picturesque (parental) sandwiches from the cold oven (only storage space left). Florence, a former teacher and dear friend, who made her fabulous sandwiches only for a select few, had sent them by taxi to accommodate me, bless her!

---

[6]Just as Madame Doolittle had predicted, these three had "come into my life again"— and welcome, indeed, they always will be!

Ruthie Johnson's regal, four-tiered holiday cake with candy cane crown, jelly bean frosting swatches, and rows of tiny red candles to be lighted later, hid a Swedish fruit cake that invariably kept guests hovering round it! Besides this, my neighbor Phyllis had brought over her own spiraling glass compote, an artistic triumph replete with ring upon ring of butterscotch bars, apricot squares, brownies, walnut crunchies, and heaven knows what-all — but all heavenly! She was expecting dinner guests but had stopped in at noon long enough to rave over everything, if only to give my morale a boost. I hoped I would live long enough to reciprocate for all this generosity!

Peter's crusty tombstones, now lying flat on large trays, had gradually changed their height and shape to form lettuce and meat-filled gardens, whose encircling frames of crisp lettuce and watercress transformed the entire kitchen table.

Ruths Hoyt and Odegard, respectively, had left tins of spritz and decorated star, Santa, and tree cookies on my school desk alongside three dozen cupcakes from Beverly Stewart's mother, Dora, an ardent *Pueblo* sympathizer. These now graced the sideboard beside a basket of fresh fruit, in the form of a cookie-cupcake tree, under and around which nestled twin brothers' boxes of ribbon candy, plus nuts and assorted cheeses and crackers. I had added my own specialty of three massive whipped cream cakes I had frozen days earlier, now topped with fresh strawberries. Surely no one should leave the premises undernourished!—The big gong was clanging again—

Everyone arrived almost simultaneously and in jouncy Holiday spirits! The partyroom closet and bedrooms were heaped with coats.

Parents ate first, while angelic hosts overhead provided dinner music to organ accompaniment in the form of repeat selections from their Christmas program. The order was then reversed and parents carried their coffee aloft, Peter's young apprentices seeing to it that the larger sandwiches and the cookie-tree replaced their daintier counterparts on the party table, and that the punch bowl was refilled. There was always cake galore left from the first shift, anyway.

Eventually all guests, regardless of size and appetite, ascended for the grand finale, a carol-sing with organ and piano combo, the children sitting on the floor, the parents in chairs or on stairs, while upcoming fragrances from the freshly-filled coffee maker vied with balsam incense for popular acclaim.

Yes, Party II measured up in full to Party I, joy-wise. How could it fail to do so with God's own Hand joining those of good friends, in mutual compassion? If any starving "guests" from the far away prison drifted in to gaze down at the lavish table this time, I did not see them.

* * * * * *

Several mothers offered to remain and help me clean up, but since the evening was yet young, I refused their kindness. Two fathers offered to drive Peter and his three helpers home. I paid the three boys, but Peter refused remuneration: "I'm the answer to a prayer, remember?" the warm, brown eyes smiled.

It was still only 10:30 p.m. when the last dish was put into the washer. I covered the party-table leftovers carefully and swept the crumbs from table and floor, turning off the heating zone completely. The room made a perfect refrigerator in winter, providing well-preserved snacks for later college visitors, former pupils returning home for the holidays. Goodies for Gilbert had already been set aside.

All under control at last, I went again to the clean kitchen table and sat down, lowering Carlo's pretty hairdo onto my arm. How different I felt this time! A strange new peace was enfolding me — for the Spirit of Christmas was indeed here with me in the quiet room. It had come in with Peter Tai and remained to smile on into my heart — "not a spirit of fear, but of power, and of love, and of a sound mind."[7]

I went upstairs to apprise Mae of the eventful evening, as I had promised her I would do. I could hardly wait to tell her that I, too, had been pulled from the Brink of Despair by the divine Ruler of Our Destinies.

"Eleanor! Eleanor!" Oh, I almost forgot to tell ye!" Mae broke in, after I had told my story. "I nearly called ye right in the midst of ye're party—but—"

"What, Mae, what?" I cried at the sudden lift in her voice—I hadn't even turned on the eleven p.m. news—

"Oh, I know it's true that God has stepped in at this dark hour to help us, for 'Not that we are sufficient of ourselves to think anything as of ourselves, *but our sufficiency* is of God'."[8] "Still I knew ye'd want to hear about 'Sister'! Eleanor, that old tiger cat jumped right out of that sweater of Ralph's yesterday morning and gobbled up two plates of Calo, she did! Then drank a pint of milk, I swear! She

[7]II Timothy 1:7
[8]II Corinthians 3:5

hasn't returned to that sweater since. She even ran over and gave her pal, 'Kitty', a friendly swipe or two with her paw, she did!"

I lay back under the flowering canopy, feeling almost a kindly willingness to start counting again those blasted—I'd make sure whether it is 203 or 204 blossoms—someday!

My eyes drifted out to the hallway where reposed a less taxing vista, the lighted portrait of the Madonna and Holy Babe. It was not one of the more celebrated works of art, but truly a lovely one. The faces were sweet and natural, the colors muted and pleasing. Each Christmas I "framed" it with small branches of Brother Bill's greens, entwined with Della Robbia fruits and the usual tiny sparklers. The illuminated faces brought to mind another countenance,—no, not Steve's, but that (and the words) of sweet Peter: "I was just walking along Main Street minding my own business, when *Something* said to me—!"

As I closed my eyes in devout gratitude, the weariness flowed like a silent river from out my body,—yet I was too spent to go to my knees: "Thou who hast been our refuge from one generation to another," I prayed, "I do thank both Thee and the Holy Family that watches over this house — for Thy divine intercession into the tribulations of this night — for this 'happy issue out of my affliction.' Amen."

* * * * * *

"Heaviness may endure for a night, but joy cometh in the morning." The little ivory and gold clock on my dressing table stood at 3:00 a.m. when the call came. I must have dozed off at that, for it startled me — yes, I hadn't even undressed — was Gilbert home?

A happy voice burst into my drowsy ears —

"Richard Bordeaux here! Eleanor, remember my telling you that some sweet day Uncle Sam would pick up your tab for a free flight to the West Coast? Well, start packing. YOUR SON WILL BE RELEASED AT NINE O'CLOCK TOMORROW MORNING!"

Act IX

MOTHER BIRDS TAKE FLIGHT

"Fear not; for I am with thee. I will bring thy seed from the East, and gather thee from the West." (Isaiah)

Signed by the Soul of a Nation
  So Nice to Meet you — Again!
    A City Opens its Heart
      Good Night, Red Teddy Bear

One hundred miles south of the bleak North Korean prison a verbal exchange was taking place at Panmunjom, which promised to elevate the status of eleven starving, brain-harrowing, pain-ridden, disease-rotting months to one of unprecedented hope,—that is, if the young Navy men dared to believe their captors this time — dared to believe the devilish tantalizers whose aim had always been to keep them in a state of anxious bewilderment, or physical anguish.

"Yay, yay! Your son-a-bitchee imperialist country maybe only be 'provocating'[1] on apology, again?—huh? So maybe won't come during Johnson administartion at all, maybe during Nixon administration,— huh?" (They seemed assured of the latter's Presidential victory.)

Nevertheless, the feverish attempts by their keepers to patch the bruised and lacerated faces of their Hell Week victims seemed to point to something definite this time.

Hot paraffin, raw eggs, steaming pads, and salves to lighten blackened eye sockets, swellings and lumps over bashed bones seemed to be the order of the day. Unfortunately, wounds hidden by the clothing of sufferers were ignored, regardless of their severity, as well as those too deep for human skill to heal. (One crewman committed suicide later on.)

Even the most hardened of the crew were praying for release now: "Home, dear God! Home for Christmas!

("We couldn't have lasted another week!")

---

[1]Did they mean "postponing," "prevaricating," "stalling," "equivocating," or maybe just plain "provoking"? Anyway, they were provoked.

When they could bear to mention it at all, i.e., the cruel mauling of the week past, they admitted they had prayed constantly during the seven days of round-the-clock terror.

> (The terrible beatings of "Hell Week" were administered in repayment for unpardonable loss of face by North Korea, occasioned by the publishing of a photograph in a National Magazine of some crewmen making derogatory finger gestures as a desperate means of conveying their predicament to the outside world. While Steve and Ralph were not among these men, they were punished along with the offenders. The gesture-makers fared worst of all. Mme. Doolittle had "gotten" the message straight, as usual.)

Miraculously, crewmens' prayers were answered, for the torture ended as abruptly as it had begun. Not only had the beatings stopped, the agonizing hours of shouted interrogations and searing invective were cut off just as suddenly. An eerie silence hung over the corridors. There was no moaning, no screaming anywhere now.

(Something else had ended just as abruptly back home in fair Melrose, leaving its own brand of silence, i.e., the high-pitched singing sound on my telephone! Ruddy Redpaws had padded off the wires at long last!)

At supper in the North Korean prison the surprises continued. Instead of slimy stew, crewmen reached hungrily for "stenchless" fish, bread, cabbage salad, and chopped pork.

A *Pueblo* corpsman, though suffering himself from a week of mauling, was summarily ordered to work alongside Korean nurses and doctors in patching up the remainder of the "wounded."

The six officers of the doomed ship were called together, at which time their smirking incarcerators explained this about-face by saying that the prisoners presently appeared to be "sincere" in their repentence and could, therefore, be "forgiven".

> "Sincere" was an overworked word by Korean interpreters. If some of the men in their quiz sessions wandered (hilariously at times) from the true paths of communism in their replies, they were not being "sincere." Steve once sat in a chair which suddenly broke to pieces. In order to maintain his "sincerity", he sat on the floor amidst the kindling, his knees still pushing into his chin, and with a perfectly straight face kept right on with his monologue. (The other fellows were cracking up.)

At the truce table at Panmunjom, "Kook" (North Korea's Pak Chung Kuk, known to captives as "Frogface") and a United States general were nearing accord on one of the most unique agreements in American military history.

Negotiations had culminated with Major General Gilbert H. Woodward (who succeeded Rear Admiral John Victor Smith) reading a strange message into the ears of North Korean and American witnesses (and eventually into the ears of the entire Free World.)

"The U. S. S. Pueblo was not engaged in illegal activity — We could not apologize for actions which we did not believe took place — "

"The document which I am about to sign *was prepared by the North Koreans and is at variance with the above position,* but my signature will not and cannot alter the facts."

"I will sign the document to free the crew and only to free the crew."

The document was dated the 23rd of December, the Monday just two days before Christmas!

Conditions set forth by North Korean formulators were a sheer pretense of moral victory over a powerful nation. Undoubtedly, as every American suspected, the paper would be divested of the General's preconditions for signing, and delivered in its original form to propaganda-impregnated vassals of the tiny Red Regime. The statement read in part:

> The Government of the United States of America, acknowledging the validity of the confessions of the crew of the *U. S. S. Pueblo* — shoulders full responsibility and solemnly apologizes for the grave acts of espionage committed by the United States ship against the Democratic People's Republic of Korea.

(Any American reading such a gross lie would be certain to know that a Ruddy Paw held the pen that composed it.)

In contrast to the grasping claw (Paw?) of communism, General Woodward's firm hand, as he bent to sign the historic statement, held within it the hearts of millions of youth-loving Americans, whose prayer-backed hopes for the return of the seafarers to their homeland was an internationally acclaimed victory over death.

With the same stroke of the pen, General Woodward scattered the "lost faces" of their barbaric keepers over the entire Free World.

(Whatever had become of that "Keep Out of the Sea of Japan or else" condition?—the one that had me and Mr. Rusk so uptight last August?)

Oh well — no matter now — I had merrier things to think about at the moment!

The "moment" was Monday afternoon, December twenty-third — 5:20 p.m. to be exact, when two deliriously happy passengers were a whole twenty minutes late for take-off on TWA's scheduled flight to Los Angeles from Boston's Logan Airport. But who really noticed? — the delay, I mean. A tiny *Pueblo* parent was the cause of it.—

Mrs. Stella Grant, mother of John Grant, Communications Technician, and his sister, from Gray, Maine, had found Portland Airport fogbound and canceling all plane departures. Maine's good governor, therefore, sent the *Pueblo* mother and daughter by his own limousine, with motorcycle escort, howling down the Maine Turnpike to Boston's Logan Airport. It was Mrs. Grant's first flight, following undoubtedly, her most exciting auto race!

Our own wild and well-photographed leave-taking at the airport being over, and finding ourselves at long last safely airborne, Mae and I unfastened our seat belts and pressed the buttons that angled the soft seats into reclining position for two weary, word-spent heads. Ah, how sweet the solitude of the heavens!

Above the drone of the big bird's engines, we welcomed the healing attributes of verbal silence.

The voice of Captain George Morehouse brought us "back to earth" with what, I must admit, was a very pleasant bump:

"We are especially happy to welcome aboard three mothers of returning men of the *U. S. S. Pueblo:* Mrs. Robert Harris, Mrs. Ralph McClintock, and Mrs. John Grant. We congratulate them and rejoice with them upon the release of their sons, and hope they will enjoy their flight with us to the West Coast."

If our respective mouths dropped open at the announcement, they were soon to be filled, for two spritely stewardesses stepped forward, young eyes smiling with the pleasure of their errand, and handed each of us a goblet containing a sparkling champagne cocktail. (The Grants had been directed to a different compartment.)

The atmosphere turned sparkling, too, for the eyes of the plane's passengers instantly turned and smiled toward us as we thanked our pretty servers. A group of six men seated along the aisle opposite "awoke" with sudden interest. Were these the Naval Security guardians my CACO mentioned would be flying with us to California?

Mae hesitated for just a second, looking at me quizzically over her champagne. Oh, I knew what she was thinking: "Eleanor doesn't drink!"

Without a qualm, and since my heart was already in my eyes, it

Rear View of Ledgewinds at Cliff's Edge

"California, here I come!" Leaving Ledgewinds for San Diego.
(Photo by Roy Hult)

was easy to smile my way into hers as I raised my glass to her own, and said softly:

"To our sons, dearest Mae!"

"To our sons, Eleanor dear!" returned the warm voice of my wonderful friend. We put the goblets to our lips—

One reason Mae and I had been blissfully unaware of the delay in take-off was because of our struggle to get all our carry-on luggage and countless gifts to our sons stashed away. My own consisted of a book on Street Railway History, a hobby of Steve's, from his Uncle Gilbert, hi-fi recordings from neighbors, a homemade holiday cake from Ruthie Johnson, Christmas cookies from Aunts Eula and Ida, nuts and candy from Florence Cheney and other easy-to-carry items too numerous to mention.

Ralph's gifts fell into the same category. We had filled completely the deep receptacle above us as well as spaces beneath the seats, babbling all the while like a couple of kids waiting up for Santa, still marveling at the speed with which friends had gotten these packages into our hands. We'd hardly had time to read the morning headlines covering our own sons' San Diego Homecoming, not to mention that other world-shaking event, the Apollo 8 Moonflight.

"Just imagine, a flight to the moon! Eleanor, can you keep up with all that's happening these days? I can't!"

"Lesson in Dynamics: *Our modern science is rolling along so fast now-a-days, we're overtaking the crystal ball!*"

"Oh my!" cried my most generous critic, "those little lessons ye're always coming out with, Eleanor, they should go in that book ye're going to write about all this that's been happening to us, all these amazing — "

"That'll be the day, Mae!" I put her off jokingly. She was forever talking about the day I'd write that book!

With the final bubbles of the cocktails warming our waistlines, we were content simply to sit with our heads back and have another go at the blissful business of gloating over our new-found freedom. But, as usual, the luxury was short lived.

Passengers, noting the empty goblets, began drifting over to us singly and in groups to shake our hands and tell us of their relief and pleasure at the outcome of our ordeal. Many told of personal pleas they had written to Naval heads on our sons' behalf. Several said they recognized us when we boarded the plane, but did not wish to disturb us until we got settled.

"You know, Mae," I commented as the last greeter returned to his seat, "there's just one person I'd like to be dragging along to Miramar Airforce Base tomorrow morning when we meet Ralph and Steve and all those returning crewmen!"

"And who might that be?" Mae asked lightly.

"That lying ESP crackpot, that cheap heartbreaker on that radio talk program who told you the men would never leave North Korea alive—that blasted, blubber-mouthed blowbrain, *'Doctor' Hellion P.* (for Poo-Poo-to-you) *Hairstander, that's who!*"

* * * * * *

Blue Boston Harbor had long since melted down into the distance, and we were out of sight of everything except a cloudbank below us as we nosed steadily to the other side of the continent. Although Mae and I had traveled abroad, we had never been all the way across our own land, and were looking forward to seeing fabled California.

"Isn't this serenity unbelievable, Mae? No reporters!" I broke in after we had both dozed, or pretended to for a few moments, and I'd felt my companion stirring. "As you put it, 'aggravation is all behind us now' — yes, no reporters, until San Diego, I suppose, then it will begin all — "

One of the men across the aisle caught my eye, smiled and handed a note to me.

I gently nudged Mae who was nodding back to Sleepsville.

"Mrs. McClintock," the note read, "I am Chick Connery of the Boston Globe. I have been assigned to cover your story on the West Coast. We six seated opposite you and Mrs. Harris are all reporters from Boston papers."

* * * * * *

"Eleanor!" Mae suddenly laughed to bridge the long silence, after we'd slept awhile, "did y'ever receive so many kisses in all ye're born days as we got there at that airport? And the way everyone moved in and stared and smiled at us! They knew who we were all right, because they all looked so happy for us. And didn't our Navy advisors look elegant! I loved the way they brought along so many of their friends in uniform! I felt like the Annapolis Queen," Mae laughed— "I suppose the Milton High youngsters and ye're fourth graders were all watching our departure! Remember that cameraman telling ye to throw some kisses 'like Marilyn Monroe' when ye were on the plane stairway? We'll have to check the papers for our pictures when we get back."

Mae's using the word "check" made me re-examine my purse for the generous one I had been saving to give Steve for a Christmas present. Mae was doing the same for Ralph. All the time I was scrimping for it, I trusted it would be God's will that I'd have a son to give it to.

There would be much for Steve and Ralph to spend it for; for by this time crewmen's personal belongings were unquestionably riding upon the backs, wrists, fingers, or in the pockets of gloating North Koreans, (that is, if not displayed on the decks of their latest "Floating Atrocity Museum," the *U. S. S. Pueblo* — Captured Imperial "Spy" Ship of those Warmongering Capitalists!)

> (There were other personal belongings aboard their ship the returning sailors must have wondered about, like for instance, where would those *Playboy Magazine* centerfolds end up they had had hanging in their quarters? Blindfolded captives on the fantail of their doomed vessel could hear Korean soldiers suddenly scream with laughter as they entered their decorated spaces. In time would such "art" framed in bamboo, perchance, hang over the royal couch of their genius-commander, peerless-patriot, omnipotent-ruler, iron-willed, ever-victorious Premier, Kim Il Sung?)

Was I, subconsciously, granting again the request on a Christmas card Steve had sent his dad and me his freshman year at Harvard? It showed a scrawny Santa dragging an empty bag behind him. The face of the card read: "Don't bother about any Christmas presents for me this year." Inside it said: "Just send money!"

* * * * * *

With the assistance of Navy guides, we changed planes at Los Angeles and boarded another for the final lap of the flight.

"It will seem strange not to have anyone we know meeting us in San Diego; so what do you say, Mae, let's live it up and take a taxi directly to the El Cortez Hotel, regardless of the distance from the airport."

"It's funny, Eleanor — I was just thinking the same thing. At least they'll be expecting us at the hotel." Mae's voice sounded wistful.

Being strangers in a big city thousands of miles from home with the prospect of badly damaged "Christmas presents" being flown directly into our arms was not one smothered in champagne and roses.

Zero Hour was programmed for 10:50 the following morning, the stage being set at Miramar Naval Air Station, a few miles out of San Diego. The same night would be Christmas Eve! Was it the Hand of God that had turned the international clock back and provided that crucial extra day for *Pueblo's* returnees?

In a matter of minutes we felt San Diego rolling under our wheels.

The choicest factor about Mae's company, regardless of the window-dressing-for-anxious-hearts aspect of our conversation, was that it had moved both flights with alacrity.

Lesson for a Long Trip: *The voice of a friend cuts the journey in half.*

"There must be someone important on our plane, Eleanor," Mae observed, leaning down across the pile of gifts on the seat to get a first window-glimpse of San Diego. "There are two official looking men standing down there at the foot of the ramp. One is in uniform. They're the only ones they've allowed outside the waiting room. Let's just take our time and see who it is they're watching for."

"We may have picked up Governor Reagan in Los Angeles," I replied, brushing *Afternoon Roses* on my lips and adding a drop or two of the flowery stuff. "They say he'll be at Miramar to meet the men, some senators, too, I hear — "

Out of curiosity I bent down beside Mae and took a cursory glance at the situation. My heart leaped. Sir Richard the Ocean-Hearted had done it again! (I hoped.)

"Mae!" I said, sotto voce, in order not to attract the attention of our newsguard stirring across the aisle. "Mae, you're simply not going to believe this, but those 'official-looking' men down there are the same two darlings who met my plane in Washington when I went to interview Mr. Rusk last summer! The selfsame two charmers!"

Mae's eyes bugged out and she emitted a soulful "Oh, my dear!" as I gave her arm an affectionate whack. (She was familiar with every detail of my D. C. kidnapping.)

I felt a sweet warmth as I recalled a certain chauffer-driven Navy limousine at the Washington airport — but there was no time for car-dreaming now. I pulled the flower-splashed Puerto Rican basket from the seat, the same one an obliging young reporter had carried into the house for me a hundred years ago. As I turned toward the aisle, I ran my hand over the flattering fur cuffs of my new coat. Butterfly's wings were not completely damaged by the ordeal —

"Of course, my friend, the joke will be on us if our two greeters down there are waiting for Governor Reagan or some other VIP," I cautioned, "but — oh well, maybe we can bum a ride from 'em!"

How satisfying it was to watch the six writers across the way scurrying to leave. Except for an occasional across-the-aisle grin they had remained disturbingly mute — but we both knew better than to regard this as anything more than a temporary news-out.

Mae couldn't resist a final window-appraisal.

"Oh my dear, just as ye told me last summer — they're two grand looking gentlemen, so friendly appearing!"

"And as your little gift book puts it, Mae, 'Friendship is the wine of life', so come on, let's get going and drink up — this seems to be our day for boozin!' "

We started for the exit with our camel's load. I pushed Mae ahead of me into the jammed aisle.

"Incidentally, the older gentleman out there isn't married," I said to the back of her new cranberry wool coat, "but don't go getting grabby, Mae. You already have that Chick Connery sending you notes!"

Mae swung a box around at my middle, and I poked her back with my basket—We wore our joy on our lips—

"Yes, as my ole Concord buddy (Henry David Thoreau) once put it: 'Nothing makes the earth seem so spacious as to have friends at a distance! They make the latitudes and the longitudes.' Which one out there do you prefer, Mae, 'Latitude' or 'Longitude'?" (The young man in uniform was Long-er than Mr. Security.)

There was no time for further jousting, for this intellectual exchange was interrupted by cordial goodbyes and multiple wishes for a happy reunion with our sons, a reaching out of friendly hands to shake hands that were already full, but we managed.

It seemed it was now Mae's turn to push me ahead of her, and after receiving the good wishes of our stewardesses, I stepped from the exit out into the warm southern sun. Two pairs of eyes below were immediately upon me.

Whether or not the Navy Security officers were awaiting us, or more illustrious passengers, made no difference at the moment. For old time's sake I decided they deserved my most charismatic smile, so I beamed it to them. The returning grins, waves and jet-powered move nearer the end of the ramp told me they were not planning to ignore us, at any rate.

As my new cocoa pumps touched San Diego concrete, the older man stepped toward me with a somewhat less formal greeting than the one at National Airport. Apparently unable to speak for the depth of emotion he felt at the liberation of his Navy brethren, he simply opened wide his arms, gathered me up, basket and all, and kissed me full on my carefully brushed-on mouth!

The younger man wrung my hand and exclaimed, "Mrs. Harris!

Isn't this simply wonderful! The whole of San Diego has gone crazy, just like the rest of the country, I suppose. You'll see what I mean!"

I presented a round-eyed Mae to the two, and after retrieving our luggage, we evaporated into that nice big, black, why-not-paint-'em-navy-Navy, chauffeur-driven limousine I was so recently dreaming about.

Funwheeling Fate had certainly been consistent about rolling into the script a big black limousine as a prop in all my major theatricals being staged in this "Something Big on the Agenda" year, from Father Mulhill's frightening vehicle right on up to this latest act of automation.

Riding the hills of San Diego, my mind's eye was slowly opening upon an extraordinary possibility: Could it be that Ole Boogey, that "Cool" Comedian who had entered my little classroom almost a year ago and followed me home, the same entity that had sat in the gold chair, and later stood by my side to receive the phone call "heard 'round the world" – had been rehearsing me all these months, and I'd finally gotten the scene perfected!??

* * * * * *

That evening in our handsome double room with its high balcony overlooking the blue swimming pool patio, Mae opened her San Diego Guide Book, endeavoring to educate my subconscious before sleep caught up with it. But I absorbed only part of it, for I kept thinking about tomorrow: ("Tomorrow, Tomorrow, How Happy We Will Be!", the old popular song Bob and I used to dance to at the Kappa Sigma Fraternity House in Cambridge, kept waltzing through my mind.) Meanwhile Mae's lilting voice read on:

" 'San Diego is the base of the United States First Fleet and a training ground for ships prior to overseas deployment. The Eleventh Naval District Headquarters, Naval Station, Naval Training Center and Commanders of Naval Air Force, Pacific, Amphibious Force, Pacific, Cruiser-Destroyer Force, Pacific and many other commands and installations are located here.' "

(Dearest Bob, if only you could be here with me now to meet our son—or are you watching all this from "out there" somewhere? I mustn't forget to write a thank you letter tonight—I'd brought my notebook along—to my Heavenly Father for bringing this all about!)

"That's all just dandy, Mae. There's a great marine museum located down on the waterfront I'd like to see, and this superb and most generous city, as you might have surmised, is noted for its art, music and scientific centers, I know," I replied, sliding off the bed to remove my pink cloud.

"But, I've had enough sightseeing for one day, haven't you? Why not withhold all the jazz about the U. S. Navy for a while, good as they were to bring us here. Turn to the part about the Balboa Park Zoo; we're both such goons about animals! (I hoped Gilbert was remembering to feed my "denizens," and that he'd eat something besides ice cream while I was away.)

"Yes, let's just skip the U. S. Navy tonight, Kiddo. After our sea-going strife of the past year, wouldn't you rather be kissed to sleep by a nice quiet baboon instead of some bloated admiral?"

As always, my captive audience responded gleefully. "Eleanor, I've heard there's a bear in that zoo that snaps to attention on his hind legs every time the zoo bus comes by with a load of sightseers. The driver tosses a chunk of bread down over the moat, and up jumps Mr. Bear, grabs it, and gives a natty salute, he does! They say this goes on all day! I wonder if it tells about that here?" She began flipping pages with new interest.—

"Well, all's I can say, Kiddo, is that he must be a *Red Bear* if he grabs the bread and gives only a salute in return."[2]

—And soon I was dreaming the very dreamiest dream of all this night-marish year,—'though wide awake—*of meeting Steve!*

---

[2]Today, the U.S.S.R. owes us over 800 million dollars—and no payday in sight! (See what I mean?)

MIRACLE AT MIRAMAR

Those "Wonderful People" of San Diego
  Crickets in the Blue
    A Flag-Draped Dream Comes True
      Sons-in-Arms!
        Merry Christmas?

While *Pueblo* families were flown to San Diego at Uncle Sam's expense, it was the great-hearted citizens of the beautiful port city who made it possible for all of us to be sheltered and fed completely free of charge, not only for the scheduled one week, but for two, at one of its finest hotels, the El Cortez, standing on the brow of one of the city's loftiest hills.

The San Diego Chamber of Commerce—to which both Mae and I later composed letters of appreciation—headed the fund-raising, aided by the local radio station.

Indeed, government leaders, labor officials, business executives and residents of the city responded so generously to the drive to raise $20,000 that $40,000 was the actual amount received! Even the swank El Cortez Hotel cut its rates sharply as its share of the gift.

Attractive signs of welcome to returning *Pueblo* sailors, and their relatives, greeted us at every turn in the handsomely appointed public rooms and hallways of the hostelry.

My craving for panoramic views should be satiated here, that is, if I could stop thinking about dear Steve long enough to look out from its outdoor balconies, ride up the glass elevator on the outer wall of the hotel, or cross the moving glass bridge that arched over the boulevard from the hotel itself to the building across the street.

The posh, red-carpeted ballroom on the first floor of the hotel had been converted into a toy-filled playroom for *Pueblo* youngsters — incidentally the most well-behaved covey of cuties I've ever "put up" with. There were big toys, too, like rocking horses and tricycles. Nicest of all, this immense nursery-kindergarden-primary-geared recreation center was staffed with Red Cross Aides, serving cheerfully as almost round-the-clock attendants.

239

A temporary reception and information center was set up for us adults on the second floor of the hotel, overlooking a palm-framed blue swimming pool down on the luxury patio.

Besides attractive guidebooks and other helpful literature covering our sojourn, all *Pueblo* relatives were issued plasticized identification badges with a big "P" centered on them, which we were requested to wear at all times.

"I'm trying to figure out whether this "P" stands for Pass, *Pueblo,* Prisoner, or 'Praise God from Whom all Blessings Flow'," Mae remarked when she pinned it on her cranberry coat.

Even Rear Admiral Horace D. Warden, commanding officer of the Balboa Naval Hospital, where the men were to be detained for medical examination and debriefings, had forwarded a letter to welcome us. He posted my own reply to it over his desk in the "Pink Palace's" administration office, "for my entire hospital staff to enjoy," he told me later.

"See? Everyone loves your letters, Eleanor! That's why ye should write our story!" Mae threw at me then.

"Mae, as old Tom Carlyle once remarked: 'All that mankind has done, thought, gained or been, it is (already) lying as in magic preservation in the pages of books!' So why sweat it?"

"Well, *our* story hasn't been 'preserved', and *ye're* the one to preserve it," Mae declared stoutly.

" 'Can' it, you mean, Mae!"

Off-duty firemen and other city workers, housewives, and "wonderful" San Diegoans in general, at a reserved section of the main lobby under Red Cross sponsorship, dropped by in droves every day, ready at any hour to use their own cars and gasoline for sightseeing trips for *Pueblo* guests after the homecoming excitement had abated and the men were hospitalized.

* * * * * *

The morning after our arrival, at approximately 10:00 a.m. on December 24th, on a Monday that was to make history, Mae and I, wearing our Plasticized "P" cards, arrived at Miramar Naval Air Station via one of the many chartered buses carrying *Pueblo* relatives from the hotel.

Once again we found our Navy watchdogs smiling into our eyes. They'd simply materialized out of nowhere just as we stepped down from the bus at the airfield to join the milling crowd of elated sky-watchers.

The younger officer ("Longitude"), after a few words with his boss as to where we would close ranks later on, walked on ahead with Mae.

"There are a few people connected with your son's mission I'm sure you'd like to meet, and vice-versa," my own good shepherd, "Latitude" suggested pleasantly, having already complimented me on my "refreshing" appearance and the exotic behavior of the weather. (This being the case, why blow the scene by describing the rotten night I'd just twisted through? Huge ventilators outside on the hotel roof had sounded to me exactly like planes arriving *all night* from North Korea!)

Lesson in Looks: *Joyful anticipation is a gal's best beauty bath.*

Neither would I disenchant my Navy nannie by revealing that I'd gleefully wring the necks of any and all "connected with Steve's mission" who'd sent him on his way to a death-dealing prison! With my emotions so close to the surface, I could see it was going to be a real go-go struggle to keep Ole Tomboy on the mat today. Yes, today would require all the ham and histrionics I possessed to emulate my angel mother!

Because there remained nearly three-quarters of an hour before Mae and I would find ourselves "on the ropes" over there (put up to restrain relatives from rushing en masse to catch their Hearts' Desires dropping down out of the blue?), I thanked my security officer for his consideration and put my cocoa pumps on the stone steps leading to the broad verandah of the main building facing the rows of seats in back of the ropes.

Although I caught a heightening of interest when I was introduced to "brass" both in and out of uniform as "the mother of *Pueblo's* Research Operations Officer in charge of the ship's Intelligence Detachment," I was too preoccupied at this frenetic hour with speculation on the well-being of "my two favorite things" to remember any more than a jumble of titles, names, ranks and Navy offices which I knew I'd never be able to sort out and match up once I'd vacated the VIP-laden verandah.

I regretted that my state of recall was in such drowsy disarray, since my escort had informed me that several of these handshakers had dropped by (down?) from loftiest echelons of Naval Security. I knew my returning Researcher would appreciate knowing which of his bosses I'd talked with. At this point, unfortunately, I couldn't even remember when I'd slept last.

My one grave disappointment on this day of days lay in my failure to bring along to the airfield a deserving son's most cherished Christmas gift, have it all stunningly wrapped and here at my side to present to him the moment he stepped down from his homecoming plane. That big check? No, that little bride, Vuokko, the *Flower of his life!*

Directly following Mae's Bedtime Bear Story, a telegram had arrived at the hotel, elevating my spirits. My daughter-in-law wired she was coming; however, her plane would arrive about the same time as Steve's and at a different airport.

Dear God, how close these two had come to bringing to fruition my most terrifying fear: that neither of the young people would live to see the other!

A scraping sound on the mounted P. A. system brought the milling airfielders to a sudden halt. Mae and I thrust aside our half-finished punch and sandwiches, being partaken of more to please our hosts than our appetites, our rendezvous having been a goodie-heaped Red Cross table manned by comely young girls. (We didn't encounter a plain one in all of San Diego!)

"Commander Bucher and his crew are now eight miles away and will be arriving shortly," a vibrant male voice called out. Even the announcer had the Sound of Music in his lungs this globe-shaking morning! Mae and I reacted as if we'd just been injected with some sort of explosive serum.

Our hosts guided us to the ropes immediately, mine sufficiently "moved" by the announcement to "move in" with another of those mouth-to-mouth reassurances. (This not unwelcome form of "reassurance" was becoming a habit. What would Gilbert say to this? "Just doing what he's paid to do"? More likely, "the guy must be crazy!")

And soon Mae and I were left to the intimacies of greeting our long-lost lambs.

"When you see Ralph, just forget I'm here, Mae dear. We can all meet back at the RX Club later." She begged me to do the same when I saw Steve.

The first speck over the horizon enlarged to become the aircraft carrying California's Governor Reagan, Senator Margaret Chase Smith, and other prize passengers I failed to identify, for my companion-in-adversity and I had chosen to stand well down the ropes away from the VIP Center[1] to our left, a huge wooden platform erected for the occasion. Shining down upon it from a cloudless sky, the California sun brought to life its appalling array of tripods, cameras and other

---

[1]For which reason we appeared in none of the widely publicized reunion newsphotos.

"Lieutenant Harris walks with his mother, shortly after the crew's arrival home, afternoon of Christmas Eve."   *(Official U.S. Navy Photo)*

What a difference a few weeks make!

audio-visual paraphernalia, their metal bases and braces bristling like miniature derricks in a Texas oilfield.

We'd had our fill of all this publicity jazz, thank you, and for obvious reasons assumed that the first of the giant Star Lifters winging its way from Midway Island since before sunrise, would be flying the ship's captain and put down directly abreast of this mechanical forest.

Why we were positive it was the *second* plane that would be carrying our sons I cannot say, unless our clairvoyant Mme. Doolittle (hopefully *not* that pretentious knave, "Dr." Hokum Poo-Poo Hairstander) was having an extended influence over our thinking.

After what seemed an eternity of skysearching, a tiny black speck appeared — hands pointed — then another speck a short distance behind it. Hands pointed again. Now, as the two specks became clearer, a deep-throated cheer rose to meet them — rose all the way to meet them, a cadence so profound that a fellow sufferer could hear within its timbre, a million hurting heartbeats, a thousand soft-shed tears, a hundred pleading prayers of lonely wives and fatherless children, the back-home victims of a faraway Holocaust of Hate!

As for the eighty-two priority passengers up there riding their celestial chariots, how much smoother this airborne passage must seem to them after their storm-tossed voyage of nearly a year before! Intrigue and duplicity, haranguing and hate, and all those miles and miles of printed words were all behind them now,—or so I believed. These cruelly used chessmen, or what was left of them after the international tournament, were almost home!

Even the children standing along the ropes who had hitherto been abnormally passive, warmed to the idea it was quite all right now to start being happy again, to become "wicked normal" kids again.

Meanwhile the two specks above us had swelled in size until —

Suddenly, as if on cue, Mae and I, our emotions brimming to the bursting point at this upcoming culmination of our long vigil, turned and threw ourselves into each other's arms, hugging and hugging with all the joyous strength we could manage. Mae's ailing arm, the one she broke "in *Pueblo's* wake," seemed to be doing its thing just perfectly now.

As if our enthusiasm were contagious, a great epidemic of this same hugging, along with hopping, leaping, jumping, back-pummeling, accompanied by the squealing and whooping of children, broke out all along the ropes.

"Lonely wives" held their little ones up to the promising skies,—

while others hurriedly called their children about them, pointing up-ward intermittently.

The older generation, mothers and fathers of crewmen, on the other hand, stood quietly by, many holding handkerchiefs to their faces.

As for Mae and me, we seemed out of character with our support-ing cast. We simply stood there, bone dry to all appearances,—on our own private little pink cloud—with lace!

"Well now, will ye just look at us, Eleanor?" Mae boomed heartily. "Everyone else our age around here bawling their eyes out, and here we stand, you and I, as happy as, as happy as —

"As a couple of mosquitoes at a nudist picnic!" I finished for her.

Mae gave me an affectionate jab. Soon she was pointing upward again.

"Eleanor, when ye write our book, be sure ye say that those two little 'mosquitoes' up there are the finest sight I ever put my eyes on! Ye write that!"

"Forget the book! 'Know something,' Kiddo? Those 'two little mosquitoes' up there look exactly like crickets to me, a couple of sweet, resurrected little luck-luggin' *crickets!*"

—"And not a bucket nor a snowbank to be seen," Mae cackled back happily.

The specks above us were fast taking shape now, bird shapes like those of the sparrow hawks over my cliffs in spring, not darting about playing love's oldest game like they, perhaps, but winging down to me the same ephemeral delight.

As the Star Lifters swelled in girth, something in my throat swelled with them.

"Mae," I began urgently, my voice calmer than I felt, "remember, we must not cry, no matter how badly they look when they step out of that plane,—we must not cry!"

Was I really warning myself? Or just being cognizant of the tell-tale effect our tears would have on our returnees?

Mae could only squeeze my arm in affirmation, so tense was her scrutiny of the approaching "mosquitoes."

Camera and TV crews had long since hopped up to their tripods and audio-visual entanglements on the busy VIP platform, while the swarm of dependents, and Navy brass in their scrambled-egg hats, had thickened just below this technical tangle of wires and wizards.

My heart warmed to the realization that Rose Bucher and teenaged sons, Mike and Mark, would be among the throng. How overjoyed I was for this family and to know we would soon be meeting them and

Pueblo's commander at the RX Club luncheon this very noon,—if the men were able to make it. But what about the parents of Duane Hodges? Would they come all the way from Oregon to "greet" a dead son? Mae and I both wondered about this, and mourned for them.

Bandsmen in impeccable Navy dress, their rows of white hats and freshly polished instruments gleaming in the morning sun, now snapped to attention and launched into "California, Here We Come!" or, if it wasn't that song, it should have been. My memory is hazy here.

But I'm positive of the second tune, for as the first great bird swelled to enormous size, hovering overhead like a giant eagle, these same musical heart-warmers went steaming into—yes, they did!— *"The Lonely Bull!"*, the *U.S.S. Pueblo's* very own theme song, (Herb Alpert's, also), the song that was playing aboard the lost ship when it sailed out of the Japanese port of Yokosuka eleven horrid months ago. I hoped the band would keep on playing it 'til every returning sailor heard it. (They all did!)

> (The man responsible for this thoughtfulness, "the most considerate man I ever met," (Cmdr. Bucher) was Admiral Edwin H. Rosenberg, a soft-spoken gentleman, who greeted the pain-ridden, hungry sailors on their return, at the Seoul evacuation hospital (at Anscom, South Korea.) He telephoned ahead to the Miramar Airfield Reception Committee to have the song played just as the men were arriving on the airfield.
>
> Crewmen later told of the outstanding kindness of this sensitive, distinguished man as he moved from bed to bed on their first stop homeward. One of the most seriously beaten of the prisoners he personally helped into bed, tucked him in and kissed him.
>
> "You are a hero among heroes," he told Commander Bucher.
>
> Every mother would agree to that! A pity some Navy brass (later on) couldn't see it that way—blinded by "tradition", perhaps?)

Just as Mae and I predicted, the first of the Star Lifters put down precisely on the block in front of the mechanical forest and VIPs.

My heart was doing its utmost to burst the gold buttons clean off the ivory silk suit beneath my new coat, for the second plane was now rolling to rest in its designated block, about 200 feet forward and to the right of us.

To add to our tenseness, both planes remained closed and appeared almost windowless.

My heart pounded on. Beside me, Mae stood as "congealed" as I.

No sound, save the strains of the band, was issuing from anywhere at this juncture, not even from the sea of faces along the ropes. The children, likewise, had ceased their hopping and swaying and were staring straight ahead.

Which plane would give them Daddy?

Mae's hand on my arm tightened so perceptibly, I tore my eyes away from this second plane just long enough to perceive a taut expression of — what was it, incredulity? — stiffening the soft contours of my companion's motherly features. Was it my imagination, or was she also turning pale?

"Eleanor! Eleanor!" she cried in a strained, high-pitched voice, the same voice I heard over the telephone when I first called her in Milton. "This is what I kept seeing all winter long. Watch the belly of that first, no, that *second* plane, watch it now! Ye'll see what I — "

Happily enough, this was not the moment to watch the second plane at all, but the *first,* and its door, at that, for it opened slowly at the exact moment a group of Navy VIP's started moving toward it from the ropes.

Out of the first plane now stepped a hollow-cheeked, wan, but handsome man wearing what looked like a brand new Navy hat with gold braid.

(Again the work of that "wonderful person", Admiral Edwin M. Rosenberg.

Commander Bucher had been using a borrowed hat from a chaplain who accompanied the men to the South Korean evacuation hospital at Anscom. Admiral Rosenberg wired ahead measurements for a new one, and at the next stop on their home-coming flight, when the ship's captain talked with Adm. John J. Hyland, Commander in Chief of the Pacific Fleet at Midway Island (at 2:00 a.m.), where the plane stopped for refueling, Adm. Hyland presented Bucher with the new hat. The captain was as moved as his crew at the compassion of Adm. Rosenberg, who, incidentally, had paid the bill out of his own pocket.

This same benefactor later forfeited Christmas Day with his family to look after crewmen in San Diego.)

After shaking hands with his greeters, the ship's captain limped gamely forward, hurrying as best he was able to get to his little family.

The concrete sea of faces in the open air theatre immediately erupted into a tide of thunderous cheers as the leading man of the globe-shaking drama, at long last, made his frail bow at this world premiere!

As he approached the ropes, beneath the new Navy hat I discerned the same "clean white smile" I had commented upon one golden October morning a hundred years ago.

To be sure, the smile I admired in the photograph in the *Pueblo Colorado Star Journal* had radiated from a rounder, ruddier face than this one, but the hero of *Pueblo's* forlorn travesty at this moment, for all his lost poundage, issued forth as personable and appealing as ever!

How robust and well nourished his greeters looked in contrast to the willowy frame they were meeting now, particularly Vice Admiral Allen M. Shinn, Commander of Naval Air Force Pacific Fleet, a "bear of a man", whose great paw completely covered the thin hand of the commander.

Mae and I are in absolute agreement, to this day, that the most rave-rated love scene of any movie—those decent types we used to view—was as nothing, compared to the real-life tenderness unfolding before a totally enthralled audience at this moment. For once, I'm certain, a couple of fans on third balcony wished they had staked out nearer the stage.

Mae and I, nonetheless, were able to see our Oscar-winner put out his arms, even before he reached his leading lady, the Rose of his Heart's Garden, spreading them wide enough to encompass his entire threesome in one loving sweep!

After a few moments of tearful hugging, the Commander's two sons stepped aside, and he took his beloved alone into these same eager arms, smothering both her tears and the fragile white orchid quivering on her pretty wool suit in a hungry, longing embrace.

A tear-dewed face, as lovely as the orchid she was wearing, lifted to the commander's lips, and I prayed there were cameramen present expert enough in their art to catch the tender pathos of this meeting. If so, it would wring the hearts of millions of Americans whether viewing it at home, here at Miramar, or seeing it in news-photos all over the world. So much for the First Act—

When would that "second plane" over there ever open?

Mae's hand, for the second time, caught my arm in a viselike grip, and oddly enough it was the first communication we'd had, so moved were we by the scene just enacted.

Silence descended once more over the entire assemblage. There was no movement along the ropes now. Even the band had ceased sending out its morale-mustering melodies. It was an eerie moment —

It reminded me of a certain January morning eleven months ago when a strange, arresting, though entirely invisible "entity" seeped in to call on a little classroom of warm fourth graders, refrigerating their teacher, at least, during its visitation. (My twenty-eight news hawks would all be watching this now, too, bless 'em.)

I felt the same netherworld coldness enveloping me now, and although the California sun was shining briskly upon me, I looked down to see the soft mink cuffs on my new cocoa coat flattening as if a stiff breeze were blowing—but I had other things vying for my attention; for at this point Mae's fingers were trying to put bruises clear through these same sleeves onto my arm—

"Eleanor! Watch the belly of that second plane!" she demanded again, as if the opening scene had been but an engrossing interruption to her agitation.

"Oh, I saw all this last winter, I did — over and over. The side of that plane will open very slowly. Six or eight sailors will march out to the plane from the ropes down there at the platform, and ye'll see that flag-draped casket I kept telling ye about taken out of the opening, placed on the shoulders of the sailors and carried over there." (Mae pointed to the right of us.)

"Then, my dear," she continued breathlessly, "they"ll play the Navy Hymn and taps — ye'll see I'm right — ye will, ye will! Oh, it was all so plain to me. Ye see, Eleanor, all the time I thought it must be poor Ralph!"

"But it wasn't Mae, dear! It wasn't your Ralph — and almost any moment now you're going to see him *alive,* walking into your arms!" I hurried on, praying my distraught friend would not break into tears.

"Just keep your mind on that, Mae, dear Ralph walking into your arms, alive!"

The *Presence* was hovering close now. I was, in fact, shivering. Mae's face was still pale, and, like everyone else, neither of us was paying much attention to what might be going on over at the VIP Centre.

But we soon found out, for the next act was a sad one; and as we stood there arm in arm, our eyes on the airfield theatre, we watched Mae's strange vision come to life. Yes, in the next few minutes, everything went off precisely "according to Mae."

Duane Hodges, the youngster who was killed, was "coming home", as well.

The plane's side did open, the casket was placed on the shoulders of six sailors, and the solemn cortege at this very moment was passing in front of us, beyond the ropes, to a place of honor to our right, to the tune of the Navy Hymn!

> "Eternal Father, strong to save, whose arm doth
>   bind the restless wave —
> Who bid'st the mighty ocean deep, its own
>   appointed limits keep —
> *O hear us when we cry to Thee — for those in*
>   *peril on the sea!"*

There was a long silence after the last notes of the famous hymn faded away.

There were some things I must attend to: First things first: "Get lost!" I mentally commanded the awesome "Thing" breathing down my neck. What in the name of sanity was it trying to tell me this time? Had something happened to Steve?

"Beat it — scram!" I demanded silently a second time, vaguely wondering if I were addressing some long-lost aunt, uncle, cousin, or even grandmother in spirit form. I'd gladly "pretend it" into being some deceased mortal enemy if that would rid me of it any sooner, only I couldn't remember having had a mortal enemy, least of all one I recalled having said a final farewell to. This was simply not the time for haunting. It could just go thumb, bum, or will its way back to Spiritsville, Cloud 9, Hades, or wherever; it could even go back and sit in the gold chair in the family room and wait there for me, if it would only get off my back!

Still shivering, I glanced behind me out of curiosity, to ascertain what effect the sad procession had had on other relatives,— and in so doing, I caught a glimpse of a familiar face watching mine. It was that of Mr. X, my blue guardian angel. He smiled radiantly and saluted, as if to say "Don't worry about Old Boogey, Sweetheart, I'm right here standing watch!"

(What eventually became of Ole Boogey, I really can't say—for events were too overwhelming from this point on to accord him (it?) a suitable niche in *Pueblo* history. It's very possible he "got my message", or simply erased himself to carry out some haunting assignment elsewhere. Who really knows?)

Mae and I closed ranks now, steadying ourselves against the tightly drawn ropes for the Grande Finale!

The glorious red carpets sailors had rolled out when the planes first arrived, leading from their exits straight to the ropes of waiting loved ones, were soon to be filled, for the moment of truth was at hand![2] Kim Il Sung's dark mountain was opening at last!

The doors of the two massive jet transports opened almost simultaneously, and two long blue lines of repatriated prisoners began their second historic walk to freedom.[3]

Endeavoring to watch both lines at once with one's heart in one's eyes, although a labor of love, was not an easy one, for at the distance all thin faces and figures looked much alike. Each man emerged carrying a white cloth bag with drawstrings, garbed in a blue Polaris submarine jump suit with blue cap (resembling a baseball cap), whose visor partially screened his youthful features.

There were some distinguishing factors, which, unfortunately, became more and more distressingly evident, as at perfectly-spaced intervals crewmen approached within close range: Some limped, some sagged a little, some had black bruises or wore face patches; some arms didn't swing quite naturally; but all walked or hobbled briskly,— and every young face, however tightly drawn the skin over its cheekbones, wore the "neatest" homecoming grin you could possibly imagine!

I shaded my eyes from the sun, for my long battle with anemia had weakened them, straining them blind to bring each approaching face into focus.

Under which visor was the one dear face I loved? At this moment, however, I loved them all!

Only the tenseness of the occasion kept me alert, for high anticipation and insomnia were taking their toll.

"Dear God, keep me conscious!" I prayed.

Mae's voice broke into my perusal: "Eleanor! Eleanor! Quick, look over there!" She was pointing to our left. "Oh, God bless that boy! Look at him, Eleanor, he's kissing the ground!"

Sure enough, one youngster had sidestepped the red carpet, dropped to his knees, spread wide his arms, flattened his hands against the ground, and now his blue-visored cap was going down to allow his lips to touch the breast of the country he loved.

---

[2]As long as I live I shall remember with deepest gratitude and affection this U. S. Navy's heartwarming, typically American tribute of welcome, *i.e.,* Rolling out the Red Carpet! God bless those planners!

[3]Over the *Bridge of No Return* from their dark prison was the first.

A strange panic lay hold of me as I heard the murmuring in back of the ropes rise to a joyous pitch as young men began falling into the arms of loved ones. I turned for a second, feeling dizzy from such tight concentration, to see tearful little circles of arms clustered about each blue cap.

What if Steve had gotten by me? Would I lose him again, perhaps forever? Had he walked by me unrecognized? He was the next to the last to cross the Korean bridge, so, perhaps being an officer —

The men came on and on. Even Mae was lost to me now; she'd moved down the ropes, perhaps. Had she spotted her Ralph?

My heart was leaping so violently it actually hurt me to breathe— Or was this cruel pounding I felt, the hoofs of Emblematic Chollima hurtling over my breast for the last time? — his flying feet bidding me a painful farewell as he made his headlong dash down the Half-Peninsula of Hate?

The men on my left had reached the ropes first, so I found myself facing them for the moment.

A shadow was moving up on my right, but I gave it only a cursory glance and turned back to my figure-watching, for it surely wasn't Steve. This son I was looking for was more robust in build, more broad-beamed, rounder-faced, stood straighter —

The shadow, nonetheless, seemed to be addressing me: "Mother — Mother, don't you know me?" it was saying incredulously, with a nervous little laugh.

My heart burst clean out of my "eyes" at the sound of the beloved voice. That, at least, I recognized as I whirled in the direction of it —

"Steve! Stevo, my Darling!" I cried, running the few steps down the rope between us. "You're home, home, home!" and I threw my arms up onto the tall, emaciated figure leaning across the rope toward me.

I felt a strange new wetness on my cheeks as I stood on tiptoe, clinging to him with all my strength, kissing the hollow cheek again and again!

How easily my arms encircled the thin shoulders I could scarcely encompass before.

"Well," he laughed softly, slowly lifting his own damp cheek from mine, "let's get on one side of this thing or the other."

Despite its dampness, the broad smile completely illuminated the wan face which still had a tiny spot of color on each cheek.

I let him go long enough to allow him to bend beneath the rope between us, wondering at the slowness with which he accomplished the simple task.

Quickly replacing my arms about the dear frame, I heard him asking over my shoulder, "Where's Esther?" (Vuokko)

"Oh, she'll be here, Stevo! She'll be arriving in San Diego just about this very moment." I started to look up my arm at the wrist-watch my housebreakers had robbed me of.

My words tumbled out in strange contrast to the inert manner in which this new son of mine spoke. I felt a hurrying compulsion to comfort him, to put the mind behind the pale, drawn face at ease. I tried to sound cheerful:

"Stevo, the sight of you is all she needs!" (The sight of you? God prepare her for the hurt of it!)

"Yes, Mother," he replied calmly, lifting his head above my persistent arms to look about him at this land, these people he had been away from so long. "We'd been told you were having a flu epidemic here and not to be alarmed if all our relatives didn't show up to meet us." He talked as if it were an effort to speak. "They'll probably inoculate us — we'll be hospitalized for awhile. By the way, Ma, you look great!" he finished in happier tones as the pain-dulled eyes looked down at me.

(He was calling me "Ma!" There was hope for his recovery!)

It was with profound relief that I realized Steve had lost none of his characteristic calmness and logic in the face of disappointment, keen disappointment such as this, although I couldn't help wondering, as I looked up at this spectre that had been returned to me in exchange for the stalwart "warrior" I had unwittingly willed to North Korea, how much he was able to feel of anything. His arms hung like lead on my body.

I studied his face as he looked about him.

Dear God in Heaven, what had those fiends done to him to make him look like this? Why, he must have lost seventy pounds![4] And why did he breathe with his mouth hanging open that way — through those oddly-puffed lips? Was it because his cheeks had sunken so deeply they made his mouth appear unnaturally large?

And his eyes! What hideous "treatment" had they inflicted upon him to rob those once-glorious "blueberry eyes" of their deep-sea coloring, leaving only this glazed pair of slate-gray? I could hardly bear to watch them grope their lustreless way over the airfield crowd.

The dark swatches beneath them looked as if they had been painted on, reminiscent of certain chocolate cookies that had gone the rounds of my classroom on a memorable January 24th!

---

[4]Fifty, to be exact.

What clever artisan had made up the face of my pleasant son for this macabre role? (I felt the blackness stealing over me again.)

"Uh, Mother," the gaunt one was saying, "I wonder if you could manage not to lean quite so hard against me — uh, my legs — malnutrition y'know — they're going to put me in a wheelchair — I — "

"Oh, Stevo! How selfish of me!" I dropped my arms quickly. Steve in a wheelchair? I felt a wave of nausea — I must get him onto the hospital bus as quickly as possible. To heck with the VIP speeches now going on over there in front of the oil derricks. Few people were paying much attention to them anyway!

"Mother, who was that woman I saw standing beside you at the ropes when I got off the plane?" the quiet voice asked. "And, by the way, did you hear them playing *This is My Country?*" he interrupted himself. "I remember you used to teach that to your junior high kids."

"I certainly did hear it, Stevo! You know what a flag-waver your mother is!" I started to steer him toward the bus, intending on the way to tell him who the wonderful friend was standing beside me at the ropes.

"That wasn't Ralph McClintock's mother, by any chance, was it?" he resumed, as if reading my mind. "He's one of my men, you know. I wonder where he — ?"

Steve turned slowly — like an old man, I thought, opening wide his poor milky eyes above the thin neck to stare back down the ropes for his mislaid technician.

If we didn't both get to the bus soon, I felt the Naval hospital would have an extra patient. Only the joy of feeling Steve's arm, warm against my own, kept me going. That and the lilting brogue of Mae McClintock coming from somewhere in the crowd to the right of us.

"Eleanor!" I heard the familiar voice calling (and shall always remember the mountain of pride she put into the next two words.) "Here's Ralph!"

Out she came from obscurity in her pretty cranberry coat, her arm leading a tall, white-faced lad in blue, whose eyes glinted pleasantly back of his glasses. I could see at once why Mae wanted to share her find.

"Hello, Mrs. Harris," "her Ralph" greeted me cordially, as if he'd known me for a lifetime. He walked toward me slowly, almost painfully.

"Well, hello, dear Ralph McClintock!" I cried joyfully, throwing my arms up and around Mae's only lamb, almost breaking my neck to reach the pale young cheek to give it a resounding kiss — for he was even taller than Steve.

"I hope you don't mind my hugging you like this, Ralph," I smiled into the friendly eyes, "but I feel as if I know you after gazing at your picture for eleven months!"

He looked down at me as if he didn't mind anyone's hugging him on this day of days, not one little bit —

"I've been looking at yours, too," he smiled, "the one you sent Mr. Harris at Easter. They took it away, though."

There was no need to introduce Mae to Steve, for while I was hugging Ralph, she was likewise greeting Steve, undoubtedly charming him out of his homecoming mind with that loving brogue of hers.

"Yes," Steve was saying, "we wore out that page from your letter with the 91st Psalm on it, Mrs. McClintock. You'll never know how much that meant to us. How it ever got past the guards is still a mystery!"

Except for Ralph's paleness and a slight receding of the dark hairline, he looked exactly like the photo beside Steve's on my dressing table, although I noticed he spoke and moved with the same deliberation as Steve. Mae had found one answer:

"Ralph's legs are hurting him so, I must get him onto the bus, Eleanor. Are Steve's legs bothering him? Ralph can't feel much in his arms," he says. Her words had a familiar ring.

We headed immediately for the buses, each of us guiding, by his lifeless arm, our precious freight, the Yuletide presents two newsmaking mosquitoes (crickets?) had dropped down to us from heaven.

It was only moments later we were delayed in our journey by the sound of taps issuing from the "place of honor to our right." We listened motionless, each thinking, no doubt, of the dead crewman, but more especially of his parents —

Young Duane Hodges was being guided Home, as well.

"It should have been me, Mother. It should have been me!" Steve whispered brokenly, as the last note rolled away over the airfield. "That shell was meant for me!"

Tears from the glazed eyes slowly coursed down the sunken cheeks — no one moved for a moment.

"God has other plans for you, my son. That is why He spared you,"[5] the Angel Mother within me whispered to him. I pressed the heavy arm against me tenderly.

---

[5]And indeed He did have! Steve speaks all over the country (on weekends) concerning the amazing faith of the *Pueblo* crew. He cannot begin to fill all his engagements. Again, I repeat: *Who says God is dead!?*

In another moment or two we became separated again from Mae and Ralph, for several of the crowd had closed in upon us, some to greet Ralph, some returnees anxious to present Lt. Harris, their detachment commander, to their parents.

I steered Steve away as graciously as I could manage, noting the all-too-familiar signs of stress and malnutrition on the faces of his fellow crewmen. Were their parents suffering inwardly as keenly as I? Several of us exchanged understanding glances. A few fathers simply shook their heads sadly.

"Dear God, don't they look awful!" Mae had whispered just before we lost each other a second time. Under the circumstances, she had borne up nobly.

"Your Ralph is a darling, Mae, a darling!" I comforted her, "and other than his paleness, to me he looks exactly like his photograph — while Steve!"—

"I know, Eleanor dear, I know (what else could Mae say?) Ye can see how much Ralph thinks of 'Mr. Harris!' Your Stephen's a darling, too. Why wouldn't he be, he's your son!" (That's my Mae!)

I started to help Steve onto the nearest of a long line of Navy buses. My mistake — he quickly turned and helped *me* aboard.[6]

"Here, you sit by the window, Stevo. It's you they want to see," I said cheerily as we made our way with others along the aisle to an empty seat.

"Who's 'they'?" he asked.

"You'll see, Old Dear," I replied affectionately, quite innocent of the full significance of my words.

Yes, little did I anticipate the magnitude of the welcoming committee that waited outside the well-guarded airfield — nor its continuation all the way along San Diego's Route 495 leading to the Balboa Naval Hospital!

We could already hear a distant murmuring, the soft beeping of car horns and general commotion up ahead of us. As we turned onto the highway, the murmurings increased in volume and intensity to become a steady roar.

Homemade signs of welcome, the thumbs-up and V signals were bobbing up everywhere amongst the shouting greeters standing three and four deep along both edges of the route.

As our bus moved slowly through them, (I estimated ours was about the third in the long cavalcade), the shouting, waving and tooting continued unabated on both sides of us. If we had to slow down,

---

[6]The memory of this simple act of courtesy by a near-dying son ("We couldn't have held out a week longer, Mother") will move me as long as I live.

happy people tapped upon the windows, threw kisses or called out, "Welcome home! Welcome back, *Pueblo* crew! Hurrah! Welcome, welcome home, sailors!" etc. etc. etc.

"S'funny, I don't know any of these people, but they seem to know us," Steve remarked in that droll way of his.

"Wave to them! You should all wave to them!" I commanded, having noted the apathy with which the quiet ones along the aisle were lifting their hands. Were they too sick to wave?[7] Their parents seemed to be doing most of it for them, and energetically too, I must say. That the men were not too sick to smile was evident, however.

"Mother, we're not heroes," Steve protested mildly. "We're just a bunch of ordinary guys who were in the right place at the wrong time." (An historic declaration if I ever heard one!)

"You are too heroes! Wave!" I commanded again, my uppity-ego waving sufficiently for both of us.

Welcome home! Beep, beep, welcome home, crew of the *Pueblo!* The sounds and signs came on — mile after mile —

One smudgy-faced little urchin eventually caught everyone's eye, even the bus driver's who pointed him out.

In his happy zeal, the little tyke appeared to jump higher than any of the other kids lining the route, his hard, tanned little body clad only in a pair of faded brown shorts. But it is what he was carrying so pridefully in his small fist that brought both joy and tears to the wan faces seated along the aisle. For, from a homemade standard, a crooked, bark-stripped branch of a small sapling, waved an American flag, the first of their country's emblems many of the crewmen had seen on their native soil. (Miramar Airfield flags flew at quite a distance from the landing place of the two jet transports.)

The impact of the sight of this first "home" flag, as well as the little patriot wielding it, had a profound effect upon all bus spectators, particularly upon the quiet ones in blue. Steve's misty eyes grew mistier as we left the little patriot to carry his fervor into the hearts of other returnees in other buses following ours in the long procession.

Slow tears came upon faces all along the aisle, parents and sons alike. An older sailor across from me — at least his hair was gray — was crying into thin, gnarled hands.

"Mother," Steve was saying pointedly, "have you kept the flag flying?"

(Now, have you ever been tempted to indulge that controversial

---

[7]As a matter of fact, many of them were!

cover-up, that curse of good conscience, unjustifiably labeled the "justifiable lie"?)

Well, it's exactly what I indulged in at this moment:

"I certainly have!" old Mother Tiger roared convincingly, if deceitfully. My claws were extended for this wounded cub and let no one reproach me for his protection now!

Uneasily I recalled Gilbert's struggle way back in early January (it *had* to be January!) to remove the badly bent and battered metal flagpole that had yielded so pitifully to those shrieking Wind Boys hosting Miss N. E. Winter's newsmaking blizzard, the below zero one that had almost rocked us off the rocks, leaving such memorable souvenirs as unpolished floors, drowned furniture and bedraggled drapes, not to mention a case of influenza.

Sadly I had folded the big banner and placed it on a back shelf in Steve's bedroom closet. Three weeks later his ship was captured. (I must get another, stouter flagpole up before he returned to Melrose!)

We were encountering more flags along the happy route now, more signs, more cars, larger crowds, louder beeps —

"Ma," Steve was saying, "did you know you're the most celebrated mother in North Korea?"

"Come again, Stevo?" I asked lightly, thinking I had not heard him correctly.

"Your letters, Mother," Steve continued. "You have no idea how much they meant to — "

"Keep waving, Stevo," the ham in me interrupted as the bus turned a corner into fresh greeters. I picked up his hand gaily — it was cold as ice.

"Yes, as I was saying, Mother, — about your letters—"

(My letters again! Blast it, maybe Mae was right. Someday I might find myself writing up a storm.)

"The men liked them, eh? I suppose you had so few from home you passed them around." I remembered Ralph's saying he had seen my Easter photo.

"The *enemy* liked them, Mother!" Steve corrected me, smiling as if in retrospect. "My gloating Communist captors liked them!"

"Ye caaats! Do you mean to tell me those — those *savages* liked my letters? Why, you know as well as I, Stevo, all I did was to let you know how much I loved you, include some Bible — "

"That's just the point, Mother," he broke in, picking every word almost painfully, yet eager to converse. "In Korea the mother-son relationship is a very strong one. Probably aside from the Premier and his own mother, Kang Ban Sock, this relationship is the most sacred they are aware of. The North Koreans worship the Premier's dead mother as if she were the Virgin Mary.

"Of all the letters they perused, and believe me, they studied them all before they handed them over to us, they said yours were the ones which showed a mother's true love for a son. They took every one away from me, the photographs, too. They liked that one of you in the pink (rose, really) dress. Sorry — I can't tell you what they said about that — they refused to believe you were the same age as Kim Il Sung."

The crowds were thinning out now, for we were nearing the hospital grounds.

"Well, Stevo dear," I commented hurriedly, "of all the statements you ever made to me, I must say this one concerning my letters is the most surprising. My frequent references to God, and my Bible quotations must have baffled those godless pirates, didn't they?"

"S'funny thing, Mother, they did keep quizzing us about our beliefs, at that. Yes, I guess you could say they were 'baffled', for they couldn't fail to see how much our religion meant to us. Sometime remind me to tell you about the time my pockets became our Bible — "

A look of pain darkened the circles under his eyes. How much anguish had his pocket Bible cost him?

I was glad we were approaching the base of the hill upon which stood the huge hospital complex. Had it ever opened its Gates of Mercy to a full ship's crew before?

Certainly no pair of eyes could fail to notice the wooden sign standing on the side of the embankment marking the entrance to the great Naval Hospital: MEN, LIKE SHIPS, NEED A HAVEN FOR REPAIR.

"Dear Stevo," I said, looking above the purple shadows into the opaque eyes, "at last you and your shipmates will receive the medical attention you require — oh, I do thank God for that!" (Had I registered my alarm too openly?)

"The Navy will take good care of us, Mother. Don't you worry about that," the quiet voice reassured me. "This hospital is considered the finest of its kind in the world. . .uh, I wonder where Esther is?"

* * * * * *

In another bus, another mother was bravely keeping her tryst with Self-Control as she, too, secretly tallied the ravages of barbaric treatment on the languid body beside her.

It's possible that at the very moment our little sprig of a boy was waving his flag on the crooked stick — or when I was noting the tear-stained faces of the quiet ones in blue along the aisle, that Mae was having an equally moving experience of her own. She sobbed pitifully when she told me about it in our hotel bedroom late that Christmas Eve, an evening reserved for both mourning and rejoicing.

Indeed, Mae said she had to summon every atom of fortitude in her makeup to keep from crying at the time.

From Mae's description, I felt certain it must have occurred when Ralph saw the little boy with his flag —

"Ma," he had pleaded softly, "Ma, please lift this arm over here by the window and wave it for me, will you?"

CURTAIN

"They have suffered enough and further punishment would not be justified."

John H. Chafee, Secretary, U. S. Navy

"We were fully prepared and would have been quite willing to die for our country — We suffered instead.

Before the ordeal I was just one of many Naval Officers. I knew my country needed military men for its system of defense. Now I know what we are defending ourselves against!

I wouldn't wish my experience on anyone, but if the people here could go through what we went through, they'd know what they have in a free country!"

Lt. Cmdr. Stephen Robert Harris

"As far as the U. S. Navy and the nation are concerned, these men acted honorably."

Rear Admiral Edwin M. Rosenberg

Merry Christmas!
  Dis-Court-eous Discourses
    Philippe et Angelique
      Little Red Writing "Hoods"
        Sorry, Wrong Bug!
          "What's This Doing in My Closet?"
            A Touch of Heaven

No Christmas morning reveille was held at the Balboa U. S. Naval Hospital barracks housing the freed captives.

"The guys all woke up smiling, so it can't be North Korea!" sailors told newsmen.

Each man reacted to his first day back home according to his personality and to the extent of damage inflicted upon his person in North Korea. Some men seemed outright bewildered, a few were strong enough to be jubilant, but the majority were pleasantly numb

261

(anemic?). Good food, a warm bed without nightmares and a loving family to meet him each day at the RX Club at lunch and dinner were destined to change each man for the better. Observing this change was one of the most gratifying experiences for Mae, Vuokko and me.

Pueblo sailors had just received a telegram from the families of the Apollo 8 astronauts who had rocketed clear to the moon. Their frail, emotionally taut, but enormously pleased ship's Commander read this to all of us in the great RX Club dining hall following Christmas dinner: *"Your reunion has brought great joy into our hearts this Christmas Day."*

Pueblo's crewmen first thanked these thoughtful families, then telegraphed their reply to the astronauts themselves: *"Although we 82 tried to monopolize the headlines, you three were just too much. We gladly relinquish the limelight."*

Crew of the U. S. S. Pueblo

There were other happy surprises. One had occurred in this same dining room just the noon before while Mae, Ralph and I were awaiting Steve's return to his wheelchair, placed at the head of the table during our first luncheon together.

As Steve himself describes the happy meeting with his beloved in the deserted RX lobby. (He refused to be wheeled to his reunion!)

> "I saw Esther (Vuokko) coming across the lobby. She was pale and thin but her green eyes sparkled. She looked like a dream to me.
>
> We fell into each other's arms. For a moment neither of us could think of anything to say. Words couldn't express our happiness.
>
> When we were able to speak, she explained that her plane had landed at the commercial airport about the same time mine had landed at the Navy field. It was the very best she could manage."

If Vuokko was alarmed at Steve's appearance, she gave no sign as she sat at the left of his wheelchair pushed up to the Christmas dinner table. I was at Steve's right, Ralph at my right, and Mae beyond her son.

Christmas dinner, cafeteria style, had, for openers, a choice of shrimp cocktail, French onion soup, tomato bisque, crackers, celery hearts and a relish plate.

Vuokko selected Steve's food this time and carried it to him to save his standing in line.

At Homecoming Party - April *(Photo courtesy of Boston Herald American)*

"Mother's Mausoleum on the Mountain" was filled, once again,
with live, happy bodies. *(Photo by Frank Amato)*

Entrées included roast young Tom turkey (I hoped my twin brothers were relishing the one I'd stuffed and roasted for them before I left Melrose), also roast prime ribs of beef au jus and even fat rainbow trout, mind you! (After rotten fish and greasy turnips day after day, all this food must have been a heavenly sight.)

Cranberry sauce, sweet and white potatoes, three vegetables and two salads were also offered, lying in great steaming or ice-sprinkled bins in a long passageway off the dining room. Wide-smiling Philippino chefs in white caps and aprons presided over the delicious array, happy to assist in filling the plates of these hungry-eyed men and their families.

Dessert was typically American as well, similar to what I'd left behind for my Homekeepers, "Bill and Bert," to consume: fruit pies, fresh fruit, candies, etc. — only I was positive Gilbert would choose only his beloved ice cream.

Cartons of milk on ice waiting to be poured into nearby tumblers proved popular to those having survived on tepid water; and children dressed in their Christmas best, crowded around the real-life fountains of orangeade and grape juice bubbling from silvery wall dispensers alongside the many Christmas trees adorning the dining hall and foyer. How different to look out these windows on December 25th and see green, growing things, not snow!

As I rose to get Mae another cup of coffee, I stopped on the way to shake hands with those I recognized, among them Ed Murphy, Executive Officer, and his sweet little family.

In passing another table, I merely saluted the Captain, his wife, Rose and sons Mark and Mike, for I did not wish to interrupt their dinner as I had already visited with them the evening before. How contented the little family looked!

I made a particularly heartwarming notation as I wandered among the diners. Most of the real feasting was done with eye and hand. For all its choice viands, this Christmas dinner turned out to be, primarily, a Feast of Love. Eyes looked longingly into eyes; hands held, not always knives and forks, but other hands across the tables. Small children had their dinner in daddy's lap, or stood pressed against his side as they ate.

There were other things besides love and food on the menu:

Senator Margaret Chase Smith (one of the very few who replied to neither of my letters) hobbled up on crutches (arthritis?) to shake Steve's hand, and several Navy VIP's as well as the club chaplain, also welcomed him. Finally, the most desirable dessert one could ask for was brought by a "scrambled eggs" officer to our table: Rear Admiral Edwin H. Rosenberg!

Although I knew nothing of the admiral's personal kindnesses to his rescued charges at the time, his sensitive face, deep brown eyes and "caring" voice impressed me profoundly. I remember turning to Steve as he was leaving us:

"There goes one of God's good men!"[1] I remarked prophetically. Steve nodded and smiled at the recollection of this familiar tag of mine. He then proceeded to review the roster of the Admiral's many good deeds.

For the first time on Christmas Day I watched Steve put a little food into his mouth. I had become so worried over yesterday's constant interruptions by the "brass" at both luncheon and dinner (causing Steve to miss each meal!) that I carried the goodies I had brought by plane from his Home Admiration Society over to his hospital room early on that same evening, i.e., Christmas Eve.

"Esther is way ahead of you, Mother. She had a whole meal sent up to me," he laughed from his wheelchair.

Steve was delighted with the Christmas packages — most of all with the check.

"Mother, this is great, great! And I know how long you must have had to save to do this — uh — I don't think I'll be able to climb the hill to the PX tomorrow (the pain never left his legs and feet). I wanted so much to buy — " (the circles under his eyes darkened even more).

"Forget the presents, Dear! You're all Vuokko and I want for Christmas!"

"It's funny, she said exactly the same thing," he smiled contentedly.

* * * * * *

On Christmas Eve a dozen or more telephones were installed on long tables along the wall of the spacious RX lounge, while the floor opposite them had a long line of divans and easy chairs pushed together.

The men were allowed to call anywhere in the U. S. A. free of charge, and to make as many calls as they wished! This went on and on from about 9:30 into the wee hours.

However badly Navy planners had goofed in sending these men

---

[1] "One of God's good men" was my own expression, one Steve would recognize. My husband used to tease me about it, as I often honored some philanthropist or do-gooder, past or present, with the phrase. "And am I one of God's good men, Dollie?" he once asked me with an angelic expression on his face. "No-o, not yet, Sweetheart," I replied. "But you do have one distinction. You're one of the Devil's *very best!*"

on a "minimal risk" mission, they were certainly doing everything in their power to try to make amends for their tragic error.

Parents and wives sat and watched this joyful process of reaching relatives and friends who could not be present. Much visiting between waiting families went on at this time. I talked with the Crowes, Stranos and the sweet little wives of Bob Hammond and James Sheppard, among others.

Uncles Robert, Gordon and the twins didn't mind a bit being awakened at 1:00 a.m. or later to hear Steve's voice, nor did his college roommates, Jack Briley and Jim Roberts, both residing at the time on the east coast.

Flashbulbs flashed, polaroids plicked, movie cameras murmered and Mr. Strano caught a "still" of Stephen, flanked by Vuokko and me at the same time Navy photographers were making a movie of "chief spy" R. S. Harris and his two dolls — or is it "molls," on one of these aforementioned divans located beside one of the many Christmas trees. We viewed the results later on TV and I hoped my twin brothers would chance upon the "show" on the 11:00 p.m. news back home in snowy Melrose.

An ecumenical Service of Thanksgiving was held at the RX Club next morning. There were no absentees among the crew!

Mae and I daily thereafter, knew no peace from the press, for they roamed the hotel ceaselessly, knocking on *Pueblo* doors. But a jovial crowd they were, really, as happy as the rest of us that the news was, at long last, "good"! Instead of sitting opposite newsmen on a plane, we now sat opposite the same six on a twin bed, Chick Connery being Mae's most constant shadow.

"We swept them off our beds every day like crumbs off a table-cloth," Mae declared picturesquely, describing the scene later.

Navy spokesmen warned us at the Information Center on the second floor of the hotel not to discuss crewmen's harsh prison treatment nor their wounds, but, as usual, their warning came a trifle late. TV camera crews had already wedged me into a corner of the hotel lounge where I had emerged from a telephone booth after contacting some of Sir Richard's Navy friends. I was dressed to meet Mae downtown.

By way of escape, and in answer to one question concerning the condition of the men, I innocently donated a graphic and gruesome description of one man's leg that his young wife had insisted he show me. It was indented with a long row of deep purple gouges. What medieval tool had his torturers wielded to accomplish this? There were other wounds besides aching legs from malnutrition. There were fractured ribs, a broken jaw, immovable fingers, and damaged optic nerves, as well as damage to internal organs from brutal kicks.

"Won't you remove your hat, Mrs. Harris? We'd like to show your hair," one cameraman asked.

"Not on your life! Did you ever see hair that's just had a tight turban pulled off it?" I laughed.

Steve was home! Newspapermen were ogres no longer, at least the ones I encountered!

(Some covering Steve's Navy Court of Inquiry, unfortunately, seemed of another breed, rather Pink of Persuasion. Some used Red ink in "reporting" secret sessions, in my opinion. *Were such writers "out to destroy the image of our Servicemen"?*

* * * * * *

On Christmas Day another "present" awaited Mae and me, probably the most singular one either of us had ever received. Strangely enough, we'd already been promised it, but we'd entirely forgotten about it.

Late in the afternoon, the usual line of chartered buses stood arrayed in front of the El Cortez Hotel to carry us on this Day of Days to a ceremony to be held up on the opposite hill where, at the "Pink Palace" the ten crewmen wounded in the one-sided sea battle were to be awarded purple hearts. (Steve and Ralph were not among these, 'though "wounded" they surely were!')

Like everyone else, I was looking forward to visiting the main building of the handsome complex, so clearly viewed from our hotel.

We ascended a long, nicely landscaped driveway, left the bus and walked through a stone archway opening from the facade of the main building. We entered, not a reception room, but a spacious courtyard with the greenest lawn I've ever seen! A glorious fountain at the center of it was sending its liquid rainbows high into the California sun, and beside it a rectangle of chairs had been set out for spectators.

On the balconies of the three walls of the quadrangle, their white uniforms standing out against its pink background, nurses and doctors lounged about, apparently stealing a few moments to catch the action below.

Navy attendants showed us to our seats after we had chatted with other visitors, among them Mrs. Alan Hemphill, a close friend of Rose

Bucher, who along with Rose and teenager Marcee Rethwish, had done so much to help the *Pueblo* cause on the West Coast.

At the open end of the courtyard, against a backdrop of lacy green foliage and one huge palm tree, in four neat rows of spanking new uniforms (a ladies' group had sewed all night to make), stood the entire crew of the *Pueblo*, the stars of this Christmas Pageant! Steve, as prophesied, stood in the front row beside Commander Bucher.

One look at the total picture and Mae and I turned in our chairs as if on cue and simply stared into each other's eyes. A pity Captain Wilcox and Poo Poo Hairstander couldn't have been present to stare along with us at this long-ago promise, this clairvoyant "portrait" come to life. It was exactly as I had described it to Capt. Wilcox!

San Diego wasn't Hawaii, to be sure — and neither was Balboa Naval Hospital the Kaiser Estate. Even the timing was off, but it was all there, every precious item of it, eighty-two proud and grateful faces of it. Madame Doolittle's mental canvas had "gotten" the picture perfect in every detail![2]

All glory to the Lord of Lords and King of Kings, the real Painter of this Christmas Masterpiece,—to Him who bestowed upon Madame her rare gift,—and willed her to share it with us!"

* * * * * *

After almost two weeks of watchfulness, Mae and I decided we could leave our men with a modicum of concern. Our bags were packed and presents for the homefolks purchased. The prospect of a Naval Court of Inquiry we found most disquieting, however.

"It will be like opening fresh wounds to bother those men in their sad condition, Eleanor. I'm afraid they'll only live their awful nightmare[3] all over again," Mae was saying as we stood on the hotel balcony looking across at the Pink Palace.

"It's Naval tradition to investigate the loss of a ship, Steve tells me," I replied. "However, I agree with you, Mae, that they should allow the men more time for recuperation. I think the reason for the promptness of the court inquiry is that they must have the facts while they're still fresh in the poor fellow's minds."

---

[2]I sent her a gold-quilted-satin dressing gown and check from San Díego. She was hospitalized at this time, and deeply touched by my gesture. Today, she is nearly ninety!

[3]Ralph later authored a series for the *Boston Globe* entitled: *My* Pueblo *Nightmare.*

* * * * * *

Our last evening in seagirt San Diego was beautiful. No smog had yet stretched its foul fingers to assault the innocence of the blue heavens. Even the night sky had a clear conscience.

Mae threw herself down on her twin bed and yawned contentedly. "Did ye bring that notebook I told ye to, Eleanor? I wish ye'd read me something out of it, I do."

"Right here," I laughed, pulling it from under the hotel pillow. "I haven't written a word in it since we've been here; it's all poetry anyway, except for a story from my mother's home in that little English village in French Quebec. I don't think you'd — "

"Oh, read me that story! I could use a good cup of coffee, too. I'll order us something to drink."

"Coffee and a story. Does this remind you of anything, Mae Dear?" I asked.

"It certainly does! Of the time you made me feel better about 'seeing' Ralph with your story about the ghost that comes to your ledges after a heavy storm at sea. I forgot to drink my coffee half the time during that story! Ye have a way with words, ye do!"

"Why, thank you Mae," Ego-Ellie promptly replied.

"This narrative is about a storm of sorts, too," I began, turning the pages of my notebook, "a story the Poet Drummond who used to visit my mother's home, would gladly have put to verse, had my mother been old enough to relate it to him; for it concerns two of his beloved 'habitants', those French Canadian country people he depicted so charmingly."

The coffee and orangeade Mae ordered arrived almost immediately. She gave the bellboy a generous tip and started to sip her favorite brew. Even these drinks were "on the house", we learned.

"'God works in mysterious ways, His wonders to perform'," I continued.

"O my dear, He does, He does! Just look at us. Eleanor, will ye? It took those North Korean 'apes' as Commander Bucher calls them, to make a good Christian out of me. They threw us both on a rocky road and ye took my hand in yours; but like all Christians, we were able to pick ourselves up again and again, and journey over each obstacle,—but—oh, go on, go on, Eleanor dear."

"Well, Mae, I'd say your story is better than mine,—about those 'apes' making us walk this rocky road. And that ship took much of my spiritual apathy and old attitudes along with it, too, some I don't want back again if it ever returns. My story also concerns a sorely-pressed Christian, a hard-working young man and his frail little wife."

"I remember my mother alluding to the remarkable faith of this fine-looking, strong-armed young French farmer, whose dainty little wife worked as a domestic for my Grandfather Westman. One summer when I went to Quebec to visit Kathleen and Doris, my cousins, we begged Grandma to tell us the story." (I began reading from the notebook. It was easier than telling it.—)

"Sweet, pale little Angelique limped as she went about her duties at the big house,[4] for she had been injured in a coasting accident in her teens (a sleigh ran over her leg) and her family did not have the means to provide her with the medical care she so badly needed.

"My Grandfather Westman repeatedly offered to pay for the operations required to put the malfunctioning limb back in working order; however, her husband, Philippe, was as proud as he was devout.

" 'My God will lead me to the money I need, merci, Monsieur Westman,' he would politely reply."

"Why didn't he take her to the famous shrine at St. Anne de Beaupre?" Mae asked.

"A good question, Mae," I replied sipping my orangeade. "I've asked myself that one many times, and I don't know the answer, unless it lies in the fact that it would have taken days to get to St. Anne's by horse and sleigh or buggy (over 125 miles of driving) and perhaps Philippe couldn't leave his farm animals in their isolated location for any length of time.

"At any rate, Angelique's leg became progressively worse, and by early spring she was no longer able to work at Grandpa's.

"Spring was an opportune time for Philippe's financial prospects, for working at one of Grandpa's sugar houses—where sap of the maple forests was converted into syrup, sugar, and other products—added to his meager savings for his adored and ailing Angelique.[5]

"He prayed beneath his bedroom crucifix at dawn and dusk with more fervor now. Surely God would find the money – lots of money – for his tiny wife before she – He must have looked down

---

[4]Which enchanting old homestead met a most unromantic demise, i.e., it burned to the ground, ignited by a spark from a steamroller! It was here that not only the poet, Dr. William Henry Drummond visited, but also Mr. William Cody (Buffalo Bill) who, with my grandfather, built the first lookout atop Pike's Peak in Colorado.

[5]Grandfather Westman's great granddaughter, Molly Williams MacKay, is wife (and helper) of the Maple Sugar King (Joseph G. MacKay) of the Province of Quebec. Molly (Mary Ellen) was born in nearby Lynnfield, Massachusetts and met her young Canadian "King" one summer while visiting her Aunts Kathleen and Doris, my beloved cousins.

lovingly at the white-faced doll still sleeping like the unspoiled angel she was.

"One morning, after collecting his buckets of sap from woodland trees, upon returning to the sugar house, Philippe overheard two other workers inside talking and laughing boisterously together:

"'Oui, that Boss, La Bossière, he bet me one thousand dollar I wouldn't have the guts to put my bare arm into that hell of boiling sap down there—and he has the money to put up, too, since his wealthy tante died in Montreal.'

"'Mon Dieu! That La Boissière, he's always betting!' cried the other habitant jovially. 'But he always pays off those he doesn't win. He's un bon homme—but myself—mais non, I am not willing to leave a good arm boiling in sugar for all his money—nor for any other man's!'

"Philippe moved silently to the cauldron: 'Tell la Boissière I'll accept his bet,' he announced in a voice that revealed no emotion. 'Tell him to be here with the money tomorrow morning—with a good fire going under the sap.'"

"Oh, Eleanor, ye do tell the most wonderful stories!" Mae cried when I stopped for a swallow of orangeade.

"That's because you're most wonderful about listening, Mae dear. Ye cats, isn't it quiet here this evening! Our scribbling bedbugs must have left town, or perhaps they're taking this all down out there beyond our DO NOT DISTURB sign!"[6]

"Well, our valiant Philippe," I read on, "prayed all the way home as he walked through the woods in what he hoped would be the last snowfall of the season.

"Yes, the sap was running fine — it was a good job to have before planting time —

"Early next morning as he turned away from his crucifix in the tiny bedroom, he asked Angelique to fetch him the small wash basket, the one with the handle. Her eyes opened in disbelief when he told her what to put inside it; but being an obedient French wife, she did exactly as he bade her, and covered it with a heavy dish towel as he had directed.

"Whatever Philippe was about to do was something not akin to his usual routine, Angelique decided; and since he had been praying most of the night, she begged to be a party to this mysterious adventure. It was only after she promised to remain by his side, keep her eyes on the basket and pray without ceasing that Philippe allowed her to go with him to the sugar house.

---

[6]True, they'd winged home to Boston!

"The new snow made it difficult for him to carry her through the woods, especially since he seemed determined to keep his left arm in the basket.

"As they approached the maple sugar house, it became apparent that the male inhabitants of the entire little French village of St. Etienne de Trois Rivières had crowded inside for the daring feat.

"The tanned young farmer's face showed no surprise as he carried his fragile angel over the threshold, wedged through the opening crowd, and gently set her down, basket and all, beside the bubbling cauldron.

"Quickly he removed his jacket and rolled up the sleeve nearest Angelique, replacing it unnoticed beneath the dish towels in the basket between them.

"Was Philippe angered at the turnout of villagers pressed solidly about him awaiting the deed, or at Boss La Bossière laughing in loud delight as he fanned the $1000 check above their stocking-capped heads in the steaming, sweetly-tepid air?

"Mais non, pas de tout — for these were his friends. As well he knew, not one amongst them wished him to fail. Unbeknown to him and pretty Angelique, moreover, many a mackinaw pocket bulged with bandages and salves, and many a weathered lip had a prayer upon it.

"Only the dark Shadow of Death hovering over the little red building in the woods would acknowledge that such a sacrifice could be fatal, result in the loss of a limb, or a wound serious enough to carry for a lifetime.

If Angelique measured the evil portent of the wager, she gave no sign, for her dark lashes were lowered against pale cheeks, her soft lips, likewise, moving in prayer.

"A hush fell over the cabin. Philippe's head bowed for a second, then, as if on signal, the sign of the cross filled the crowded room. The moment had arrived.

"As quickly as it takes to tell it, Philippe withdrew the strong brown arm from the basket and plunged it into the heart of the seething hot syrup.

"There was a hissing, spattering sound as steam rose into the young farmer's averted face — but just as quickly, the arm was withdrawn and replaced under the dish towel!

"With his free arm, Philippe drew his jacket over one shoulder, gathered up Angelique, basket, and yes, the $1000 dollar check — and quickly departed amidst the cheering crowd. La Bossière himself rushed out after them and insisted upon placing Angelique on his own woodland sled for Philippe to pull home, giving him the day off in the bargain."

* * * * * *

I drained my glass of its frosty orangeade.

"And I suppose ye're going to tell me t'was *God* was in that basket," Mae chortled happily over the last of her coffee –

"Well,—yes, in a way He was, Mae," I answered—"for it was filled with heaven's own fresh-fallen snow!"[7] –

"Put down that coffee cup, Mae," I ordered gaily as I went over and tossed the notebook into my suitcase. "You know neither of us is going to sleep. Now that we've both pulled our arms out of the *Pueblo* cauldron, let's cool off by going out and having a last look at beautiful San Diego. I shall always remember its generosity!"

"Eleanor, I'm not sleepy either. Let's walk down to that pretty ice cream parlor at the foot of the hill, and if it's still open, I'll buy ye *a basket of snow!*"

* * * * * *

Mae and I deplaned at Boston's Logan Airport directly following an ice storm so widespread it delayed our first stop at O'Hare Airport in Chicago (we spent over an hour circling it), then got us to Buffalo (for more circling) and eventually home to Boston at 3:00 a.m.!

Ole January greeted us by blowing his frigid breath straight into our faces as we came down the plane's ramp. (There were no movable jetways at that time.) I wished I had Ole Racoon over my shoulders now, for Mae and I had soared from sunny streets over a Bridge of Blue into a glacial, beautiful, but dangerous world.

Both Commander Peter Nelson and Richard Bordeaux had been waiting hours to meet us, yet were as felicitous as if they'd freshly arrived on the scene. Sir Richard, as bombastic as ever, drove the (yes, that's correct) big black Navy limousine over the icy roads to Melrose as skillfully as a figure skater. As we rolled along I gave him a day-by-day rundown, including the greetings and well-wishes of his host of Navy friends in San Diego. (He had hoped I'd go in person to meet a couple of his banker friends, but I simply couldn't find the time [or nerve!] to do so.)

My account was avidly received when I resumed it at Ledgewinds' kitchen table over hot chocolate malteds and fresh bakery rolls my sleepy homekeeper got out and heated up for us at 4:00 a.m. Uncle

---

[7]Philippe suffered no ill effects, losing only a layer or two of skin for his trouble. Angelique, after a series of operations, was completely cured, and never limped again. She worked for Grandfather until her first baby was born.

Gilbert wanted to be in on the latest news of his nephew, too. I clicked off my Gay Nineties lamp at 5:00 a.m.

* * * * * *

Another storm was brewing now, more newsworthy than the blizzard Ole January had racked up almost a year before, a storm whose foul winds were to carry their false fragrances from coast to coast — icy ones, too, that would freeze up whatever faith I had left in the American press.

Forewarnings of this newest blow emanated to Mae's home in Milton via telephone from the indefatigable Madame Doolittle:

"Tell Mrs. Harris she must now prepare herself for a second hell! Her son will become the target of Communist writers bent on destroying the image of U. S. Servicemen." (The words had a familiar ring!)

First the ship's captain would be hanged from the black-columned yardarm, rationale told me,—to be immediately followed by Executive Officer Ed Murphy? No, to be immediately followed by the *U.S.S. Pueblo's* Intelligence Commander, Stephen R. Harris, their second "goat" for the slaughter.

Why?...Why, no doubt, because his secret work was directed against Communism. (Alma Mater of Pink Penwielders.)

I wonder what tack Madame Doolittle's Pink Monsters will take? I asked myself. Will they hold Steve responsible for the Navy's lack of foresight in failing to provide the proper destructive devices for a contingency such as this one? *He'd requested such devices himself!*

Steve was such a quiet, above-board guy, the solid, hard-thinking type, cautious in his maneuvering, not the fighting, gung-ho bomber the Captain was. (The very fact their personalities are so complementary keeps them friends, I believe.)

Well, time enough to worry about that. There were a few things that demanded my more immediate attention, like, for instance, rejoining my news-hungry fourth graders.

My clique in Coop 12 demanded an on-the-spot, tear-by-tear, hug-by-hug description of my meeting with the returning POWS at Miramar. Despite the fact my chicklets arrived en masse and early, pink-cheeked and puffing with mittensful of newsclippings covering every moment of the grand reunion, they still preferred the story straight from their horse's mouth. They crowded about me so closely, the weight of their small bodies nearly "creamed" me; but it was "wicked nice" to be back with them again despite the discomfort.

Now that their long-incarcerated hero had returned, my clique made me a formal presentation of the *Pueblo* scrapbook. (Now in Steve's hands.)

I was "wicked" sorry I had failed to evict "wicked" from their vocabulary; but my corrective prowess was no doubt impaired, due to the fact I had more "wicked" things to wrestle with!

At home, answering the phone resumed its time-consuming rôle. Newsmen asked the same questions as my fourth graders, yet I managed to replenish the larder, cook, write thank-you letters for Steve's goodies, and make plans for Steve and Vuokko's homecoming party, in addition to performing several de-frustrating exercises.

Exercise Number One consisted of climbing atop my canopy bed, scene of much sad introspection, yanking from aloft the faded garden of "funeral flowers," and replacing it with a pure white satin arch.[8] As Steve had done upon the bare, cracked walls of his prison cubicle, I could now project "home movies" (with less sleeping-robbing plots— and no nerve-cracking countdown of posies).

Exercise Two took place "down in the hold behind the boiler," where I dusted, scrubbed and painted in regal gold a certain musty-eyed queen of Hindu origin,—not Chinese after all. I replaced her wandering onyx orbs with two gloriously blue Western eyes, dug with a kitchen knife straight out of a costume jewelry brooch and Elmer-glued to her royal skull. (And not a black jumper anywhere around to crick about the workmanship, either!)

A few hours later, bang by bang, huff by puff, I bopped the garden girl up over the cellar stairs and wedged her onto her greenery throne. "Know something, Mae?" I reported later by phone. "She seems to be smiling (laughing?) at me now!"

* * * * * *

The correctness of my hypothetical reasoning, along with the dire prophecy of You-know-who, soon materialized in both West and East Coast papers. Yes, the countrywide Word-Blizzard came storming in, straight from Court of Inquiry reporters. Since not one of them was allowed to attend the secret sessions of the court, they simply imagined the proceedings, and most imaginative this "reporting" became.

Why must these unfortunate Servicemen be subjected to a second round of torture through conjecture of reporters whose hearts beat as tenderly as the click of a typewriter, and whose regard for their fellow man stretches only the length of a ball point pen!? *Who appoints such newswriters both Judge and Jury?*

---

[8]In a bargain basement store, I had bought for five dollars a big-name display-dusty wedding dress (original price $375.00), cut off its many yards of satin and lace-studded train, laundered it, trimmed it, and voila, a luxury canopy!

Just as I surmised, Commander Bucher was the first to be "pressed" onto the roasting rack. Oh, by-my-scrambled-eggs, yes, he had broken the Navy code, surrendered his ancient but tradition-bound barque, complete with sacks of papers there was not sufficient time nor means to destroy (minus its millions in sophisticated equipment Steve had smashed to "powder")—but evidence sufficient to sink "Navy honor" straight down to Davy Jones' locker and Uncle George. The captain had even handed over eighty-two defenseless underlings to incorrible wretches without firing so much as a slingshot!

Whole forests of newsprint were wasted on torture-hacked[9] Commander Bucher, a memory-wracked, sobbing man, doing his utmost to state the facts, despite his broken health:

> ("I consider that the primary thrust of the Court of Inquiry's recommendation for a trial by general Court Martial for myself boils down to my being *charged for refusing to order my men to commit suicide.* I do not regret that decision and in fact would make the same decision in similar circumstances every time.")

Thank you, Commander Bucher![10]

After news stories covering the Captain-at-Court soured when the general public refused to swallow them hook, line and lynching, the ship's Intelligence Officer, just as I suspected, was next on the news-griddle; and a fine fish to fry he turned out to be! For Steve, bolstered by his own honesty and devotion to duty, was not one to bark back, but stand quietly on his record, however imperfectly it was served up to the eyes of the reading public.

Despite the general news assault upon Steve's good character, *Navy publications praised him!*

This son of mine, as usual, throughout the senseless tirades about super-spy Steve Harris handing over whole "mattress covers" full of "secret documents" to the enemy, (mostly old publications in triplicate he had been unable to offload before sailing, and of no use whatsoever to the North Koreans) showed remarkable self-control. Hardly able to walk into the courtroom because of malnutrition pains in his feet and legs, when asked by a **sympathetic newsman** how he was

---

[9]Commander Bucher was tortured so badly that he has never fully regained his health. As a consequence, he recently decided to retire from his beloved Navy!

[10]Mae and I will always remember the last comment of this remarkably considerate officer when we said goodbye to him in San Diego, thanking him for bringing our sons home *alive*. "Ladies, I didn't bring *them* home, they brought *me* home!" he corrected.

bearing up after tedious days of court grilling, he grinned and answered (on a TV newscast), "Well,—I'm *still standing.*"

"If it were my Ralph, Eleanor, I'd call the Captain in California
and find out what he's doing about these wild statements they're
making about *him!* Ralph says he's sick of reading all these lies about
Mr. Harris and the Captain, he is!" Mae seemed even more enraged
than I.

I did just that. Such flagellation of the facts was getting out of
hand. Each new account added more "mattress covers" to the tally.
I began to wonder who this scoundrel of a counter-spy was they
were ranting about. The Red Claws were really scratching!

"There isn't a word of truth in it, 'Miz' Harris," replied the good
captain in that easy-going nasal voice of his.

Commander Bucher went on to say as much as, "Look what
the press is doing to me, and *there isn't one single thing you can do
about it!*"

* * * * * *

After the Naval Court of Inquiry closed—at which a pompous
array of "judges", with little compassion, had succeeded only in
using half-sick sailors to point up their own ineptitude at rescue—
Steve and Vuokko bought a car and drove to Washington state to
visit her older brother and his family, then continued across the
North Central States toward Boston.

"The country never looked so beautiful and so free," Steve said
later. "No Check-Point Charlies at every change of state."

The happy couple reached Melrose on April 16th and I opened
Ledgewinds' doors to a homecoming reception four days later which
was attended by over one hundred guests.

The Melrose Board of Aldermen, soon after my party, presented
Steve with a framed resolution commending him for "courage and
loyalty as a member of the *U. S. S. Pueblo* crew during its unjustified
incarceration by the Republic of North Korea."

Also, among many other presentations, crewmen each received
a handsome plaque presented to them by movie actor John Wayne.

* * * * * *

At 10:30 a.m. on a May morning, while preparing to leave Ledgewinds for Washington, D. C. and the new assignment he had requested
(now promoted to Lieutenant Commander), Steve received a long
distance phone call from none other than Admiral Francis J.
Fitzpatrick, Assistant Chief of Naval Operations for Communications

and Cryptology. He read Steve a statement from Secretary of the Navy, John H. Chafee. It took almost fifteen minutes.

In substance, as a result of the Court of Inquiry decisions, Steve was both charged and forgiven. The statement ended: "They have suffered enough and further punishment would not be justified."

"Punished? For what? For coming home alive? Or in Steve's particular case, for doing all that was humanly possible with only the crudest of destructive devices available?

> Steve's testimony, in short, brought out that his men could not jettison material over the side of the ship because seaman Duane Hodges lay mortally wounded in the passageway and because of heavy Communist gunfire across the deck. Five fires were set, but a blaze could not be started in the main research area because there was no ventilation, and the ship's fuel tanks lay just beneath this area.
>
> (Vast amounts of secret material were thrown out port holes, and to crewmen's delight, onrushing Korean war vessels "innocently" plowed it beneath the ocean's surface!)
>
> Steve said that most of the information including codes and cryptographic material was "torn apart like confetti," the newest of the sophisticated electronic instruments "reduced to powder." (2½ million dollars worth of super-secret devices!)
>
> "We were united in doing the very best we possibly could during that day," the young lieutenant finalized.[11]

* * * * * *

A world-shaking atrocity such as this piracy on the high seas followed by the world-warming miracle of rescuing its 82 imprisoned crewmen alive, deserves a memorable ending, and in my own little corner of "Pueblo-vigiling" the grand finale held out several:

Of course, in reviewing the episode, there are some things one would like to undo, such as the foul turn some press took toward an honorable son and his honorable ship's captain. Yet, above and beyond all those miles of newsprint, the very strength of their nation

---

[11]Cmdr. Bucher's first order to destruct was given over a speaker that had no outlet in Steve's quarters, a delay which baffled even Steve's men. One man later apologized to Steve for first taking the matter of destruction into his own hands. Bucher had no knowledge of the vast amount of materials to be destroyed, and said he felt *"completely responsible"* for any papers there was no time to jettison. *Few newscarriers revealed these facts!*

and Navy-loving characters, I was certain, would transcend false criticism.

I knew this U. S. Navy I respected so cordially would not be *promoting* Steve and *giving him his choice of assignment* had they been honestly dissatisfied with his performance during the ship's seizure.[12]

How I wished Mae had not had to suffer all winter long from the foul prognostications of a false prophet who dared predict to a listening audience that *Pueblo's* men would "never return," thus saddling her with a flag-draped casket to carry to bed with her each night!

As to the pleasanter aspects of the grand finale:

The first occurred on a beautiful Saturday morning in May while Steve was still at Ledgewinds. Walking out onto the sunny ledges where Vuokko and I stood watching my sparrow hawks playing their annual spring game of tag, gliding playfully up and down, swinging in wide arcs across the garden pool mirrors, we turned to see what it was Steve was holding in his hand.

"May I ask, Mother, what these two valuable things of Grandmother's happen to be doing on the back shelf of my closet under the big flag folded up there?" (No, we hadn't been able to get a permanent new flagpole put up before Steve returned!) There was a look of disbelief on his nicely rounding face.

On his open palm, to my profound relief and delight, lay Grandfather Westman's silver Service Medal from Queen Victoria—and though tarnished, quite unharmed and unstolen! Beside the medal lay my mother's diamond engagement ring![13]

Evidently I had removed both these keepsakes from great, great Grandpa's secret drawer and hidden them under the flag before leaving the house on some extended trip or weekend — and had completely forgotten having done so!

Another surprising bit of information was supplied me by Steve, also, a sort of serves-me-right culmination to the cricket controversy. It came after I had entertained him and Vuokko at dinner one evening with the story of the destructive advent of my *Pueblo* New Year, my "Something Big on the Agenda" year!

"You mean to tell me that you thought mashing up a batch of crickets would bring you bad luck? Why, Mother, U. S. A. crickets

---

[12]Steve had already been decorated as a result of a previous mission.

[13]I suggested that Steve give this to Vuokko when they became engaged—but he refused. He appreciated the sentimental attachment I had for it, I believe.

bear no resemblance, and probably are a wholly different breed from
Oriental crickets. Our bugs are little beauties compared to theirs.
Those Oriental brutes are big, ugly creatures. I can't understand why
they revere them so!" (No wonder they keep 'em in cages!)

In June, one of the most rewarding of Pueblo's denouements
danced in via telephone (and TV) from Milton, Massachusetts:

"Eleanor! Eleanor!" Mae cried one evening as I reclined under my
lacy canopy, writing some closing lesson plans for Grade Four;
"Turn on your TV quick! That old fake forecaster, Dr. Hellraising
Hairshambler, or whatever ye called him, is on television this time,
on Channel XY. Turn on your TV! It's one of those phone-in
programs. Here's where I tell him off!"

I called downstairs to tell Gilbert to listen in, also!

" — and ye broke a great many hearts that night, ye did!" I heard
Mae's enraged voice saying to an obese-faced man. *"Ye told the
world,* and don't say ye don't remember saying it either; for ye said
that *'few if any of Pueblo's men would ever return!'* In fact, ye
told ye're listeners that probably none of them would ever live to
get out of North Korea!"

Then followed one of the most ludicrous attempts at self-
excusing I ever witnessed; for the pudgy-faced prophet, yes, just
"couldn't seem to remember saying it at all." In fact so vehement
was his negation that his wattles wagged as vociferously as his head.

Well, *I* remembered! I turned toward my bedside phone, but
heard Mae's voice again putting it strongly:

"And one of the men ye said 'would never return' is an engineer
at that station where ye are now, *standing right there beside ye in
that studio!"* (The engineer being "her Ralph", of course!)

—And a fine man he is, too, Mrs. McClintock!" broke in the voice
of the channel's Master of Ceremonies.

"This is the best show I've seen on TV this year!" my sphinx
co-viewer called upstairs with unusual warmth.

From that moment on, Dr. Poo-Poo petered out. He ended his
defense on such an irreverent note it must have made his listeners
squirm, for he lamely stated that "only Jesus Christ never made a
mistake, and he simply wasn't the man Christ was." (the acme of
understatement!)

Friends who viewed the debacle kept our lines so busy after the
telecast that Mae and I were unable to phone each other until the

following morning! I doubt, after his stunning defeat, if the flabby-jowled prophet is ever invited to haul his hallucinations into any of our local channels again!

* * * * * *

Words I especially like to remember came from the Chairman of the Armed Services Committee (Mendel Rivers) who told Congress:

"If we don't learn something from this (*Pueblo* seizure), we should forget about being a world power.

This should be an everlasting reminder that if we are to send men out to the far corners of this earth, we should be ready to protect them."

While both Commander Bucher and Steve were "relieved" by the U. S. Navy Secretary's statement, the charges levied against them brought a shared conviction of unfair judgment. Like his ship's captain, Steve actually would have welcomed a Court Martial, which constitutes a trial by Navy judges, for both knew they could *disprove the charges made against them if given the opportunity.* As it was, "forgiveness" by their Navy Chief of Staff erased the opportunity.

As Steve told me later:

"It would have cost the Navy a fortune to have held a Court Martial for the captain and me, for we would have had to bring witnesses from all parts of the world. This way (via 'forgiveness'), the Navy got itself off the hook."[14]

* * * * * *

I have little trouble getting the driveway shovelled when Gilbert is at work on wintry days, for at the first flake of snow, I receive a phone call from one of my three most ardent *Pueblo* fans, those small feisty refugees from a ladies' dress shop, who know I'll pay their bus fare over from Malden, plus wages and a good meal to boot.

Or, if the white stuff piles up during the night, the dawn cracks with the familiar sound of a plow on my driveway. Yes, thankful

---

[14]As to the oft-repeated press statement that Steve and Commander Bucher were continually at war with each other, nothing could be farther from the truth. (It was the quote about Steve from the Commander's book which cleared up the matter.

"I quickly discovered a penetrating awareness and brittle sense of humor behind Steve's facade—a mild soft-spoken manner that was nevertheless direct. I liked and trusted him at once and felt we would be able to get along well on a basis of mutual respect." From: *Bucher: My Story* by Cmdr. Lloyd Bucher and Mark Rascovitz.

am I that my smiling plow*man* (I don't refer to him as my plowboy anymore) is safely back from Hue, happy to be alive, as he always was.

* * * * * *

The first Saturday morning after my return from San Diego, (Ole January was hard upon us now!), I walked out into my upper hallway, wondering what Funkilling Fate would "scythe" out during this very newest of ever-luckless Januaries. The month thus far had proved super!

Regardless of my apprehensions, I felt refreshed and vaguely expectant after my morning shower; and looking out the music room windows, I beheld spread out before me, a "pretty day," as one of our southern teachers would describe it.

I walked on into the sun-filled room,—my Prayer Room,—grateful that Steve and I, Mae and Ralph, and all those loosed from their Dungeon of Death were able to behold such a day in freedom, "to rejoice and be glad in it!"

My eyes fell to the snow-blanketed ball park lying below me, but I couldn't find the floor of it, for a billowing white mist hung over it, the morning sun spreading a coverlet of gold upon its back. I was actually standing above a cloud, watching the God of Nature netting it in a seine of sunbeams!

I closed my eyes, for the scene was almost overpowering in its beauty, quite as lovely as the giant cloud-cradle that had hung suspended on its silvery spiderwebs across this same valley the autumn before.

The closing episode of this seaswept odyssey of mine, if it is closed, is one which will throw its incandescence upon my little stage of life right up until the final curtain,—most assuredly "a lamp unto my feet" for the remainder of my earthly journeying.

Yes, while I often longed to feel some token of divine receivership of my prayers, some affirmation that I had achieved a one-to-One relationship with this Heavenly Father, to whom I had steadfastly beamed, for eleven months, both silent and written supplications,— ultimately I reached the conclusion that there could be no one-to-One relationship at all—only a one-*in*-One.

I realized, further, that only when I was able to fall free from this overwhelming *self* so manifest in my make-up, could I enter in and become one-in-One Body with Christ, my Lord. "He in I, and I in Him!"

Well, I was far from that attainment, as no one knew better than I—(except One?). *Had some of my loathesome "self" sailed off with the Ship That Never Returned?*

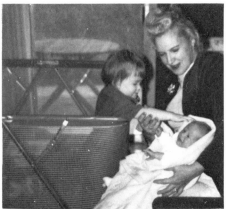

"My desire to become a Wonderful Person has long since been shelved.
All I want to be now is a Wonderful Grandmother!"

Truly a private little miracle was about to take place: With eyes still closed, I sensed rather than saw this misty aura begin to rise and drift upward toward me, as if drawn by the power of an unseen Hand. Slowly and silently, as I stood mesmerized by an indescribable "peace that passeth all understanding," I felt it drifting over, around and even *within* me, suffusing my whole being in a sensation so pure, so uplifting and glorious, that I felt I was bathing in a holy fountain whose waters cleansed and healed me. Time and place were of another world—

At the same time I was receiving this Baptism of Joy, my mind seemed to be acquiring a message of divine assurance—My *mind,* did I say? It was breathing itself into my very *heart!* As if saying:

"You see, you really didn't have to reach so strenuously for Me; I was right here in this room with you—here within you—all the time."

Was this "God's marriage with the soul"?

* * * * * *

Lying in bed under my new white canopy that same evening, I looked up at the shining arch of satin over my head. Yes, as Steve had done upon the dreary walls of his prison cubicle, I could now view some "home movies" of my own, with no bright blossoms challenging a no-longer-distraught mind to count them!

I strained my imagination to project on the shimmering "movie screen" a picture worthy of portraying my immeasurable gratitude to my Heavenly Father for returning Steve to me — alive!

—But all that came into focus in the opening scene was a lone choir member—a most familiar figure—dressed in a red robe with starched white surplice. She was singing my favorite passage of praise and thanksgiving—from the sacred oratorio, *Eli,* by Costa:

> "I will extol Thee, O Lord, for Thou hast lifted me up
> and hast not made my foes to rejoice over me —
> I will praise my God while I have my being!
> I will sing unto the Lord as long as I live!
>
> Amen"

—So be it!—

ACKNOWLEDGEMENTS

When one is fortunate enough to have a following of empathic friends, *i.e.,* teachers, pupils, neighbors, relatives and "unclassifieds," all inquiring (because they know my reasons for writing it), "How's the book coming?—and performing all manner of kind acts to hasten its completion—which ones does a writer acknowledge, and which ignore?

I choose to ignore no one, for I love them all, even if there isn't sufficient space here—or anywhere else—to list them individually.

A philosopher close to my nature-loving heart, Henry David Thoreau of Concord, Massachusetts, where 1 once lived, helps solve my dilemma. Says he:

"The most I can do for my friend is simply to *be* his friend. I have no wealth to bestow upon him. If he knows that I am happy in loving him, he will want no other reward."

I'd like to be as broadminded as Henry—yet I seek an "other" reward, *i.e.,* that this book, my first brainbaby of its kind, though born out of wedlock with tragedy, will be taken into loving hands and considered worthy of continued concern for its welfare!

First to be "acknowledged," I suspect, should be my good son, Lt. Cmdr. Stephen R. Harris, U.S.N.; for, without his capture and subsequent incarceration in a barbarous prison, there would be no story.

Then, of course, there's that darling, Mae McClintock, who made me write it—as well as those I made read it,—in part or in whole: Professor William Hooper Reynolds, Dr. Harry Foot, Rev. Dr. Harold W. Richardson (a high-school classmate), as well as Mary Edwards, May Milliken, Evelyn Morehouse, Elaine Arsnow, Gertrude Miles and three of my four delightful Ruths: Ruths Marlin, Odegard and Johnson, respectively. Most important of all in this category, of course, is my charming young editor, Susan I. McMonagle, and Enid Peterson and Claire Gagnon of The Christopher Publishing House.

It would do no harm, I suppose, to list here for posterity those six personable (teasing) gentlemen, plus one gentle lady, in the Music Department of our Melrose Schools; for, if they noticed I was red-eyed from writing all night, they brightened them with their wit, to keep me singing all day: Mr. Warren D. Wood (Director of Music), Tom Reed, Bob Love, Ted Leutz, Joe Messina, Roger Gagnon, and Jane Kniffen.

"Principal favorites," whose sympathetic inspiration should be recorded here, as well, are: Irma Pendleton, Imrie Dixon, George Mac-Pheters (former teacher), Bill Ferreira, Bill Nagle, Ed Barry, Claude Croston, Dr. Bob Bachelder (Associate Superintendent of Schools), and Eleanor Evans (former Director of Elementary Education).

And by all means, don't let me forget to include my typists, those patient, efficient puzzlers who put up with my cross-outs, write-ins, and page-wanderings hieroglyphics, *i.e.,* Kathryn Hopkins, Jean Le-Royer, Kathy Shanley, Barbara Perrotti and Georgia Brewer.

Those affable gentlemen in the Melrose Post Office deserve a special vote of thanks here, also, for taking such a personal interest in speeding on their way, my love letters to a lost lamb,—as well as helping me launch my two Word-Bombs on Washington: Joe Martorana, Fred Mahoney, Cliff Luke, and Ricky Festa.

Then there are those dear gals plus their boss in the Melrose Savings Bank, who always gathered back of my "window" asking for Steve: Sarah Barnes, Vera Maloney, Bertha Emery, Barbara Dalton, Lieke Lucas, and Archer (Archie) Thompson, President (a classmate of Melrose High School days). Archie passed away last summer.

I mustn't forget Clemmie Reich either, who had her bakery (Wyoming Bakery) make the big cake for Steve's homecoming party, a perfect replica of his lost ship! The Sugar and Spice and Muffin Man girls were sympathetic, too!— And Casey Florists sent a huge red, white and blue floral centerpiece as a gift for Steve's homecoming party. My pretty neighbor, Janet Morehouse, her mother, Evelyn, and Grandma, Gertrude Miles were enthusiastic backers, also, as well as my poetess friend in Newton Centre, Victoria Everding.

Don't think for a minute I intend to exclude two of my jolliest, "helpfullest" fourth grades in the history of education, either. They were my greatest brain boosters, the exhilaration of living out the better part of every week with these cheer-charged cherubs, keeping me attuned to the Joie de Vivre, despite its damaging vicissitudes.

Notably contributive to my brainchild's mental health were my learned and accomplished peers in the Thoreau Society of Concord, Massachusetts. (also, The Beethoven Society of Melrose.)

Among the former are Anton and Gertrude Kovar, Roland and Gerry Robbins, Frank and Grace Bramley, Dr. Al and Flora Bussewitz, Mary and "Fuzzy" Fenn, Rev. Harry and Helen Foot, Robert and Lucille Needham, Betty and Lloyd Rathbun, Lillian Walker, Lois and Olive Goddard, Joan Nolan, Marilyn Nickerson, Professor Herbert and Greta Ulig, Ruth Wheeler, John Duston, Gladys Clark, Elliott and Kay Allison, Bob Wilde, Larry Whipple, David and Miriam Dean, Professor Bill and Bonnie Howarth, Dr. Vernon Ramon, Dr. Walter Harding, Ted and Emily Thomas, Debby Coulter, Mr. and Mrs. Eugene Walker, Paul and Bernice Jones, Gilbert Van Buskirk, and Leonard Kleinfeld.

In recognition of the Good Neighbor Policy on this Prettiest Hill in Town, may I say that not only is it kept pretty (with the exception of the lawn at the top of the hill), but they're all Pretty Nice Neighbors, taking more than a passing interest in whatever I happen to be dabbling in, particularly if I happen to be dabbling in catastrophe. My loving appreciation for:

Muriel and Bill Edwards	Ruth and Arthur St. Germain
Evelyn and George Morehouse	Gladys and Bill Askin
Phyllis and Lewis Crosby	Gwendolyn and Everett Eggers
Mary and Alan Bigwood	Betty and Stan Mason
Mary and George Boyle	Mary and Donald Favorat
Jean and Richard Leone	Fran Goineau and Ray Dimock
Louise and Victor Leone	Jinny Varney and Marcia Burnham
Ruth and Cliff Luke	Sally and Cliff Lydiard
Florence and Bill Pretti	Alice and Gordon Graham
'Tense and Rayford Williams	Margaret Davis Sowerby (former neighbor)
Marie Greenlaw	Marian and Ralph Anthony

Other inspirers dwelling within or near my favorite city include author Mary Stetson Clarke, Dr. Nurhan Adrian, Florence Cheney, Ruth Beshong, Betty Marshall, Margaret Taylor, Helen Knorr, Vera Roache, Loraine Hamm, Phyllis Colluci, Janet and Leslie Stark, Mabel Otis, Marjorie Howe, Helen Walters, Herbert and Florence Oberg, Mary Magnasco, Marion Roos, Dot Raymond, John Perkins, Edwin Johnson and Dr. Richard Evans Schultes of Harvard.

I must mention, also, those "Wonderful People" in the Teachers', Highlands Woman's and *200* Clubs of Melrose, in addition to those members of Trinity Church, the First United Methodist and the First Baptist Churches where I soloed over the years.

As to the immediate family, there's my darling Vuokko and her two brothers and wives: Dr. Kyosti Uotinen (and Fanny), and Veikko (and Kaye), their dad, Rev. William Uotinen, and of course Vuokko and Steve's beautiful children: twins Colby Gyles and Christiana Louise and little Robert Somerby (my three grandbabies), as well as dear Aunts Eula and Ida, Bab and Mel and sons, cousins Alex and

Frieda and their six daughters, and cousins Kathleen and Doris and sons, as well as Ted, Lillian and Louisa; Amos and Ellie Moore and family, and college roommate, Lorraine Shaw Clark.

I must likewise laud with singular gratitude and affection my first voice teacher, Edith Weye Wilson, whose insistence upon my memorization of all church solos—particularly of those containing Scriptural passages—provided me a sacred storehouse of spiritual strength, from which to draw in times of stress.

I'd acknowledge my brothers—although, with the exception of Alden, who's been in Saigon so long he's forgotten what his sister is like,—probably not one of the five handsome devils will take more than a cursory glance at their kid sister's great epic. They're all too busy doing their own thing—which always tops mine![1] They are Robert (and Doris), Gordon (and Martha), Alden (and Kaye) and twin brothers, Gilbert and Willard. My favorite nieces and nephews are Rob (and Jean), Bob (and Mary Wallace), Lauren (and Dean), Priscilla and Robin, and Robert and Russell.

And lastly, I gratefully acknowledge any and all you good people who ventured to read my story.

Cordially yours,
Eleanor Van Buskirk Harris

---

[1]For instance, it was Brother Gordon who unearthed and partially developed an early American settlement on his seagirt property in Pemaquid, Maine. This trading post village predates Plimoth Plantation here in Massachusetts.

The State of Maine Parks Commission purchased the property from Gordon and plans to reconstruct the village as a national historic monument.

Gordon built a museum on the site. It now houses more than 50,000 artifacts dug from the ruins, as well as projected murals in oil depicting life in this frontier settlement of the early 1600's.

A Journey in Faith

Dear son of mine, torn from my heart,
Behind unyielding walls you wait —
Walls that promise no escape
Without the Will of Time and Fate!

But I shall find your prison walls;
God's ... es hear; —

... d

By ...

... yer — ...